ON
THE
X
CHROMOSOME
OF
MAN

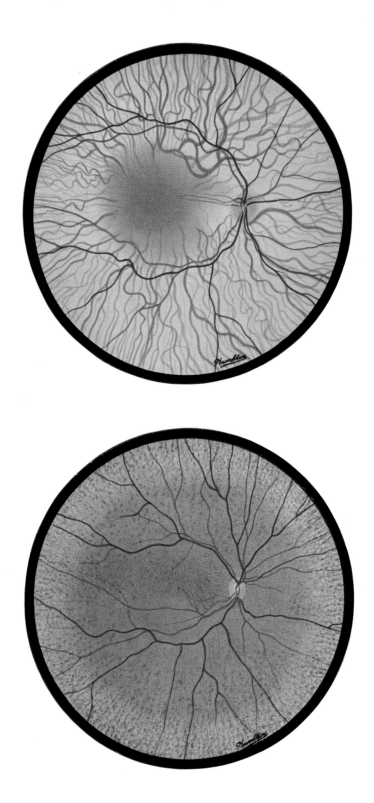

Appearance of the fundus of the eye in a male with ocular albinism (above) and in a female carrier (below). The mosaic pattern of pigmentation in the heterozygote is consistent with the Lyon hypothesis.

ON THE X CHROMOSOME OF MAN

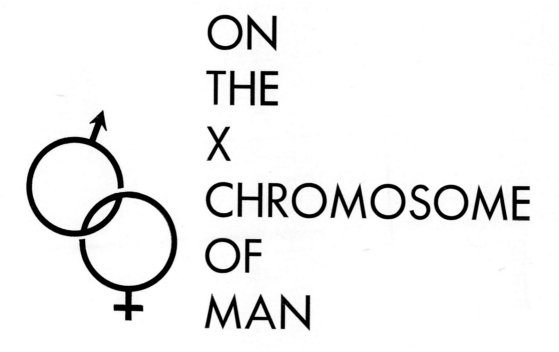

By Victor A. McKusick

Division of Medical Genetics,
Department of Medicine,
Johns Hopkins University
School of Medicine,
Baltimore

American Institute of Biological Sciences

2000 P Street, N.W.
Washington 6, D. C.

STECHERT-HAFNER SERVICE AGENCY, INC.
31 EAST 10th STREET
NEW YORK 3, N. Y.

On The X Chromosome of Man, by Victor A. McKusick,
was originally published in an abbreviated form in *The
Quarterly Review of Biology*, volume 37, number 2, June, 1962

Editorial Assistant A. Willard Bellais
A.I.B.S. Publications

PRINTED IN THE UNITED STATES OF AMERICA
BY Waverly Press, Inc., Baltimore, Md.

ACKNOWLEDGMENTS

I am indebted to many colleagues who in the last few years have participated in the work of this department along lines covered in this review. The contributions of Drs. Samuel H. Boyer IV, Malcolm A. Ferguson-Smith, Alan W. Johnston, E. A. Murphy, Ian H. Porter, James H. Renwick, Peter Bowen, Catherine S. N. Lee, Alan E. H. Emery, and David Wise, and of Mrs. Jane Schulze deserve particular mention. It has also been my privilege to engage with Drs. R. R. Race and Ruth Sanger in a trans-Atlantic collaboration in the use of the Xg^a blood group for X-chromosome mapping and study of the origin of X–aneuploid states. The catalog of X–linked mutations and/or the manuscript were reviewed helpfully by Dr. Carl J. Witkop, National Institutes of Health, Bethesda; Professor P. E. Becker of Gröningen; Professor A. Franceschetti of Geneva; Dr. Harold J. Falls, University of Michigan, Ann Arbor; Dr. F. Clarke Fraser, McGill University, Montreal; Dr. John B. Graham, University of North Carolina, Chapel Hill; Dr. James V. Neel, University of Michigan, Ann Arbor; Dr. A. G. Bearn, Rockefeller Institute, New York City; Dr. Park S. Gerald, Boston; Dr. Oliver Smithies and Dr. John M. Opitz, University of Wisconsin, Madison; Dr. Arno G. Motulsky, University of Washington, Seattle; Prof. J. A. Böök, Uppsala; Dr. H. Werner Kloepfer, Tulane University, New Orleans; Prof. Curt Stern, University of California, Berkeley; Dr. Mary F. Lyon, Harwell, England; Professor D. Klein, Geneva; Dr. L. B. Russell, Oak Ridge; Dr. R. J. Gorlin, Minneapolis; Dr. R. R. Race, London; Dr. Ruth Sanger, London; Dr. Susumu Ohno and Dr. Ernest Beutler, Duarte, California; Drs. Bernice H. Cohen, Bentley Glass, Clement L. Markert, Carl P. Swanson, William J. Young, and William H. Zinkham, Baltimore. For pertinent statistical discussions I am indebted to Drs. Allyn W. Kimball and A. M. Lilienfeld of Baltimore and Professor C. C. Li of Pittsburgh.

TABLE OF CONTENTS

FOREWORD

The history of our knowledge of the X chromosome of man is reviewed with appropriate reference to the contributions made through study of other forms. It is noteworthy that sex-linkage was first observed in man.

X–linkage has been established for about 60 traits in man. Unlike a majority of autosomal traits in man, most of the observed X–linked traits are recessives (or incomplete recessives).

The genetic map of the X chromosome is known only in the most sketchy manner but is likely to be filled in rapidly in the next few years through the use of newly discovered markers, such as the Xg^a blood group, and cytogenetic investigations of cases of X chromosome anomalies. It appears that the color-vision locus (or loci) is on the short arm and may be rather far from the kinetochore. Based on chiasma counts of autosomes, estimates of the genetic length of the X chromosomes are of the order of 150 mapunits (1.5 morgans). Independent segregation of color blindness and night blindness, of color blindness and hemophilia B, and of Xg^a and hemophilia B is consistent with this estimate.

Cytologic observations of the male meiotic chromosomes make it unlikely that any significant portions of the X and Y chromosomes are homologous. Furthermore, the pedigree data on all traits for which partial X-linkage has been suggested are at the best inconclusive.

The Barr body is formed from one X chromosome (or part thereof) which retains heterochromatic properties during interphase.

The Lyon hypothesis suggests that on a random basis one X chromosome in each cell of the female becomes the Barr body and genetically is relatively inactive; that the decision as to which X chromosome will behave in this manner is made early in development and once made is fixed in all descendants of a given cell. The cytologic basis of the hypothesis is presented. The genetic consequences which the hypothesis would predict have been outlined and the evidence available to date reviewed.

Mutation, the sex ratio, selection, consanguinity, evolution, and genetic counselling are discussed as they bear on the X chromosome and vice versa.

The limited information about the Y chromosome is reviewed briefly.

V. A. McKusick

I · INTRODUCTION

CYTOLOGIC advances have undoubtedly been a leading factor in the recently renewed interest in the X chromosome of man. Meaningful questions to which answers can be sought include the following: How much and what genetic information is carried by the X chromosome? What is the genetic topography of the X chromosome; that is, what is the relative linear position of X–borne loci, and what specific parts, e.g., the short-arm or the long-arm, carry particular loci? Is there any effect of the double dose of X–borne genetic information in the normal female as compared with the normal male? If not, what is the mechanism for the "dosage compensation"? What is the role of the X chromosomes in sex determination? What is the relationship between the Barr body ("sex chromatin") and the X chromosome? What is the functional significance of the Barr body? What is the rate of mutation at X–borne loci? What are the disturbances of X chromosome behavior in meiosis and mitosis which lead to the aneuploid states involving this chromosome?

At least three methods for getting information on some of these matters exist:

1) *Pedigree analysis* with demonstration of typical patterns of inheritance often can establish that specific traits are determined by X–borne genes.

2) *Linkage studies* sometimes can confirm X–linkage when pedigree studies are inconclusive and, furthermore, can quantitate, at least in a relative manner, the distance separating loci on the X chromosome.

3) *Cytogenetic studies* of normal and abnormal morphologic features of the X chromosome in relation to functional, that is, phenotypic, aspects can provide information on what part of the X chromosome carries particular genetic information. Such studies have, furthermore, suggested a mechanism for dosage compensation, and provide other information on the normal and abnormal function and behavior of the X chromosome.

The following is a review of information on the constitution of the X chromosome of man provided by these and other approaches. Information from study of other species will be cited only when particularly relevant to man. First, the history of our knowledge of the X chromosome will be briefly surveyed.

II · HISTORICAL NOTE

PRE-MENDELIAN *observations* (Zirkle, 1946). The occurrence of hemophilia in brothers and in male cousins, the offspring of sisters, was recognized by the writers of the Talmud (cf. Neel and Schull, 1954; Webb and Dixon, 1960). An American newspaper account of 1791 described the family of a man named Zoll who had six hemophilic sons among the children by one wife and all normal sons by a second wife (McKusick, 1962a). Two hemophilic families were described in Germany later in the 1790's (Bullock and Fildes, 1912). Otto (1803) described the transmission of hemophilia in the following terms: "...males only are subject to this strange affection,... all of them are not liable to it.... Although the females are exempt, they are still capable of transmitting it to their male children." In 1813 Hay (McKusick and Rapaport, 1962) and in 1817 the Buels described other American families with hemophilia affecting only males and transmitted only by females (McKusick, 1962b). Nasse (1820), a medical professor at Bonn, reiterated the mode of transmisson which with the frequent injustice and illogic of eponymization became known as Nasse's law.

Color blindness was a matter of interest to three British physical scientists: Joseph Priestley (1777), John Dalton (1798), and Lord Rayleigh (1881). At least Dalton was himself color-blind, probably a protanope (Brockbank, 1944; Sloan, 1961, personal communications, Baltimore), and had a color-blind brother. The characteristic pattern of inheritance was established by the Swiss ophthalmologist Horner (1876).

Before its chromosomal mechanism was understood (1911), sex-linked inheritance (then called sex-limited inheritance) was also recognized for ichthyosis vulgaris (Sedgwick, 1861), night blindness (Pagenstecher, 1878), peroneal muscular atrophy (Herringham, 1889), pseudohypertrophic muscular dystrophy (Gowers, 1879, and others), nystagmus (Owen, 1882), and anhidrotic ectodermal dysplasia (Darwin, 1875, see No. A25 of catalog). Gee (1877) and McIlraith (1892) described families with diabetes insipidus in a pattern consistent with X–linked inheritance with occasional expression in heterozygous females.

The two types of pedigree patterns which we would now distinguish by the designations sex-limitation and sex-linkage were recognized by Darwin (cited by Harris, 1948). In 1906, in his address on Mendelian heredity in man before the Neurological Society, Bateson referred to the pattern of inheritance of X–linked recessive traits as "knight's move" descent. However, he misinterpreted the mechanism of inheritance, drawing an analogy to horned-hornless sheep, a sex-influenced autosomal trait. Also, in the draft of his 1909 monograph which was sent to press, Bateson was confused about what he called "sex limited" inheritance: he defined it as dominance in the male and recessiveness in the female and considered that male-to-male transmission was possible. Nettleship, the ophthalmologist, called the error to his attention so that the following erratum was published as an inset (p. 231):

> Mr. Nettleship has called my attention to a fact which must greatly modify the sug-

gestions here given. The statement made (p. 172) that colour-blind men frequently have colour-blind sons is not true. On my scheme, half the sons of a colour-blind man should be colour-blind. ... in the fact that the sons of colour-blind men are normal we perhaps see the complement of the peculiarity already ascertained in other sex-limited conditions, that the number of daughters transmitting is greater than the scheme contemplates. It will be evident that the question of a sexual dimorphism among the spermatozoa is thus prominently raised.

Early cytologic observations. The chromosomes of man were first described in tumor cells by Arnold in 1879. In 1891 Henking (Wilson, 1925) found in an insect a "peculiar chromatin-element" which in the second spermatocyte division lags behind the separating anaphase chromosomes and then passes undivided to one pole. Because of his uncertainty about its nature he labelled it "X". Thus, the X chromosome, like Q fever (Derrick, 1953), owes its name to the obscurity of its nature at first discovery. The X chromosome was studied by others in insects and other animals and its nature as a chromosome was established. McClung (1902) first suggested its role in sex determination. The X chromosome was referred to by several terms, of which one widely used was McClung's *accessory chromosome*. The term derived from McClung's misconception that the male had an extra chromosome which was missing in the female; actually the XX female in the grasshopper he studied has one more chromosome than the XO male. The designation X chromosome became firmly fixed in the literature mainly through its use by Wilson (1911, 1925).

Winiwarter (1912) counted 47 elements in the human testis and 48 in the ovary, concluding that man has an XX–XO sex chromosome constitution. Painter (1924) concluded that the chromosome number of man is 48 in both sexes and that the sex chromosome constitution is of the XX–XY type. Winiwarter and his pupils continued to insist on the absence of a Y chromosome in man so that some European writers have until quite recently (Rostand, 1961) viewed the matter as unsettled. The application of improved technique of studying human chromosomes in 1956 not only established the correct diploid number of man as 46 but confirmed Painter's observation that the human sex chromosome constitution is XX–XY.

The cytologic explanation of X–linkage. Sex-linkage was discovered in poultry before the rediscovery of Mendelism (Cushman, 1893; cited by Zirkle, 1946), and later in moths by Doncaster and Raynor (1906) and in birds by Durham and Marryatt (1909; cited by Zirkle, 1946). In the same period both Charles B. Davenport (1906) and Raymond Pearl (1910) studied *barred*, a sex-linked color trait in the domestic fowl. However, in all these species the female is the heterogametic sex so that sex-linked traits affect mainly females but are transmitted through males. In 1905 Stevens and Wilson (1905) showed that in certain insects the X chromosome passes into all eggs and into female-producing sperms and that it is absent or replaced by a small homolog in male-producing sperms. In 1908 Stevens demonstrated the XX–XY sex chromosome constitution of *Drosophila*.

T. H. Morgan's discovery in 1910 of a sex-linked trait, white eye, in *Drosophila melanogaster* (1910a, b) clarified the mechanism of the inheritance of conditions such as hemophilia and color blindness. In 1911 E. B. Wilson, like Morgan, a professor at Columbia University, pointed out simultaneously with Morgan (1911a, b) that X–linkage accounts for this pattern of inheritance in man. The term *sex-linked* was introduced about that time. The term generally used hitherto (e.g., by Sedgwick (1861 and 1863), Bateson (1909), Davenport (1909, 1911), and Morgan (1911a) himself) had been *sex-limited*. As now used, *sex limitation* is the extreme case of sex influence on an autosomally determined genetic trait. In 1913 Morgan (p. 83) wrote as follows: "These cases, as already stated, were formerly included under the term *sex-limited inheritance*, that implies that a character is limited to one sex, but we now know that characters such as these may be transferred to the females, hence the term is misleading. Their chief peculiarity is that in transmission they appear as though linked to the factor for sex contained in the sex chromosome, hence I prefer to speak of them as sex-linked characters."

At about the same time that X–linked traits were being discovered and explained in *Drosophila* and other organisms, Doncaster (1911; 1912; Doncaster and Raynor, 1906), at Cambridge University, and Little (1912), in this country, pointed out that *orange*, a coat color trait in the cat which in the heterozygote expresses itself as "tortoise-shell," is X–linked. The "tortoise-shell" cat has attracted renewed interest recently (p. 63).

Mapping the X chromosome. In 1909 Janssens studied chromosomal chiasmata and suggested that exchange of material between chromosomes occurs in the process of chiasma formation. Morgan (1913), and his student Sturtevant (1913), discovered genetic crossing over (recombination) in X–linked traits of *Drosophila*, demonstrated the usefulness of data on crossing over in mapping the X chromosome, and suggested that there is a cause-and-effect relationship between chiasma formation observed cytologically and recombination observed genetically. In 1911 Morgan (1911b) wrote: "...the proportions that result [through recombination] are not so much an expression of a numerical system as of the relative location of the factors in the chromosomes." Thus, X–linked traits figured prominently in another of the major advances in genetics after the rediscovery of Mendelism, the discovery of linkage.

Demonstration of linkage, crossing over, and chiasma formation was important to acceptance of the chromosomal basis of heredity. Considering independent assortment to be a general law, recognizing that organisms must have more genes than chromosomes, and not knowing of the exchange of material between chromosomes, early geneticists like Bateson (1906, 1909) and Punnett (1950) were for some years unwilling to accept the Sutton-Boveri hypothesis (McKusick, 1960b), that the chromosomes carry the Mendelian factors.

Sex determination. In 1905 Stevens demonstrated the XX–XO mechanism of sex determination in several insects, thereby correcting McClung's (1902) misinterpretation of the "accessory chromosome." Elaboration of the mechanism of sex determination and the role of the X chromosome therein was provided by Goldschmidt (see review, 1955) and later by Bridges (1916), who from the study of various non-disjunctional states affecting the sex chromosomes of *Drosophila* concluded that the Y chromosome is largely a "dummy" as far as determination of sex phenotype is concerned (although it is essential to fertility of the male) and that the sex phenotype is a function of the balance between male determiners on autosomes and female determiners on the X chromosome. The

exceptional patterns of inheritance of X–borne genes, when correlated with the cytologic findings in aneuploid states involving the X chromosome, provided final conclusive evidence for the chromosomal basis of Mendelism.

Since the sex chromosome constitution is the same, and since such a close parallelism in the transmission of X–linked traits had been observed, the same mechanism of sex determination was presumed to obtain in man. Not until 1959 did the study of aneuploid states of the sex chromosomes in mice (Welshons and Russell, 1959) and men (Ford, et al., 1959; Jacobs and Strong, 1959) show that the mechanism of sex determination in these mammals is different from that in *Drosophila melanogaster*. With reports beginning in that year, newer methods for study of the human chromosomes were applied to the investigation of the Turner syndrome, Klinefelter syndrome, and other sex anomalies which were found to have their basis in a quantitative abnormality of the sex chromosomes. Independently and about simultaneously an extra autosome was discovered in Mongolism by Lejeune and his colleagues and an extra sex chromosome in the Klinefelter syndrome by Jacobs and Strong (1959). The report on Mongolism was read at the *séance du 26 Janvier 1959* of the *Académie des sciences* in Paris (Lejeune, Gautier, and Turpin, 1959); the report on the Klinefelter syndrome appeared in the issue of *Nature* dated January 31, 1959.)

In 1937 Geitler and Smith (1945) found that in insects (the waterskater and the spruce budworm) interphase nuclei show differences according to whether one or two X chromosomes are present. In 1949 Barr and Bertram discovered a similar sex dimorphism of the cell nuclei of mammals (the "sex chromatin," or Barr body), and in 1954 Davidson and Robertson Smith found a sex dimorphism in the nuclei of leucocytes, "drumsticks" in the female. Application of the Barr and Davidson techniques for determining "nuclear sex" uncovered thought-provoking inconsistencies with sex phenotype in three conditions: 1) some cases of the Klinefelter syndrome, 2) some cases of the Turner syndrome, and 3) cases of testicular feminization. Until chromosome analysis was applied in 1959 (Ford, et al., 1959; Jacobs, et al., 1959a; Jacobs and Strong, 1959) all three were believed to be examples of sex reversal. Only in the third condition did such prove to be true.

X *chromosome phenomena not yet demonstrated in man*. The behavior of the X and Y chromosomes in spermatogenesis in man was demonstrated in 1932 by Shiwago and Andres, who found end-to-end association which would not seem to allow crossing over. The cytologic evidence was aparently considered inconclusive by Haldane (1936, 1941) who, stimulated by genetic and cytologic observations in fish (Aida, 1921) on *partial sex linkage* (i.e., determination of traits by genes on a homologous portion of the X and Y chromosomes between which crossing over might occur in meiosis) and by cytologic suggestions of homologous segments in the rat (Koller and Darlington, 1934), which he assumed behaved the same as man (Koller, 1937), sought evidence of partial sex linkage in human pedigrees. Studies by Sachs (1954), Ford and Hamerton (1956), Kodani (1957), Ferguson-Smith (1961), Hamerton, et al., (1961) and others of spermatogenesis confirm the findings of Shiwago and Andres. (See p. 39.) Furthermore, re-examination of the pedigree data by Morton (1957), among others, lends no support to the partial sex linkage of those traits of man for which this mode of inheritance has been suggested.

In 1922 Lilian V. Morgan (Mrs. T. H. Morgan) described in *Drosophila* the phenomenon of *attached-X chromosomes*. In some flies two X chromosomes become permanently attached. Such females (X̄X̄Y) produce two classes of ova, X̄X̄ and Y. Fertilization of the first by an X sperm results in a triple-X fly which usually dies; by a Y sperm, in another X̄X̄Y female. The other two types of zygotes expected are XY (normal male) and YY (which turned out to be lethal). If the attached X chromosomes are homozygous for a recessive allele, then the resulting trait will be expressed in the fly, who although X̄X̄Y is a fertile female in *Drosophila*. Furthermore, essentially all females in the line will show the trait, which will be transmitted in direct descent, so-called hologynic inheritance.

At the stage when sex determination in man was thought to be identical to that in *Drosophila* it was presumed that *hologynic inheritance* due to attached-X chromosomes might obtain, and

two possible examples were discovered in the literature (Gowen, 1933; Haldane, 1932; Zirkle, 1946). In 1645 Sir Kenelm Digby described a condition of double thumbs affecting all the females and none of the males through five generations. In 1838 Cunier published an extensive pedigree of color blindness transmitted from mother to all daughters through many generations. It is now known, of course, that the XXY human individual is an infertile male with the Klinefelter syndrome. The attached X chromosome mechanism cannot, therefore, obtain in the pedigrees of Digby and Cunier. Furthermore, close study of Cunier's description by Stern and Walls (1957) indicated that the phenotype was no conventional form of color blindness but rather a "lost syndrome" with cataract as a feature.

In *Drosophila*, X chromosomes with part of a Y chromosome attached were used by Stern (1931) in classic experiments demonstrating that genetic crossing over is accompanied by the physical exchange of chromosomal material between homologous chromosomes. The same investigator (1936), in other classic experiments demonstrating somatic crossing over (somatic recombination), made use of two X–linked traits, *singed*, a bristle mutant, and *yellow*, a pigmentation mutant.

V–type (variegated) position effects have been observed in *Drosophila*, *Oenethera*, and recently in mice (Russell, 1961; Russell and Bangham, 1961). Although the phenomenon was discovered in the 1920's (Lewis, 1950), Schultz in 1936 referred to it as *variegation* because of the mottled or mosaic phenotype. When through translocation a wild-type locus, which normally lies in euchromatin, is moved into the vicinity of heterochromatin its dominance becomes uncertain, or modified, so that a recessive allele, if present on the homologous chromosome, may be expressed. In mice, autosome/X chromosome translocations are the ones productive of V–type position effects and they occur only in the female or the Klinefelter (XXY) male, presumably because only these have a heterochromatic X chromosome. (See p. 64.) This phenomenon may be found in man in due course.

III · PEDIGREE DATA ON THE CONSTITUTION OF THE X CHROMO-SOME OF MAN

T HE catalog, which is given in Table 1 and elaborated in the Appendix, lists those mutations which have, with varying degrees of confidence, been identified as X–borne in the human species. In the Appendix a description is provided of each trait, other genetic forms are indicated, and the expression of the gene in the heterozygous female is described when known. For the traits listed in part B the evidence for X–linkage is incomplete. Some of these are probably indeed X–linked; others probably are not. Part C discusses certain conditions for which sex-linkage has been suggested but is almost certainly *not* the mode of inheritance. In many of these cases inclusion in the enumeration (especially in part B) is largely for heuristic purposes.

For reasons given on p. 26 the term *X–linked*, rather than *sex-linked*, will be used throughout.

The diseases and aberrant traits listed in the catalog are like a photographic negative from which a positive picture of the constitution of the X chromosome can be produced. Here is an illustration of William Harvey's observation made in 1657, that "in almost all things, . . . what they contain of useful or applicable na-

ture is hardly perceived unless we are deprived of them, or they become deranged in some way." Nature's experiments in these X–linked traits inform us that genes on the X chromosome are concerned with the formation of normal proteins, such as antihemophilic globulin and glucose–6–phosphate dehydrogenase, and with normal functions such as gamma globulin formation, and color discrimination.

Pedigree patterns of X–linked inheritance. On p. 21 methods for detecting X–linkage of *common* traits are discussed. Evidence for the X–borne nature of *rarer* mutations is provided by demonstration of a typical "sex linked" pedigree pattern (Figs. 1a–c, 4), of which the critical feature is absence of male-to-male transmission.

For an *X–linked recessive* trait, one-fourth of the sons of all daughters of carrier females are expected to be affected (Fig. 3). In Table 2 this test of the X–linked recessive hypothesis has been applied to the pedigree shown in Figure 2.

The pedigree pattern characteristic of X–linked recessive traits such as hemophilia creates practical problems in tracing families. Osler (1885) pointed this out in writing about hemophilia: "As the tendency is chiefly transmitted through the female members of a family, who

6

TABLE 1

A catalog of X–borne mutations in man

A. *Conditions for which X–linkage is considered proved or very likely.*

1. Partial color blindness, deutan series
2. Partial color blindness, protan series
3. Total color blindness
4. Glucose–6–phosphate dehydrogenase deficiency
5. Xg blood group system
6. Muscular dystrophy, Duchenne type
7. Muscular dystrophy, Becker type
8. Hemophilia A
9. Hemophilia B
10. Agammaglobulinemia
11. Hurler syndrome
12. Late spondylo-epiphyseal dysplasia
13. Aldrich syndrome
14. Hypophosphatemia
15. Hypoparathyroidism
16. Nephrogenic diabetes insipidus
17. Neurohypophyseal diabetes insipidus
18 Lowe's oculo–cerebro–renal syndrome
19. Hypochromic anemia (Cooley–Rundles–Falls type)
20. Angiokeratoma diffusum corporis universale
21. Dyskeratosis congenita
22. Dystrophia bullosa hereditaria, typus maculatus
23. Keratosis follicularis spinulosa cum ophiasi
24. Ichthyosis vulgaris
25. Anhidrotic ectodermal dysplasia
26. Amelogenesis imperfecta, hypomaturation type
27. Amelogenesis imperfecta, hypoplastic type
28. Absence of central incisors
29. Congenital deafness
30. Progressive deafness
31. Mental deficiency
32. Börjeson syndrome
33. Spinal ataxia
34. Cerebellar ataxia with extrapyramidal involvement
35. Spastic paraplegia
36. Progressive bulbar paralysis
37. Charcot–Marie–Tooth peroneal muscular atrophy
38. Diffuse cerebral sclerosis (Pelizaeus-Merzbacher)
39. Diffuse cerebral sclerosis (Scholz)
40. Hydrocephalus
41. Parkinsonism
42. Ocular albinism
43. External ophthalmoplegia and myopia
44. Microphthalmia
45. Microphthalmia, with digital anomalies
46. Nystagmus
47. Megalocornea
48. Hypoplasia of iris with glaucoma
49. Congenital total cataract
50. Congenital cataract with microcornea
51. Stationary night blindness with myopia
52. Choroideremia
53. Retinitis pigmentosa
54. Macular dystrophy
55. Retinoschisis
56. Pseudoglioma
57. Van den Bosch syndrome
58. Menkes syndrome
59. Albinism-deafness syndrome

B. *Conditions for which the evidence of X–linkage is considered inconclusive.*

1. Inability to smell cyanide
2. Incontinentia pigmenti
3. Wildervanck's syndrome
4. Male hypogonadism
5. Male hypogonadism and ichthyosis
6. Testicular feminization syndrome
7. Male pseudohermaphroditism
8. Kallmann syndrome
9. Anosmia
10. Zonular cataract and nystagmus
11. Myoclonic nystagmus
12. Combined Charcot–Marie–Tooth disease and Friedreich's ataxia
13. Choroidal sclerosis
14. White occipital lock of hair
15. Diffuse cortico-meningeal angiomatosis
16. Albright's hereditary osteodystrophy
17. Aptitude for spatial visualization
18. Microcephaly with spastic diplegia
19. Familial obstructive jaundice
20. Paget's disease of bone
21. Phosphorylase-deficient glycogen storage disease of liver

C. *Conditions probably not X–linked although this genetic mechanism has been suggested.*

1. Leber's optic atrophy
2. Gynecomastia
3. Acrokeratosis verruciformis
4. The OFD syndrome
5. Plain radial loop, right index finger
6. Spiegler-Brooke's tumors
7. Familial periodic paralysis
8. Mohr syndrome

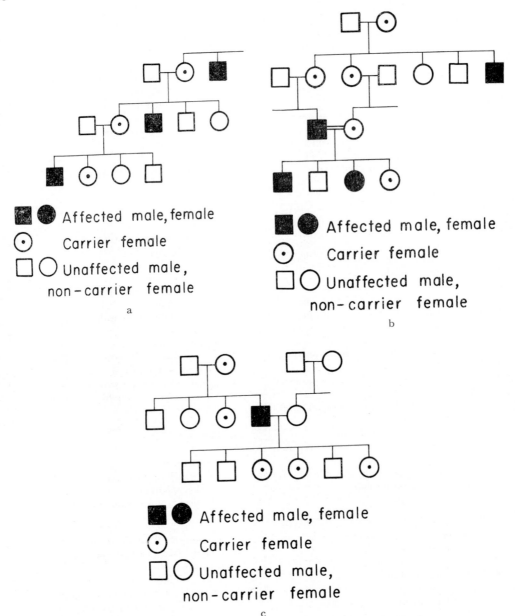

FIG. 1. SCHEMATIC AND IDEALIZED PEDIGREE PATTERNS OF X–LINKED RECESSIVE TRAITS

a. The "oblique," or "knight's move" pattern created by involvement of males and transmission through females. b. The occurrence of a homozygous affected female through a consanguineous (first-cousin) mating of an "affected" male and a carrier female. Note that there is no inconsistency with the rule of no male-to-male transmission; the "affected" male in the last generation inherited the trait from his carrier mother. c. Among the children of an "affected" male all daughters are obligatory carriers and all sons are normal.

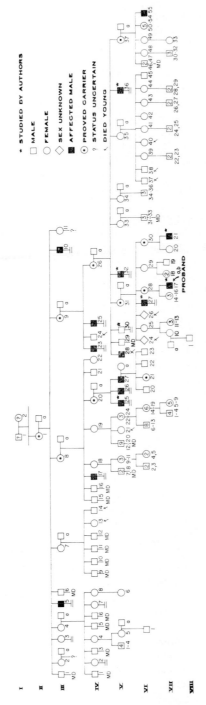

Fig. 2. Pedigree of X-Linked Recessive Spastic Paraplegia

See Table 2 for analysis of the X-linked recessive hypothesis. V 30 should be indicated as the oldest member of his sibship. The birth order of the others is as indicated. VI 24 and 26 were female offspring who died in the first two weeks of life. Males VII 19 and VIII 1 show no detectable abnormality at the ages of six months and three months, respectively. Except for V 30 the males indicated as dying young died of accidental causes or tuberculosis after the age of 10 years and can, with reasonable confidence, be considered unaffected. (Pedigree extended from that published in *Am. J. Human Genet.* (Johnston and McKusick, 1962).)

lose the patronymic by marriage, it is often difficult to trace the relationship. I think if we had fuller genealogical details we should find that several of the bleeder families now thought to be distinct belong to the same stock."

In the case of X–*linked dominant traits*, affection of all daughters of affected males is, like absence of male-to-male transmission, an essential feature (Fig. 4). (Nos. A14 and A23 are examples of X–linked dominance (Fig. 5).) X–linked dominance superficially resembles autosomal dominance in pedigree pattern. The difference becomes obvious, however, when the children of affected males are analyzed (Table 3). With autosomal dominant traits, half, on the average, of both the sons and the daughters of an affected person are affected; with X–linked dominant traits, although the same is true for the offspring of affected females, all the daughters and none of the sons of affected males are affected. An excess of affected females should make one suspect X–linked dominant inheritance. With an X–linked trait which is always evident in the heterozygous female, the number of affected females in an extensive pedigree approaches twice the number of affected males, and the same is true in the population at large. The last is true, however, only if the gene frequency is fairly low. For example, with the X–linked dominant blood group Xg^a (Mann, et al., 1962) the frequency of "affected" females is not twice that of affected males; 62 per cent of males and 89 per cent of females have the blood group. (Since $p = 0.62$, the expected frequency of $Xg(a+)$ females is $p^2 + 2\ pq$, or 0.86. See Fig. 11, p. 17.) Figure 11 gives the female:male ratio for X–linked dominant traits with various gene frequencies. Full penetrance in the female is assumed.

Other characteristics of X–linked dominant inheritance are the following: 1) Barring new mutation and incomplete penetrance, affected males always have an affected mother. 2) One-third of affected females have an affected father and two-thirds an affected mother.

If the disorder for which X–linked dominant inheritance is suspected on the basis of more frequent involvement of females is also more severe in females, then sex-influenced autosomal dominant inheritance is more likely than X–linked inheritance. On the average, females heterozygous for an X–linked dominant trait have less marked expression than do hemizy-

TABLE 2

Grandsons of identified carriers through their daughters

Carriers	Grandsons through Daughters		
	Total	Affected	Unaffected
II 1	16	3	13
III 8	14	3	11
III 9	5	4	1
IV 20	—	—	—
IV 26	13	2	11
V 31	2	2	0
V 37	3	0	3
Observed	53	14	39
Expected		14.25	38.75

gous males. For this reason, discussed further on p. 15, X–linked dominant traits might more appropriately be called X–linked intermediates.

X–*linked dominance with lethality in the hemizygous male* can result in a pedigree pattern (Fig. 6) showing affection of females (and only females) in direct descent through several generations, a deficiency of males among the offspring of affected females, and an unusually high frequency of abortion in affected females. This mode of inheritance has been invoked for at least two disorders, *incontinentia pigmenti* (No. B2) and the OFD syndrome (No. C4), and might be suggested in connection with two others, Wildervanck's syndrome (No. B3) and a variety of congenital cataract (No. A48). (See Figure 7a and b.) Female-limited autosomal dominance cannot be excluded. An autosomal "partial trisomy" lethal in the male has been claimed for the OFD syndrome by Patau and colleagues (1961). Demonstration of linkage with an established X–linked trait is the only conclusive proof that the locus in question is on the X chromosome. Also difficult to exclude is cytoplasmic inheritance, for example, through the mechanism of a virus-like agent. Indeed, in *incontinentia pigmenti*, cytoplasmic inclusions suggesting virus have been identified in acute inflammatory stages of the disease (Murrell, 1961, personal communication, Richmond) and the associated congenital malformations could be easily explained on this basis (see B2 of the appendix).

Partial, or incomplete, sex-linkage resulting from the location of genes on homologous, or pairing, portions of the X and Y chromosomes

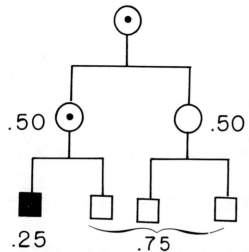

FIG. 3. TEST FOR X–LINKED RECESSIVE INHERITANCE
   One-fourth of the sons of daughters of carrier females are expected to be affected. See Table 2 for applications of this approach to analysis of pedigree in Figure 2.

would be expected to have characteristic patterns of heredity. If the trait is dominant most of the affected children of affected males will be of the sex of the affected paternal grandparent. If the trait is recessive, partial sex linkage is tested for as in autosomal linkage, the locus of the trait in question and the homologous segment of either X or Y being the two elements for which linkage is tested. The simplest case is when the linkage phase of the father (i.e., on his X or his Y chromosome) is known from the type of first cousin marriage (see Fig. 43b).

Morton (1957) concluded that so far the evidence for any example of partial sex-linkage is unacceptable. A possible exception was the large pedigree of familial nephritis with deafness reported from Utah (Perkoff, et al., 1960). However, as more pedigrees of this disorder accumulate, autosomal inheritance with an abnormal segregation ratio seems more likely (Cohen, Cassidy, and Hanna, 1961; Graham, 1959b; Shaw and Glover, 1961; Whalen, et al., 1961). It has been suggested (Berlyne, Bulmer, and Platt, 1961) that *pseudoxanthoma elasticum* may be a partially sex-linked recessive trait, since most of the reported sibships have contained affected males or affected females and rarely both. In fact in only one family out of 22 reported with adequate information did Berlyne and his colleagues find affected sibs of both sexes. However, we can add two further families of this type: in one sibship four males and one female out of seven sibs are affected; in a second unrelated sibship a brother and sister are affected. As pointed out by Macklin (1952), among the offspring from consanguineous marriages an excess of affected females can be expected if the trait is partially sex-linked. The pseudoxanthoma pedigrees in which the parents are related show no excess of females (D. Wise, Baltimore, personal communication). Any intra-

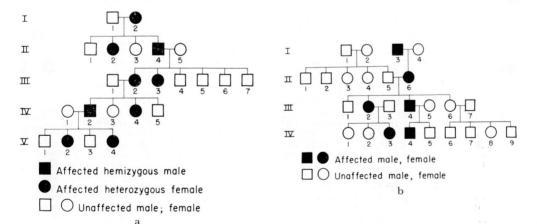

FIG. 4. SCHEMATIC AND IDEALIZED PEDIGREE PATTERN OF X–LINKED DOMINANT TRAITS

   a. Among the offspring of "affected" males *all* daughters are "affected," *all* sons are normal. Compare with the idealized pattern of *autosomal dominant trait*. b. If the trait were autosomal dominant, the probability that all six sons of affected males would be normal and all four daughters affected is $(\frac{1}{2})^{10}$, or 0.001.

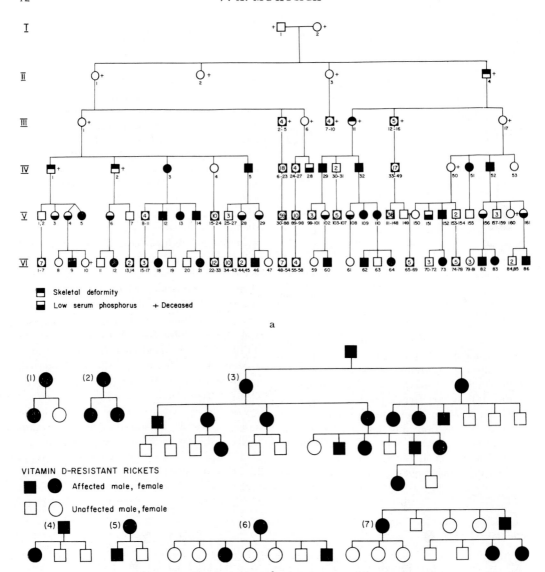

FIG. 5. X–LINKED DOMINANT INHERITANCE OF HYPOPHOSPHATEMIA
a. Pedigree redrawn from Winters, et al. (1957). (The symbols consisting of a circle within a square represent a group of unaffected males and females in the number indicated, e.g., V 99–101 are three unaffected males.) Williams, Winters, and Burnett (1960) make the useful point, which is of general pertinence in human genetics, that if skeletal disease is taken as the trait for genetic study the mode of inheritance is unclear, whereas use of the trait *hypophosphatemia* results in a distinctive pedigree pattern. b. Seven pedigrees of *hypophosphatemia* (vitamin D resistant rickets) which in the original publication were interpreted as indicative of autosomal dominant inheritance. However, the pedigree pattern is equally consistent, in fact more consistent, with X–linked dominant inheritance. Pedigrees 1 and 2 are re-drawn from Tobler, Prader, and Taillard (1956); pedigree 3 from Mitchell and Mitchell (1957); pedigrees 4–7 from Dent and Harris (1956).

familial correlations with sex, such as those Haldane (1935, 1936) observed, could also be due to modifying genes segregating in families and affecting the expression in different sexes. The

cytologic evidence (p. 39) also makes partial sex linkage unlikely.

Simulation of X–linked inheritance can result through several mechanisms. In those condi-

TABLE 3

*Hypophosphatemic progeny of hypophosphatemic males
and hypophosphatemic females
(From Winters, et al. (1957))*

	Progeny of 7 Males			Progeny of 9 Females		
	Normal	Affected	Total	Normal	Affected	Total
Male Progeny						
Expected:						
If autosomal dominant	5	5		7	7	
If sex-linked dominant	10	0		7	7	
Observed:	10	0	10	6	8	14
Female Progeny						
Expected:						
If autosomal dominant	5.5	5.5		6.5	6.5	
If sex-linked dominant	0	11		6.5	6.5	
Observed:	0	11	11	9	4	13
All Progeny						
Expected:						
If autosomal dominant	10.5	10.5		13.5	13.5	
If sex-linked dominant	10.5	10.5		13.5	13.5	
Observed:	10	11	21	15	12	27

The observed distributions in the progeny of affected females could have readily occurred by chance under the hypothesis of autosomal dominant inheritance. However, the probability that seven affected males would have had all sons normal and all daughters affected is extremely small.

tions in which the severity or the nature of the trait precludes reproduction by affected males, X–linked recessive inheritance is difficult to distinguish from male-limited autosomal dominant inheritance (Fig. 8). Nos. B4, B5, and B6 in the catalog are examples of this dilemma. As in a previously cited situation (p. 10), critical proof that the gene is X-borne is demonstration of linkage with a trait independently proved to be X–linked. (Alternatively, the demonstration of linkage with an autosomal trait would prove that the trait is *not* X–linked.) Another proof of X–linkage is demonstration of the trait in question in cases of the Turner syndrome of the XO type; this approach is, of course, not applicable

in the case of male hypogonadism or the syndrome of testicular feminization.

Yet, another approach which theoretically is applicable in these conditions was suggested by Morton (1962) and applied by Morton and Chung (1959) to data on Duchenne muscular dystrophy. The method, based on the relative proportions of sporadic and familial cases, is described in more detail on p. 72. For an autosomal dominant trait with no reproduction by affected males, about ½ of cases are expected to be sporadic, i.e., to arise by new mutation, whereas an X–linked recessive trait with no reproduction by affected males is expected to be sporadic in about ⅓ of cases.

Levit (1936), who emphasized the problem of distinguishing X–linked recessive from autosomal dominant male-limited inheritance, suggested that before X–linkage can be considered proved nine unaffected sons of affected males should have been observed, with, of course, no affected sons. Such an experience, neglecting the possibility of carrier status of the wives of said affected men, reduces the probability of autosomal dominant inheritance to $1/2^9$ or 0.002. Many of the conditions listed in the catalog have not passed such a rigorous test.

If two sisters marry two brothers (or even unrelated men) and sons of each couple are affected by an autosomal recessive disorder, then a superficial similarity to X–linked inheritance is created. Some of the pedigrees (e.g., Fig. 9) of families with multiple instances of the translocation type of Down's

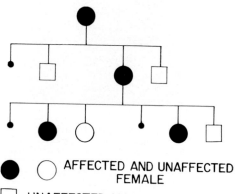

FIG. 6. IDEALIZED PEDIGREE PATTERN OF X–LINKED DOMINANT TRAIT LETHAL IN THE MALE

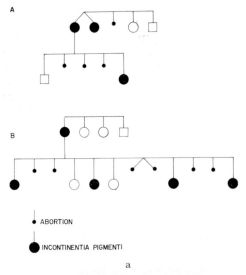

A

B

↓ ABORTION

⬤ INCONTINENTIA PIGMENTI

a

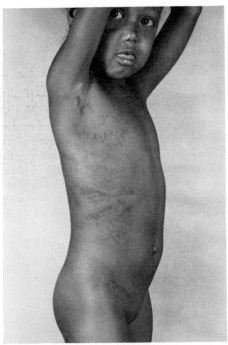

b

FIG. 7. INCONTINENTIA PIGMENTI
a. Pedigrees of *incontinentia pigmenti* which is thought to be sex-linked dominant trait lethal in the male. After Lenz (1961). b. *Incontinentia pigmenti*. (See No. B2 in appendix for clinical description.)

syndrome (the preferred term (Allen, et al., 1961) for Mongolism) suggest X–linked inheritance (Carter, et al., 1960). Only female carriers of the 21/group D translocation have affected

children (Hamerton, et al., 1961) and by chance the affected persons may all be male.

The opposite error—simulation of autosomal dominant inheritance by a sex-linked recessive trait—is possible. There was, for example, male-to-male transmission of hemophilia (later shown to be of type A) through four successive generations of Treves' family (1886) in which, furthermore, consanguineous marriages resulted in homozygous hemophilic females (Merskey, 1951; Gilchrist, 1961) (Fig. 10). Assuming that the reporting was accurate, hemophilic males in three successive generations may have married heterozygous female carriers and had hemophilic sons for that reason. This is the same sort of quasi-dominant pattern as that which results with an autosomal recessive trait and much inbreeding, e.g., alkaptonuria in the Dominican Republic (Milch, 1960).

Oswald's family (1911), frequently cited as an example of X–linked myopia, and Herringham's (1889), considered to be an example of X–linked Charcot–Marie–Tooth's disease, contained instances of male-to-male transmission in the first two generations. Both may be errors of recording since Charcot–Marie–Tooth's disease is known to have X–linked inheritance in certain families; and myopia, although not to our knowledge X–linked as an isolated finding, is a component in several syndromes (No. A42, A50) whose other features might have been overlooked by Oswald (1911). Other possibilities are 1) that the son was affected by a mimicking condition, genetic or nongenetic, and 2) that the son inherited the X–linked recessive trait from his mother, a heterozygous carrier.

Significance of dominance and recessiveness in X–linkage. As the terms are used in medical genetics, which is concerned in the main with rare traits which when dominant occur almost only in heterozygous individuals, the definitions of dominance and recessiveness differ from the classic ones of Mendel, who introduced the terms, but parallel the usage of *Drosophila* genetics. In medical genetics a trait is said to be dominant if it is manifest when the responsible gene is present in the heterozygous state and to be recessive if the gene must be present in double dose, or homozygous state, for manifestation of the trait. As used in connection with X–linked traits, these definitions apply to the female, but not to the hemizygous male,

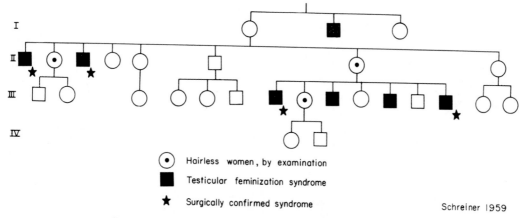

Hairless women, by examination

Testicular feminization syndrome

Surgically confirmed syndrome

Schreiner 1959

FIG. 8. PEDIGREE OF THE "TESTICULAR FEMINIZATION" SYNDROME
Note that autosomal dominant inheritance with male limitation equally well explains the
prima facie pedigree evidence. Adapted from Schreiner (1959).

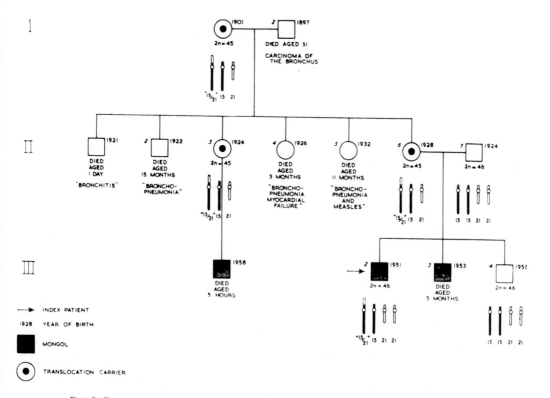

FIG. 9. FAMILIAL DOWN SYNDROME OF TRANSLOCATION TYPE WITH PATTERN SIMULATING
X–LINKED RECESSIVE INHERITANCE
From Hamerton, et al. (1961)

who always (at least for practical purposes this is true) expresses the gene.

The Mendelian definition of dominance includes the additional concept that the phenotype of the homozygous individual is indistinguishable from that of the individual heterozygous for the same gene. No trait in the catalog (Table 1) is truly dominant in the Mendelian

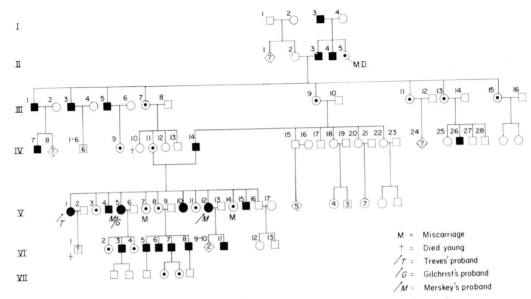

FIG. 10. HEMOPHILIA A IN THE FAMILY FROM THE SAFFRON WALDEN DISTRICT, ESSEX, ENGLAND, STUDIED BY TREVES (1886), BULLOCK, AND FILDES (1912), HANDLEY AND NUSSBRECHER (1935), MERSKEY (1951), AND GILCHRIST (1961)

sense. For example, the female heterozygous for the gene for hypophosphatemia has less marked depression of serum phosphorus and less severe skeletal deformity than does the hemizygous male. (The female homozygous for this X–linked mutation has not been observed (Graham, 1962).) If the Lyon hypothesis (p. 59 ff) is valid, one would expect most heterozygous females to have less full expression than hemizygous males.

(Actually Mendel's own definition of dominant and recessive does not demand such absolute identity of the homozygous and heterozygous dominant phenotypes as some writers suggest (e.g., Allison and Blumberg, 1958). What he wrote was as follows (Peters, 1958): "Henceforth in this paper those characters which are transmitted entire, or almost unchanged in the hybridization and therefore in themselves constitute the characters of the hybrid, are termed the *dominant*, and those which become latent in the process *recessive*." If one substitutes "heterozygote" for "hybrid" and recognizes the qualification "almost unchanged", Mendel's definition does not differ significantly from the current working definition of dominance.)

As Levit (1936) emphasized, few or no X–linked traits are completely recessive. As in many autosomal recessive traits, many of the X–linked traits in the catalog, when subjected

to close study, are found to have partial expression of the gene in the heterozygote. Dominance and recessiveness are relative matters. Furthermore, possibly because of the conditions of the Lyon hypothesis (p. 59), fully expressing heterozygotes for X–linked traits occur rather more often than in the case of autosomal recessive traits.

The homozygous state of at least seven X–borne mutations has been described: hemophilia A (Pola and Svojitka, 1957; Israëls, Lempert, and Gilbertson, 1951), two types of color blindness (François, 1961), glucose–6–phosphate dehydrogenase deficiency, megalocornea (Grönholm, 1921; see Fig. 52); the Xg[a] blood group (Mann, et al., 1962); and ichthyosis (Czösz, 1929; Orel, 1929). In none is the homozygous female any more severely affected than the hemizygous male. (The homozygous hemophilic female dog has a clinical and hematologic picture indistinguishable from that of the hemizygous hemophilic male dog (Graham, 1962; personal communication, Chapel Hill, North Carolina).) Hardisty's female patient with hemophilia B (1957) could be an example either of heterozygous expression or of a homozygote. She was the daughter of an affected male. No hemophiliacs were known in the mother's family. In

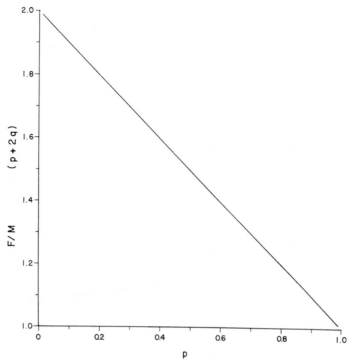

FIG. 11. THE RATIO OF FEMALES TO MALES "AFFECTED" BY AN X-LINKED DOMINANT TRAIT
DEPENDING ON THE FREQUENCY OF THE DOMINANT ALLELE, p

such a situation the only proof of heterozygosity is the genetic one provided when the hemophilic female bears normal sons. Often in X–linked traits one can prove heterozygosity and thereby exclude homozygosity, but one cannot provide absolute proof of homozygosity. One of the more interesting biological features of hemophilia elucidated in recent years is the survival of homozygous hemophilic females, a fact first demonstrated in the dog by Brinkhous and Graham (1950). Earlier it was presumed that all such individuals died. Hemostasis probably is not as much of a factor in keeping menstruation within bounds as had been thought.

The detection of X–linked traits. Some of the mutants listed in the catalog might be called "private" mutations, having probably been described only in a single family (e.g., No. A22, A45, A48, A58). Undoubtedly the X–linked recessive inheritance of a few conditions has escaped recognition because only brothers in a single sibship have been affected. Theoretically, support for the X–linked recessive hypothesis in such families can be obtained by demonstrating an intermediate phenotype in the

mother (but not in the father) and perhaps also in some of her first degree female relatives. For example, Williams and Field (1961) in a family with hepatic phosphorylase-deficient glycogen storage disease found that of three children two sons were affected and one son was normal. Low leukocyte phosphorylase activity was demonstrated in the affected sons. All other members of the family including the father had normal leukocyte phorphorylase levels, except the mother, who had an intermediate level. The combination of findings suggests X–linkage, with the mother a heterozygous carrier. Teller, Rosevear, and Burke (1961) used the same reasoning in a group of cases of the Hurler syndrome.[1] There is, however, an important pitfall in this approach: studies of the carrier state in persons heterozygous for autosomal recessive genes frequently reveal only one parent with definitely abnormal findings in the test applied. If that parent is the mother and if only sons are

[1] Dorfman (personal communication, Chicago, 1961) has been unable to detect any abnormality in either parent in the case of either the autosomal recessive or the X–linked form of the Hurler syndrome.

affected, X–linked inheritance could be falsely suspected. Indeed, females affected by the phosphorylase-deficiency type of glycogen storage disease of the liver have been described (Hers, 1959), a fact suggesting autosomal recessive inheritance.

Other legitimate additions to the list of X–linked mutations are no doubt buried in the literature and have not been exhumed in the preparation of the catalog. For example, Deraemaeker (1958), in describing a pedigree of X–linked recessive congenital deafness, referred to a convincing X–linked pedigree previously reported without comment by Stevenson and Cheeseman (1956) in a large series from Northern Ireland. From the excess of affected males in several large series in the literature, Chung, Robison, and Morton (1959) estimated that 1.5 per cent of deafmutism might be on the basis of an X–borne mutation. Fraser (1962; personal communication, Seattle) has identified several X–linked pedigrees of deafmutism.

Some autosomally inherited conditions occur with greater frequency in males than in females (Harris, 1948). The Laurence–Moon–Biedl syndrome (Bell, 1958), gout, familial periodic paralysis (see C7), and galactosemia (Hsia and Walker, 1961) are examples. The more frequent occurrence of hereditary hemochromatosis in males probably has its basis in the fact that females lose iron in the menses and through pregnancies. An apparent excess of males affected by some conditions such as alkaptonuria is almost certainly due to social factors (e.g., the more frequent examination of men for employment, insurance, military service, etc.). It is doubtful that genetic heterogeneity with X–linkage in some families can account for a male excess which seems genuine in some hereditary conditions. One possibility tested by Csik and Mather (1937) was that an X–borne gene must also be present in hemizygous state in the male or in homozygous state in the female for expression of, let us say, an autosomal recessive gene present in homozygous state. Since this necessary condition would be obtained more often in males (q) than in females (q^2) a male preponderance might be explained. Suffice it to say that with the data analyzed, no evidence for such a mechanism could be found. One must resort to the alternative possibility, that differences in penetrance of the autosomal trait are a result of more general physiologic differences between males and females.

Certain lethal congenital malformations, which occur predominantly in males, may be X–linked and may contribute in reducing the high primary sex ratio to the lower secondary sex ratio observed at birth (p. 73). Bilateral renal agenesis is such a condition, which has, furthermore, been observed in brothers (Rosenfeld, 1959).

Other conditions (such as Whipple's disease of the intestine) which occur almost exclusively in males should also be investigated from the point of view of possible X–linkage. Brothers affected by Whipple's disease have been described (Gross, et al., 1959; Puite and Tesluk, 1953; Scott and Hosie, 1957), and in one of the families (Puite and Tesluk, 1953) the mother may have been affected. (Electron-microscopic identification of "cigar-shaped" cytoplasmic inclusions, "bacillary bodies" (Yardley and Hendrix, 1961), and some of the clinical features suggest an infectious etiology.)

Some X–linked dominant traits have probably appeared in the literature under the guise of autosomal dominance. For example, small pedigrees of hypophosphatemia (Fig. 5b) were interpreted as showing autosomal dominant inheritance (Dent and Harris, 1956; Mitchell and Mitchell, 1957; Tobler, Prader and Taillard, 1956), although re-examination shows the pattern to be consistent with X–linked dominant inheritance.

Despite all the difficulties, the pedigree pattern method is a finer screen for X–linked traits than for autosomal traits. In fact, the catalog of X–linked traits in man represents probably the largest group of genes which have been located to one chromosome in any metazoan other than *Drosophila melanogaster*, certainly the largest in any mammal. At least one advantage of man as an object of genetic study is illustrated, namely the very extensive anatomic, chemical, physiologic, and pathologic descriptions of phenotypes.

The relative frequency of dominant and recessive mutations in man. As just stated, in man a more complete enumeration can be achieved for X–linked mutations than for autosomal mutations. Experience in other species, including mammals such as the mouse, suggests that recessive mutations are more numerous than dom-

TABLE 4

X–linked traits of man and mouse[2]

	Man (Verschuer, 1959)	Mouse (M. C. Green, 1961)
Autosomal dominant	285	35
Autosomal recessive	89	123
Sex-linked	38	7

Most X–linked traits of both man and mouse are recessive.

inant ones (Haldane, 1939b; Levit, 1936). In man the relative proportion of *observed* autosomal traits which are dominant is much greater than the proportion which are recessive (Table 4). In part this is because many pedigrees contain only a single case of a recessive disorder, giving no hint of a genetic basis. However, the main reason that in man autosomal recessive mutant phenotypes are less likely to be detected than dominant ones is the low frequency of consanguineous matings. Haldane (1939a) expressed this well:

Inbreeding has been relaxed during historical time in most civilized communities. This has resulted in a rapid decrease in the frequency of lethal and sublethal recessive conditions, followed by a slow increase in the frequency of the genes responsible for them. The frequency of recessive conditions will rise slowly to its old level, but the time needed for the half completion of this process is of the order of at least 2000 years in most cases, and may be longer. This gives one reason why dominant abnormalities appear to be commoner than recessives in man.

Finally, as Levit (1936) pointed out, explanation of the difference may also reside in part in the fact that only the homozygous state of a gene is recognized in animals and the milder

[2] The number of autosomal recessive traits recognized in man is increasing rapidly, possibly more rapidly than the number of newly identified dominant traits. In time the ratio of dominants to recessives may be reversed. The identification of many recessives can be attributed in part to the burgeoning of the field of biochemical genetics. Most inborn errors of metabolism are recessive. Demonstration of a pronounced enzyme deficiency in the proband and a partial deficiency in both parents is generally accepted as strong evidence for recessive inheritance even in the absence of enough affected families to permit formal testing of the recessive hypothesis. Awareness that parental consanguinity is strong evidence for the recessive inheritance of a rare trait has also helped extend the list of recessive traits.

heterozygous state escapes attention, unlike the situation in man in which analysis of phenotype is often more penetrating.

On the other hand, an X–borne mutation, even if recessive and not expressed in the heterozygous female, is always expressed in the hemizygous male.[3] For example, hemophilia A occurs once in about every 10,000 males. The gene frequency for X–borne mutations is identical to the phenotype frequency in males; therefore, the gene frequency for hemophilia A is about $1/10,000$. If the responsible gene were on an autosome and were recessive, if the gene frequency were the same, and if breeding were random the frequency of affected persons would be $(1/10,000)^2$, or only 1 in 100 million.

Furthermore, if the proportion of males affected by hemophilia is $1/10,000$, the proportion of affected females (again disregarding consanguinity) is 1 in 100,000,000. The occurrence of hemophilia in the human female was not established unequivocally until 1951 (Israëls, Lempert and Gilbertson, 1951; Merskey, 1951), after its demonstration in the dog (Brinkhous and Graham, 1950) had proved that the homozygous state is not necessarily lethal. Since the homozygous state of the gene is required for expression in the female, the delayed recognition is consistent with the above argument. Writing in 1912, Bullock and Fildes stated: "So far as we can find, after studying the contents of some 900 papers on hæmophilia, no case has yet been described in a female which bears more than a superficial resemblance to the disease as found in the male." Actually it has more recently been demonstrated by Merskey (1951) and by Gilchrist (1961) that the female with hemophilia reported by Treves in 1886, but considered unacceptable by Bullock and Fildes, was indeed a female homozygous for antihemophilic globulin deficiency (Fig. 10).

It is true to state that, in animals and for X–linked traits in man, those mutations *we can recognize* are most often recessive and that in man autosomal mutations that we can recognize are most often dominant. The generalization that mutations are more often recessive than dominant does not necessarily follow, since we may not be able to recognize many dominant

[3] Richterich and colleagues (1963) suggest that Duchenne muscular dystrophy is non-penetrant in a certain significant proportion of hemizygous males but this seems highly improbable.

lethals. On the other hand, one would anticipate a tendency for mutations to become recessive through a change in the genetic background against which they occur. This phenomenon (Haldane, 1939a) was referred to by Fisher (1931) as "the evolution of dominance" on the part of the wild, more "normal" or beneficial allele. Haldane (1930) summarized the hypothesis as follows: "Fisher has suggested that on its first appearance a mutant gene usually produces a marked effect in the heterozygous condition, and becomes recessive to the wild type only as the result of natural selection acting over very long periods. He regards this process as due to the selection of specific modifying genes which render the appearance and viability of the heterozygote approximately the same as those of the wild type." (It is, of course, the phenotype, not the gene, which becomes recessive.) Levit (1936) referred to the same phenomenon as follows: "It has become generally recognized in recent years that wild genes (normal allelomorphs) did not always so generally dominate over their mutant allelomorphs as they do now, but that at least some of them became dominant through natural selection. There is a difference of opinion, however, as regards the question of the mechanism of this evolutionary process." (Again it is the normal phenotype, not the normal gene, which "became dominant through natural selection.")

Phenocopies and genocopies of X–linked traits. A risk which is carried by lists such as the catalog of X–linked traits is that the uninformed will conclude that a particular trait named therein is always hereditary or is always X–linked. The heterogeneity of genetic disease and the occurrence of environmentally determined phenocopies of genetic disease are fundamental principles of medical genetics. Although several of the conditions listed in the catalog are indeed always hereditary and always X–linked (e.g., A51 and A55), many others have autosomal genocopies, or genetic mimics (e.g., No. A3, A6, A11, A30, A53). Sometimes phenotypic differences between autosomal and X–linked forms can be detected on close comparison; for example, the X–linked form of the Hurler syndrome lacks corneal opacity, a feature of the autosomal form (McKusick, 1960a). Nystagmus (No. A46) and Parkinsonism (No. A41) are really only symptoms; not only are there autosomally inherited forms but also these symptoms occur with environmentally induced damage to the central nervous system on a toxic, traumatic or infectious basis.

In Charcot–Marie–Tooth peroneal muscular dystrophy and in retinitis pigmentosa, autosomal dominant, and autosomal recessive forms of inheritance are observed as well as X–linked inheritance. In these and possibly other conditions, severity, as gauged by age of onset and age of incapacitation, tends to be greatest in the autosomal recessive form and least in the autosomal dominant form, with the X–linked recessive form intermediate (Allan, 1939).

Deficiency of antihemophilic globulin in von Willebrand's disease ("vascular hemophilia"), which is transmitted as an autosomal dominant (Graham, 1959a; Raccuglia and Neel, 1960), may be evidence that (Graham, 1959a) both autosomal and X–borne loci are concerned normally with the same phenotype protein. (See No. A8 in Appendix for another interpretation.) Both autosomal and X–linked loci are concerned in the synthesis of gamma globulin, witness, the X–linked inheritance of agammaglobulinemia (A10) and the identification of two autosomal loci *Gm* and *Inv* concerned with immunologic specificities of gamma globulin (Steinberg, 1962).

Can mutation at more than one locus on the X chromosome result in some of these disorders? In the Waaler hypothesis two loci have been postulated for X–linked color blindness: one locus with an allelic series for the protan type and a second locus with an allelic series for the deutan type (Kalmus, 1962; Stern, 1958). (Tritanopia is by the evidence of Kalmus (1955–1956) autosomal in its genetic control. Total color blindness is also autosomal (François, 1961) in the experience of most, although one clearly X–linked pedigree has been studied; see No. A3.) X–linked hemophilia, previously considered a single entity, is now known to consist of at least two physiologically distinct entities which may be genetically distinct as well; linkage studies (Whittaker, Copeland, and Graham, 1962) suggest that they are determined by genes at loci rather widely separated on the X chromosome.

Are some of the separately listed X–borne traits actually determined by allelic genes? Multiple allelism seems adequately established for each of the two loci for partial color blindness. However, nothing is known about possible allelic relationship of other traits listed here as separate mutations. Is there an allelic relationship between the Duchenne (No. A6) and Becker (No. A7) forms of pseudohypertrophic muscular dystrophy; between nystagmus (No. A46) and myoclonic nystagmus (No. B11); between congenital deafness (No. A29) and progressive deafness of later onset (No. A30); between retinitis pigmentosa (No. A53), choroideremia (No. A52), and choroidal sclerosis (No. B13), all rather similar conditions? One notes the occurrence of myopia with stationary night blindness in one mutation (No. A51) and with external ophthalmoplegia in another (No. A43). Thrombocytopenia occurs with at least two X–linked syndromes (No. A13 and A21). Phenotypically distinct types of spinocerebellar degeneration are X–linked (Nos. A33, A34, A35). Might these be determined by allelic genes? At least two X–linked forms of diffuse cerebral sclerosis (Nos. A38, A39) are phenotypically similar although, in the opinion of most, they are distinct entities.

As Neel (1961a) points out, arguments of allelism based on phenotypic similarities must be pursued with great caution, however.

There appear to be four separate X–linked mutations affecting glucose–6–phosphate dehydrogenase (see Appendix, No. A4). As indicated later (p. 35) linkage studies in man can prove non-allelism but cannot be expected to provide absolute proof of allelism. However, the evidence to date is consistent with the hypothesis that all four mutations are allelic.

The complementarity test of allelism so useful in bacterial genetics has been applied to the variant hemoglobins and to genetic coagulation defects in man. Since an artificial mixture of blood from a classic hemophiliac and blood from a case of Christmas disease has normal clotting capacity, the genes are known to be members of different cistrons and therefore nonallelic (Benzer, 1957). Nonallelism of the genes for the two types of clotting defect is further supported by the difference in linkage relationships with color blindness and Xg (p. 30).

Other comments. Most X–linked mutations in man have been detected by recognition of a characteristic pedigree pattern. Discussion to this point has, therefore, been appropriately focused on this approach. In the case of *common traits* the approach to detection is somewhat different. X–linkage of frequently occurring traits is in the first place suspected from the rela-

tive frequency of affected males and females. If the trait is recessive, the frequency of affected males is q and of females q^2; thus males are more frequently affected. If the trait is dominant the frequency of affected males is p and of affected females is $p^2 + 2\ pq$; females are more frequently affected.[4] Color blindness and glucose–6–phosphate dehydrogenase deficiency are examples of the first, and the newly discovered Xg^a blood group antigen (No. A5) is an example of the second.

A second step in detecting X–linkage of common traits is to determine whether the types of matings in a randomly ascertained collection of marital couples agrees with the proportions expected on the basis of gene frequencies derived from the phenotype frequencies in the male (Table 5).

A third step in detecting X–linkage of common traits is to determine the proportion of affected males and females among the children of different types of matings. The critical type of mating in the case of an X–linked dominant is affected male by normal female; all daughters and no sons should be affected. In the case of an X–linked recessive trait, matings of affected male by affected female result in all of both sons and daughters affected, just as with autosomal recessive traits. The Chapel Hill group (Graham, 1962; personal communication, Chapel Hill, South Carolina) has observed 10 such matings of hemophilic dogs and all 47 offspring of both sexes have been hemophilic. Among the offspring of a male affected by an X–linked recessive trait the frequency of affected sons is determined by the frequency of heterozygous female carriers in the population.

In man *graded characters*, whose genetic component is presumed to be polygenic, are also influenced by X–borne genes. Intrafamilial comparisons, essentially an application of the pedigree method, must form the basis for a conclusion on this point. In a large study, Winge (1921) noted a tendency for the eye color of the child to take after that of the parent of the opposite sex. Hogben (1932) pointed out that any contribution of sex-linked genes to the observed variance will tend to lower the correlation between father and son and between brother and sister. It will raise the correlation between father and daughter or between sister and sister.

---

[4] The relation between gene frequency and the ratio of females to males for an X–linked dominant trait is shown in Figure 11.

TABLE 5

The expected distribution of mating types in a randomly ascertained series of couples and the distribution of phenotypes in their children

(p and q are frequencies of dominant and recessive alleles, respectively, and p + q = 1)

Parents		Proportion of Mating Types	Sons		Daughters	
Father	Mother		Dominant Phenotype	Recessive Phenotype	Dominant Phenotype	Recessive Phenotype
Dominant phenotype (p) X	Dominant phenotype ($p^2 + 2pq$)	$p^3 + 2\,p^2q$	$1 - pq$	pq	1	0
Dominant phenotype (p) X	Recessive phenotype (q^2)	pq^2	0	1	1	0
Recessive phenotype (q) X	Dominant phenotype ($p^2 + 2pq$)	$p^2q + 2\,pq^2$	$1 - pq$	pq	$1 - pq$	pq
Recessive phenotype (q) X	Recessive phenotype (q^2)	q^3	0	1	0	1
		1				

Two sisters are more alike than two brothers, for in brothers the one X chromosome may be either of the mother's two; while in sisters one X chromosome (the paternal one) is identical and the other is, with 50 per cent likelihood, identical. (Because of crossing over the maternal X chromosome contributed to two daughters is never completely identical, of course.) Hogben (1932) made the interesting comment: "If an appreciable proportion of the total variance [in intelligence quotients] is due to sex-linked genes, it is of more importance that a boy should have a clever mother than a clever father."

Finney (1939) applied a method for testing for sex-linkage in a quantitative character to records on stature obtained by Galton. There was a suggestion of effects of X–linked gene(s), but he warned that "in view of the various seeming contradictions found in the data, it would be undesirable to place trust in any results derived therefrom without first testing them on other records." Brues (1950), by linkage studies using Penrose's sib-pair method, concluded that X–linked factors may be involved in body-build. However, so many assumptions and corrections were necessary to permit comparison of male and female sibs that no firm conclusion is, as she pointed out, possible.

In an earlier study Brues (1946) presented some evidence for the occurrence of dominant

TABLE 6

The occurrence of dominant or partially dominant eye-color gene(s) on the X chromosome

	Sibs of light-eyed males		Sibs of light-eyed females	
	Brothers n = 65	Sisters n = 77	Brothers n = 40	Sisters n = 79
Light-eyed	64.6	29.9	57.5	50.7
Not light-eyed	35.4	70.1	42.5	49.3

or partially dominant eye-color gene(s) on the X chromosome—evidence supporting the finding of Winge (1921). Blue-eyed ("light-eyed" was Brues' term) males had more brown-eyed ("not light-eyed") sisters than brown-eyed brothers, whereas blue-eyed females had brown-eyed brothers and sisters in about the same numbers (see Table 6). Both brothers and sisters could get the brown-eyed factor from the mother and the sisters, but only the sisters could get it also from the father.

Schaefer, Adlersberg, and Steinberg studied intrafamilial correlations for serum levels of cholesterol (1958a) and phospholipids (1958b). Whereas the parents showed no correlation, the parent-child and sib-sib correlations were significantly different from zero. Because of age and sex effects, all values were converted to the equivalent levels for males age 20 years before correlations were determined. In the case of both cholesterol and phospholipid these workers concluded that the data "do not support the hypothesis of an important sex-linked component in the genetic causation of the serum level." However, since father-son correlations were considerably lower than the others, the matter may not be completely closed.

It is of interest that hemophilia is X–linked also in the dog, and that in the dog, as in man, two varieties of X–linked hemophilia, A and B, have been found (Hutt, Rickard, and Field, 1948; Mustard, et al., 1960).[5] In each type the physiologic defect is seemingly identical in man and dog. The findings suggest that the loci concerned with two factors essential to clotting, AHG (antihemophilic globulin) and PTC (plasma thromboplastin component), may be older than either species. Hutt (1953) points out that in cattle a condition seemingly identical to anhidrotic ectodermal dysplasia is transmitted as an X–linked trait as in man. It is difficult to believe that all three of these cases are chance coincidence. Possible X–linked homologies in mice and men will also be worthy of study from this point of view.

"Streaked hairlessness" in Holstein-Friesian cattle (Eldridge and Atkesson, 1953) is possibly analogous to incontinentia pigmenti (B2) in man and like the latter condition may be inherited as an X–linked dominant, lethal in the male. Falconer and Isaacson (1962) described a sex-linked anemia of the mouse which may be homologous to the Cooley-Rundles-Falls anemia of man (A19). Histocompatibility genes of mice are blood group genes. The description of histoincompatibility associated with the X chromosome in mice (Bailey, 1962) raises questions of possible homology to the Xg blood group system of man. Color-vision is widespread in the animal kingdom (Francois and Verriest, 1957) and cebus monkeys with color blindness of the protanopic type were described by Grether (1939). Seemingly nothing is known of the inheritance of the defect in monkeys, however. Glucose–6–phosphate dehydrogenase deficiency is described in monkeys (Eng, 1962), but again no information on heredity is available. Sex-linked cerebellar degeneration has been de-

scribed in pullets (Mackson, Carnaghan and Young, 1959) but the birds may be too remote from man to make homology to similar disease in man (cf. p. 77) convincing. Homology which has been a corner-stone for work in almost every other area of biology may be useful also in fine-structure genetic analysis. If the genetic content of the X chromosome and its organization is similar in man and mouse, knowledge of the X chromosome of man might be extended by study of mice in which experimental genetics can be done. The evolution of the X chromosome can also be studied.

In organisms other than man there is evidence 1) that genes responsible for similar functions are often linked (Ames, Garry, and Herzenberg, 1960; Demerec and Hartman, 1959), 2) that genes functioning at the same time in ontogeny, although with quite different functions, may be linked (Paigen and Noell, 1961), and 3) that genes controlling successive steps in a chain of biochemical reactions are sometimes linked in a similar sequence on the chromosome (Ames, Garry, and Herzenberg, 1960). In the case of the genes controlling hemoglobin synthesis in man there is evidence for a "remarkable . . . clustering of related genetic functions on a single mammalian chromosome" (Neel, 1961b).

Is there any evidence of a concentration of genes with related function in the X chromosome? One wonders at the large number of X–linked ocular characters, 18 out of 58. In some part this may be due to the fact that ophthalmologists have, from the work of Leber, Horner, Nettleship, Usher, Waardenburg, Sorsby, Franceschetti, Falls, François, and others, long been informed about the typical pedigree pattern of X–linked traits. Furthermore, the phenotype is more accessible to study in the case of ocular traits than in many others. A valid way to examine the question of whether there is a concentration of "ocular loci" on the X chromosome is to determine whether more than 5 or 6 per cent of the numerous hereditary traits affecting the eye are X–linked. A perusal of the large monographs on heredity and the eye (François, 1961; Waardenburg, Franceschetti, and Klein, 1961) would suggest that the number of X–linked traits is *not* out of proportion to the number of autosomal traits.

In the discussion above and in the catalog, the term *mutation* has been used in a general sense. It is possible, for example, that some of

---

[5] Classical hemophilia is apparently X–linked also in the horse (Nossel, Archer and Macfarlane, 1962).

the X–linked traits enumerated in the appendix, perhaps particularly the rarer ones and those which are especially complex disorders (e.g., No. A21, A22, and A57), are the result, not of point mutation, but rather of deletions, inversions, or similar grosser derangements in the X chromosome. Furthermore, the terms *mutation* and *mutant* have often been used interchangeably. Strictly speaking, *mutation* is a process and *mutant* is the result.

IV· LINKAGE DATA ON THE CONSTITUTION OF THE X CHROMO-SOME OF MAN

DEFINITIONS. *Linkage* in general and *sex linkage* specifically are terms often misused in the clinical literature. Linkage is sometimes used for syndromal relationship (p. 37), when in fact the occurrence together of several hereditary traits has its basis in the multiple ramifications of the effect of a single gene. Linkage is also confused with *blood-group-and-disease association*. It is not generally appreciated that genetic linkage has no influence on the association of two traits in a population, except under the special circumstances of close linkage and insufficient time in number of generations for complete "mincing of the germ plasm" through crossing over (p. 36).

Sex-linkage is often confused with *sex-limitation*, or *sex-influence*. For example, loose-jointedness is often cited as a "sex-linked trait" on the basis of a paper (Key, 1927) entitled "Hypermobility of joints as a sex-linked hereditary character." However, the family in point consisted of an affected father with all three sons affected and all five daughters unaffected. Obviously this is not sex-linked, at least not X–linked, inheritance. Another example: Dorn's "dominant–geschlechts–chromosomen–gebunde-

ner Erbgang bei Trichoclasie" (Dorn, 1956) is an instance of male-to-male transmission through four generations and not of the usual pattern of X–linked inheritance, although in the last generation the unaffected sister of two affected males had an affected son. A third ex-

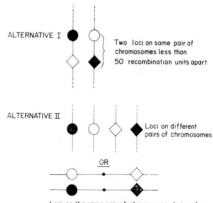

FIG. 12. THE ALTERNATIVES (I and II) WHICH STUDIES OF AUTOSOMAL LINKAGE SEEK TO DISTINGUISH

At the same time, linkage having been found, one determines the relative distance separating the two loci on the chromosome. Usually the issue in X–linkage is only the distance separating the two loci.

ample: in 1951 Barker, Commons, and Shelton described what they called "sex-linked juvenile diabetes mellitus" based on a sibship in which of six children three males were diabetic and three females were non-diabetic. Diabetes was present in a paternal great-aunt and one of her daughters but not on the maternal side, and both parents were non-diabetic. Their conclusion that "the diabetes is probably inherited as a sex-linked recessive characteristic with heterozygous parents" is obviously genetic nonsense.

Linkage is a genetic phenomenon displayed by two or more traits determined by genes at loci sufficiently near each other on the same chromosome pair. Two loci may be on the same chromosome pair but lie so far apart that through crossing over free recombination occurs between them and differentiation is impossible from the independent assortment of Mendel's second law, as observed with loci located on separate chromosome pairs (unless, of course, a third locus situated between the two is known or both of the loci are by other evidence clearly X–linked).

X–linkage has been used throughout this discussion because it is a more precise and specific term than sex-linkage. Y–linkage is also a form of sex-linkage. *Gonosomal*, the term contrasting with "autosomal," likewise does not distinguish between X–linkage and Y–linkage. *Partial*, or *incomplete*, *sex-linkage*, a somewhat confusing term, refers, as previously indicated, to the pedigree pattern which would be displayed by traits determined by genes on homologous parts of the X and Y chromosomes. In the sense that in a given sibship one or the other sex is more likely to be affected by the trait, partial sex linkage is meaningful.

Study of no X–linked trait in a kindred can be considered complete until the possibility of determining the linkage relationships with one of the "marker traits" has been explored. The existence of at least three frequently occurring X–linked traits, color blindness, glucose–6–phosphate dehydrogenase deficiency, and the blood group antigen Xg^a permits estimation of how close on the X chromosome these loci are situated and how close one of these loci is to those of rare X–borne genes. In those populations which show the polymorphism, the electrophoretic variants of G6PD (for which the heterozygous female can be identified) will probably also be useful for X chromosome mapping

and for study of X chromosome aneuploidy (Boyer, 1962; personal communication, Baltimore). Peculiarities of the distribution of marker genes in populations present difficulties in the study of linkage. For example, Negroes with the highest frequency of G6PD– deficiency have a low frequency of hemophilia, making it unlikely that one will easily find families segregating for both traits. Graham (1962) found only two Negro hemophilic families in a group of 60 families, despite the fact that Negroes represented about a quarter of the population studied and relatively complete ascertainment was achieved.

Quantitative analysis of linkage. The questions to which answers are sought in studies of autosomal linkage (Fig. 12) are the following: Are locus *alpha* (let us say, the ABO blood group locus) and locus *beta* (for example, the locus occupied by a gene for achondroplastic dwarfism) on the same chromosome pair and, if so, how far apart are they? In practice the second question is answered first. The distance separating two loci is determined by the amount of genetic recombination that goes on between them, as indicated by the frequency of so-called recombinants in the progeny. With closely situated loci the proportion of "recombinant individuals" among the children of informative matings is small. If the loci are far apart on the same chromosome pair or if they are on separate chromosomes, then half the offspring of appropriate matings will be of the two recombinant types as contrasted with the parental types. Note that it is impossible to distinguish between location on separate chromosome pairs and separation by 50 or more recombination units (centimorgans). The morgan, the measure of genetic map distance, is named, obviously, for the early student of linkage (p. 4). One centimorgan, or map unit, is that distance separating two loci which show recombination in one out of 100 gametes in the doubly heterozygous person.

In X–linkage the question usually asked is, how far apart on the X chromosome are the two loci? That both are located on the X chromosome is usually clear from pedigree analysis. Such is, however, not always the case. For example, in the testicular feminization syndrome (No. B6) and in male hypogonadism (No. B4) male-limited autosomal dominant in-

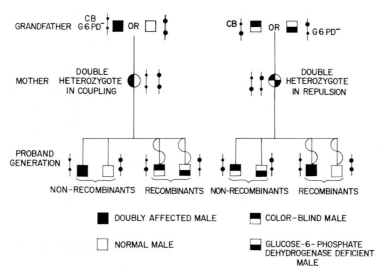

FIG. 13. THE GRANDFATHER METHOD FOR DETERMINING LINKAGE OF COMMON X–BORNE RECESSIVE TRAITS
Males showing one trait are ascertained. Then all males in the sibship of said probands are tested for the second trait. The families of those sibships in which both traits are segregating are subjected to further study. Most mothers of such sibships will be double heterozygotes. (The mothers are tested for both traits to exclude the relatively rare situation of a mother homozygous for one or the other gene or both.) The coupling phase in the doubly heterozygous mothers must be known and is determined by testing their fathers, the maternal grandfathers of the probands. The recombination fraction, χ, is the proportion of males in the proband generation who are "recombinant individuals."

heritance is a possible alternative (p. 13). In such cases studies (with color blindness or other marker traits) can be used to determine whether the gene is in fact X–borne. Note that if linkage is demonstrated in such studies, the gene can be said to be X–borne; but if linkage cannot be demonstrated, the locus in question may still be X–borne but far away from the marker locus. If chiasma counts in the autosomes can be used to estimate the amount of genetic crossing over in the X chromosomes (see p. 68), then one would conclude that there is ample opportunity for independent segregation of many of the X–borne loci.

X–linkage has interesting properties distinct from autosomal linkage, properties which have pertinence in the design of mapping studies. Information on recombination is provided by the phenotypes of the sons of doubly heterozygous females. For the simplest analysis the father is irrelevant, a circumstance fortunate for linkage studies in populations with a high illegitimacy rate. It is necessary, however, to have information on whether the two traits are in coupling phase or repulsion phase in the doubly heterozygous mother. This can be ascertained from the phenotype of her father (the maternal grandfather of the proband) as in-

dicated in Figure 13. Here, of course, illegitimacy, as well as other practical considerations such as availability of the grandfather for testing, does become a factor. This approach can conveniently be referred to as the *Grandfather Method*. It is applicable to both dominant and recessive X–linked traits.

Doubly heterozygous mothers are ascertained through sibships containing sons with both traits either alone or in combination. Bias is avoided by first ascertaining sibships by the presence of one male with one of the traits and then testing all males in said sibships for the second trait. It would, for example, be inappropriate, and certainly inefficient, to ascertain only doubly affected males as probands. See Figure 14 for the description of a study using the Grandfather Method.

(When both the traits whose linkage relationships are under study are relatively frequent in the population and recent new mutation is not likely to be encountered in any but a negligibly small proportion of the "doubly affected" families, the Grandfather Method is applicable. In a disease like hemophilia, which arises by recent new mutation in a considerable proportion of families, the Grandfather Method cannot be applied without due consideration of this factor.

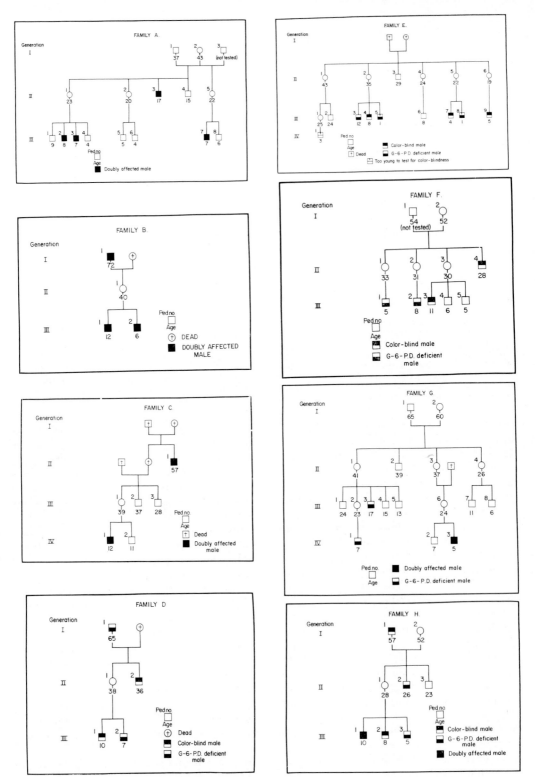

Fig. 14. Linkage of Color Blindness and Glucose–6–Phosphate Dehydrogenase Deficiency
Among 3,648 Negro school boys, color blindness was found in 134 (3.7%). All males (totalling 236) in the sibship of 106 of the color-blind probands were tested for glucose–6–phosphate dehydrogenase deficiency. In 10 sibships both traits were discovered. Of these the eight families diagrammed above could be studied. In six the deutan type and in two (c and f) the protan type of color blindness was present. Only one definite instance of recombination was discovered (in family h). See Porter, Schulze, and McKusick, 1962

28

Consider, for example, the family with hemophilia B shown in Figure 18. A two-by-two table would suggest that the mother is in coupling with regard to hemophilia and Xg(a+) and that five of 12 sons are recombinants. It is not much less likely, however, that the mother is in repulsion and that the other seven sons are in fact the recombinants. No other hemophilia had occurred in this rather numerous kindred and chances are that a new mutation for hemophilia occurred in the X chromosome of the egg or the sperm which formed the mother. The maternal grandfather was nonhemophilic. Even if he were available for testing, if he was Xg(a+) it would not be proper to conclude that the mother is in repulsion, because mutation has such a high probability. Of course, if the mother's mother could by test be shown to be a hemophilia-carrier, the Grandfather Method would be applicable.

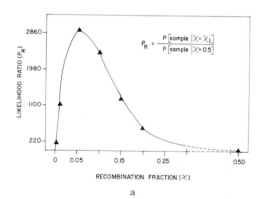

$$P_R = \frac{P\left[sample \mid \chi = \chi_1\right]}{P\left[sample \mid \chi = 0.5\right]}$$

a

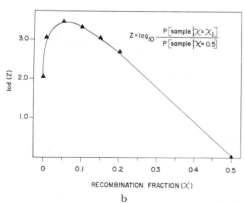

$$Z = \log_{10} \frac{P\left[sample \mid \chi = \chi_1\right]}{P\left[sample \mid \chi = 0.5\right]}$$

b

FIG. 15. THE MAXIMUM LIKELIHOOD ESTIMATES OF LINKAGE DERIVED FROM THE PEDIGREES SHOWN IN FIGURE 14, WITH THE ASSISTANCE OF THE DIGITAL COMPUTER

a. The results for the six deutan families. b. Those for the two protan families shown in Figure 14.

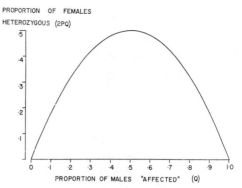

FIG. 16. RELATIONSHIP BETWEEN FREQUENCY OF MALES AFFECTED BY X–LINKED TRAIT (Q) AND FREQUENCY OF HETEROZYGOUS FEMALES (2PQ)

In practice greater efficiency is achieved if one uses data on the family in the larger sense (kindred) rather than merely the three generations indicated in the diagram of the Grandfather Method (Fig. 13). The data can be analyzed for linkage with the assistance of the digital computer, using a modification of the program written for autosomal linkage (Renwick and Schulze, 1961; Schulze, 1962). Fisher's maximum likelihood method (1921), as applied to linkage analysis by Smith (1953), is used. The question asked is as follows: assuming various values of χ, the recombination fraction, and given the combination of phenotypes and possible genotypes found in the family under study, what is the likelihood of linkage? The value of χ yielding the highest probability is taken as the maximum likelihood estimate of linkage. The role of the computer is to perform the tedious, time-consuming, and painstaking task of solving a complex polynomial in ν, to provide the values used in construction of graphs such as those in Figure 15.

Other methods of linkage analysis have also been used, e.g., Fisher's μ statistics (1935), as elaborated by Finney (1940), were applied to a problem of X–linkage by Adam and colleagues (1962).

For linkage studies of rare X–linked conditions, the only marker available until recently has been color blindness. Accumulation of data has been hampered by its relative rarity. Discovery of the X–linked blood group Xg^a is fortunate for linkage studies. Since the frequency of Xg(a+) males is about .62 (q) the frequency of heterozygous females is about 0.50 (2

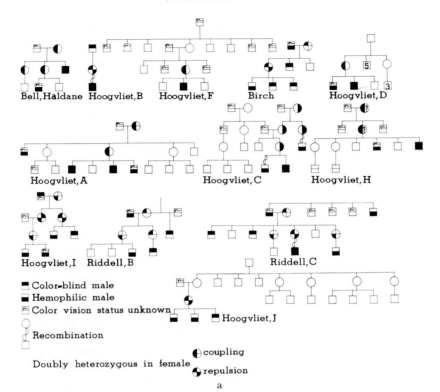

FIG. 17. LINKAGE OF COLOR BLINDNESS AND HEMOPHILIA; SOME OF THE REPORTED PEDIGREES

The large proportion of recombinations in Rath's family (1938) suggests that the variety of hemophilia was Christmas disease which is more loosely linked with color blindness than classic hemophilia (Whittaker, Copeland, and Graham, 1962). For other pedigrees, see François, et al. (1956), Jaeger (1952), and Murakami, et al. (1951).

$pq = 2 \times .62 \times .38 = .47$). Consequently, the likelihood of finding informative doubly heterozygous mothers is relatively high. Figure 16 graphs the simple relationship between the frequency of affected males (or the gene frequency) and the frequency of heterozygous females.

The following *X–linkage observations,* some of them unfortunately meager, have been made:

1. *Deutan color blindness and hemophilia A.* Whittaker, Copeland, and Graham (1962) find these linked with a recombination fraction of about 6%.[6] See also earlier estimate by Haldane and Smith (1947) made in 1947 before the two types of hemophilia were distinguished and using data in which the type of color blindness was often not specified. (See Fig. 17a.)

2. *Protan color blindness and hemophilia B.* In one large kindred Whittaker, Copeland, and Graham (1962) found a recombination fraction of about 50 per cent. In Figure 17 Rath's family is presented (1938) which, in view of the high

[6] Analysis of this pedigree with the assistance of the digital computer yields a maximum likelihood estimate of χ of about 12%.

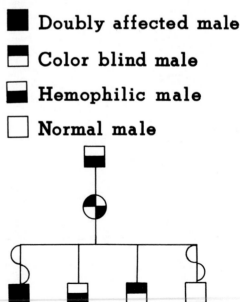

Rath (1938)

FIG. 17b.

proportion of recombinants, may have had hemophilia B.

3. *Hemophilia A and Xg blood groups.* In three informative families, O'Brien and his colleagues (1962) found six apparent noncrossovers and four crossovers. More extensive data indicate that the two loci are probably separated by about 40 recombination units (Davies *et al.*, 1963).

4. *Hemophilia B and Xg blood groups.* In a very informative family (Fig. 18), we found five apparent crossovers out of 12. See Davies, et al., 1963, for further data indicating independent assortment.

5. *Color blindness and glucose–6–phosphate dehydrogenase.* These are closely linked with a recombination fraction of about 5 per cent in both African (Porter, Schulze, and McKusick, 1962) and Mediterranean peoples (Adam, 1961; Siniscalco, et al., 1960, 1961) and probably for both the protan and the deutan types. (See Appendix, No. A4, and Figs. 14 and 15). Concluding that the protan and deutan loci may be rather far apart (see item 13 below), and recognizing the rather close linkage of both loci to the G6PD locus, Kalmus (1962) suggested that the G6PD locus may lie between the two color blindness loci.

6. *Glucose–6–phosphate dehydrogenase deficiency and Xg blood groups.* In Israel, Adam and colleagues (1962) studied 11 informative families with 51 children of doubly heterozygous women. The recombination fraction was estimated at 25.3%. The lowest likely level of recombination was estimated at 18.6%; only one in 20 samples of families of the same size would be expected to give a recombination fraction lower than this value (see also Adam, et al., 1963).

7. *Deutan color blindness and stationary night blindness.* These are very loosely linked with a recombination fraction of essentially 50% (White, 1940).

8. *Color blindness (type unspecified) and retinitis pigmentosa.* A recombination fraction of 21% (with wide confidence limits) was estimated by Falls and Cotterman (1948).

9. *Color blindness (type unspecified) and congenital nystagmus.* The recombination fraction was estimated at 0.213 ± 0.196 (Norton, 1949; Rucker, 1949).

10. *Color blindness (type unspecified) and Duchenne-type muscular dystrophy.* Two of eight

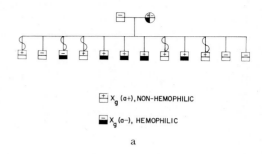

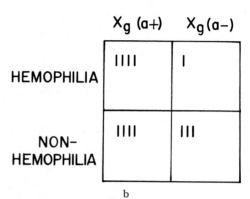

FIG. 18. LINKAGE OF XG AND HEMOPHILIA B

A very informative family (a) shows five probable cross overs out of 12 possibilities. In addition to the 12 boys the sibship contains two girls, one Xg(a+) and one Xg(a−). The mother is probably in coupling; her father is deceased. Even if the maternal grandfather were available for testing, the information would not in this instance settle the matter of whether the mother is in coupling or repulsion, inasmuch as she appears to be a new mutation for hemophilia. No hemophilia is known in this kindred other than in her sons. She had four brothers, all nonhemophilic, and the father, who died at age 70 years, was nonhemophilic. The 2 x 2 table (b) is a simple way to arrive at a guess as to the coupling phase of the mother. Whittaker, Copeland, and Graham's comment (1962) that Xg and hemophilia B may be closely linked is in error. (Personal observations, with blood groups courtesy of R. R. Race and Ruth Sanger, London, and classification of hemophilia by Dr. Dudley P. Jackson, Baltimore.)

persons showed recombination (Philip, 1955; Philip and Walton, 1946). Extension of the pedigree permitted an estimate of recombination of $0.25 \pm .11$ (Walton, 1957). (See also pedigree of Frézal, et al. (1957).)

11. *Xg blood groups and Duchenne muscular dystrophy.* In seven informative families, studied by Clark and his colleagues (1962), 14 of 21 sons were apparent non-cross overs and seven cross overs.

12. *Xg blood groups and spastic paraplegia.* In the large kindred reported by Johnston and

McKusick (1962), two doubly heterozygous females, both in coupling, were found. Each had one son; one of the two was a recombinant (unpublished observations).

13. *Protan color blindness and deutan color blindness.* Vanderdonck and Verriest (1960)

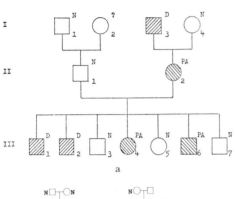

a

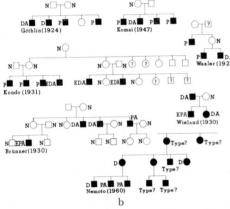

b

FIG. 19. LINKAGE OF DEUTAN AND PROTAN TYPES OF COLOR BLINDNESS

a. The pedigree from Vanderdonck and Verriest (1960) suggests that the loci are rather far apart. N = normal color vision; D = deuteranopia; PA = protanomaly; ? = unknown. Color blindness was expertly determined and typed. Nuclear sex agreed with apparent sex. The authors suggested that one of the mother's X chromosomes carries a protan gene and the other a deutan gene. The two normal sons were considered recombinants. It may not be surprising that pedigrees of this type have not been found even if the two loci are in fact far apart. Doubly heterozygous women are rather rare (about one in 250) and can be detected only through their sons. Furthermore, there must be at least one protan son and at least one deutan son for detection of the doubly heterozygous mother and at least a third son to demonstrate recombination (Kalmus, 1962). b. Any findings shown here are equally consistent with two closely linked loci or with allelism of the deutan and protan series. If allelic, one must assume that the DP female can have normal color vision. D = deuteranopia; P = protanopia; DA = deuteranomaly; EDA = extreme deuteranomaly; PA = protanomaly; EPA = extreme protanomaly.

found two recombinants out of five male progeny (Fig. 19a). If the postulated separate loci for the two main types of dyschromatopsia are as far apart as this experience might suggest, then the value of linkage studies in which the type of color blindness is not specified is doubtful. The experience in previously reported pedigrees (Fig. 19b) in which both types of color blindness are segregating but no recombination observed might suggest that the two loci are very closely linked. Renwick (1961) estimated that one could conclude with 95% confidence that the two loci are not more than 12 units apart. Indeed in the earlier studies the one locus hypothesis was not completely excluded. However, since doubly heterozygous women (only about one in 250) with at least three sons, one deutan, one protan and one normal, are required, it is not surprising (Kalmus, 1962) that families such

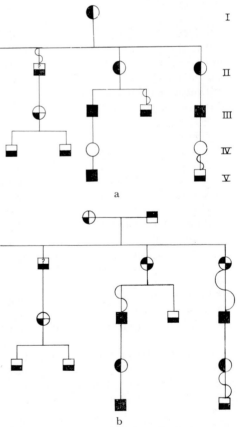

a

b

FIG. 20. LINKAGE OF COLOR BLINDNESS AND OCULAR ALBINISM

Two alternative interpretations, both requiring three crossovers, are schematized (a, b). From Waardenburg and van den Bosch (1956).

as that of Vanderdonck and Verriest have not been previously described.

Henceforth, any X–linkage study using color blindness as a marker trait, must, for full value, determine the type of color blindness.

14. *Xg blood groups and color blindness.* Jackson, Symon, and Mann (1962) have reported nine noncrossovers and five crossovers for the protan type, 20 noncrossovers and 10 crossovers for the deutan type.

15. *Ocular albinism and protan color blindness.* Probably three recombinants out of eight possibilities (Waardenburg and van den Bosch, 1956). (See Fig. 20.)

16. Linkage with traits which are certainly sex-linked, such as color blindness, provides a method for differentiating X–linked recessive from sex-limited autosomal dominant inheritance (p. 13). *Color blindness and the testicular feminization syndrome* may show independent segregation; in the two families of Stewart (1959) one recombinant out of five occurred, a finding which neither proves nor excludes X–linkage. Southern and Saito (1961) described two cases who also had deutan type color blindness. (No other data on color blindness in the family were given.) (See Fig. 21a.)

17. *Hemophilia A and the testicular feminization syndrome* may also show independent segregation (Nilsson, et al., 1959). (See Fig. 21b.)

18. *The Xg locus and the testicular feminization syndrome.* We have recently studied a family in which there is one crossover out of four (Fig. 21c). The accumulation of linkage information with three other loci suggests that the testicular feminization locus may be autosomal, although no autosomal linkage with the markers available has been demonstrated (Fig. 21d). No definite statement is possible, however, since the markers used are all in a short segment (Fig. 23) and ample room remains for independent assortment of the feminization locus.

19. Kallman, Schonfeld, and Barrera (1944) reported three families in which both *color blindness and the hypogonadism-anosmia syndrome* (Kallmann's syndrome) were segregating. The two traits were apparently in repulsion in one family (A) and in coupling in one (B); the third family (C) is uninformative from the point-of-view of linkage. No definite (or necessary) instance of recombination was observed in any (Fig. 22). All three families were of Russian, probably Russian Jewish, extraction. Color blindness has not been described in other reported families with Kallmann's syndrome.

20. Linkage was invoked by Lynch and his colleagues (1960) as an explanation of the association through four generations (three after the original progenitors) of *male hypogonadism and ichthyosis.* If indeed this is an example of linkage between the X–borne ichthyosis locus and an X–borne locus determining male hypogonadism, then the linkage is probably close (95% confidence limit less than 20 map units). In the catalog ichthyosis-hypogonadism is listed (No. B5) as a mutation separate from ichthyosis (No. A24) because linkage can only be suggested. Pleiotropism, that is, polyphenic expression of a single gene, is more often the basis of such syndromal association of traits.

21. Graham and colleagues (1962) have studied the five sons of a female triply heterozygous (for protan color blindness, Xg blood group and hemophilia B). The order of the genes appears to be cb—Xg—hem B or Xg—cb—hem B. Whatever the order and whatever the configuration of the three loci on the X chromosomes of the mother, at least one double crossover is required to explain the findings in the sons. The findings suggest that the three loci may span as much as 100 map units of the X chromosome.

22. Sanger and Race (1963) concluded that crossing over between *the Xg locus and locus for agammaglobulinemia* (A10) probably exceeds 20 per cent.

Accumulating data on Xg^a linkage and correlation of these with the other linkage information suggest that the order of loci on the X chromosome may be Xg-G6PD-color vision-hemophilia A (Fig. 23). Because of the considerable number of loci which seem to be unlinked with *Xg* it is possible that the *Xg* locus is near one end of the X chromosome, e.g., the end of the short arm if the color blindness locus is on the short arm (p. 69).

Other comments. Linkage studies involving X–linked traits provide an indirect test of nonallelism. One will not often enough encounter two rare conditions such as hemophilia A and hemophilia B in the same kindred so that a direct test of allelism can be applied. An indirect test, by separately determining the linkage of the two traits with color blindness, suggests nonallelism of hemophilias A and B (Whittaker, Copeland, and Graham, 1962). (See

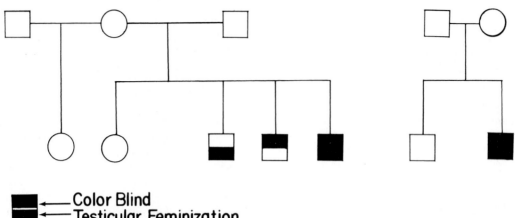

Color Blind
Testicular Feminization Syndrome

a

Hemophilia
Testicular Feminization
Syndrome

b

FIG. 21. LINKAGES OF COLOR BLINDNESS AND THE TESTICULAR FEMINIZATION SYNDROME; HEMOPHILIA AND THE TESTICULAR FEMINIZATION SYNDROME; XG BLOOD TYPE AND THE TESTICULAR FEMINIZATION SYNDROME; AND OF THE TESTICULAR FEMINIZATION SYNDROME AND AUTOSOMAL MARKERS

a. The findings are consistent with independent segregation. Knowledge of the coupling phase of the mother from information as to whether her father was color-blind would increase the information provided by these two families, but only if her mother was a certain carrier of the gene for testicular feminization. From Stewart (1959). b. The findings are consistent with independent segregation. However, if the testicular feminization mutation occurred in the ovum, which produced the doubly affected individual, the pedigree is uninformative from the linkage point of view. Said mutation may have occurred earlier, in light of the large number of "females," four of them without offspring, in the third generation shown. From Nilsson, et al. (1959). c. The findings are consistent with independent segregation. The three affected persons indicated here are pictured in Figure 55a. Three other affected persons are known in this kindred—the offspring of daughters of a sister of the mother in the pedigree as shown here (p. 108). (Personal observations through courtesy of Drs. Howard W. Jones and Lawson Wilkins, with blood groups determined by R. R. Race and R. Sanger, London.) d. In the family shown in Figure 21c no close linkage could be demonstrated with the autosomal markers, the ABO, MNS, P, rhesus, Duffy, and Kidd systems (p. 13).

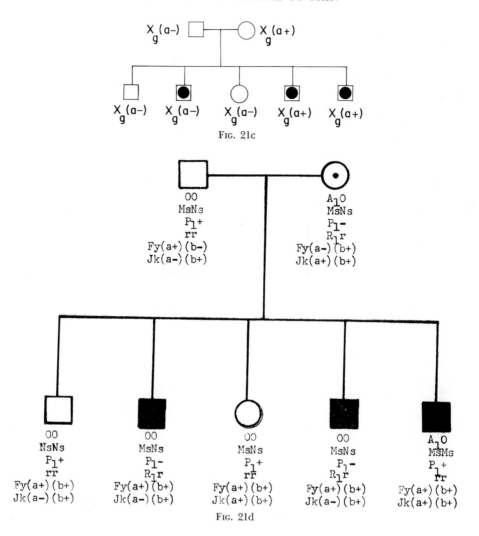

Fig. 21c

Fig. 21d

above.) The evidence is not completely conclusive, however, because in the one large kindred with hemophilia A the type of color blindness was deutan whereas in the kindred with hemophilia B it was protan. These two types of color blindness may be determined by genes at loci fairly widely separated (Kalmus, 1962) and part or even all the differences in linkage found by Whittaker, Copeland, and Graham (1962) may be on this basis.

Note that linkage studies in man, because of their relative crudity, can prove nonallelism but not allelism. Boyer, Porter, and Weilbacher (1962) point out that to date all cases of the Negro type of G6PD–deficiency (in both the American Negro and the native African) have had the anomalous fast (or A) electrophoretic type. Logically the finding is equally consistent with close linkage of two genes or allelism in the form of a double mutation in the functional genetic unit, although the latter possibility is perhaps more plausible. In human genetics, and the hemoglobin variants specifically, chemical studies have been resorted to for indirect evidence on the question of allelism versus linkage. The same may be possible in the case just discussed.

(The linkage test might answer some of the questions about allelism raised on p. 20).

The closer two loci are situated on the same chromosome, the longer the time in generations required for crossing over to result in equal frequency of coupling and repulsion heterozygotes, the equilibrium state. For autosomal link-

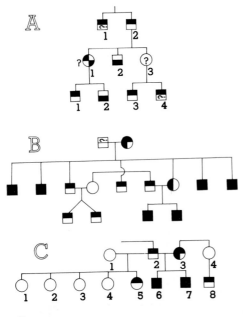

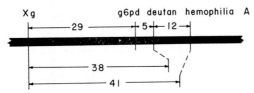

◐ Doubly heterozygous female in repulsion

◑ Homozygous color-blind female,
heterozygous for Kallmann syndrome

■　◐ Color-blind male, female

▬ Male with eunochoidism, anosmia and
mental deficiency

Fig. 22. Linkage of Color Blindness and
Kallmann Syndrome

Pedigree C is uninformative from the standpoint of linkage. The other two are consistent with close linkage. (After Kallmann, et al. (1944).)

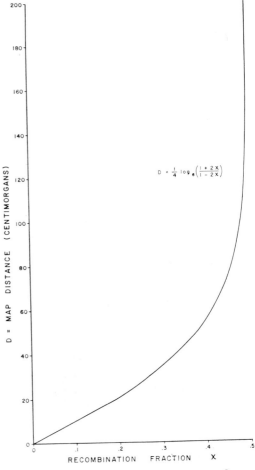

$$D = \frac{1}{4} \log_e \left(\frac{1 + 2X}{1 - 2X} \right)$$

Fig. 24. Relationship of Map Distance in Centimorgans (or Map Units) to the Recombination Fraction

After Kosambi (1944)

Xg　　　　　　g6pd deutan hemophilia A

Fig. 23. Tentative Map of Segment of
X Chromosome

Data from studies of five linkages are considered. The recombination fractions have been converted to map units by the formula of Kosambi (see Fig. 24).

age, the problem was treated by Jennings (1917) and Robbins (1918), and more recently by Li (1955) and Falconer (1960). Since for the X chromosomes crossing over occurs only in the female, appreciably longer is required for equilibrium to be attained. For example, if a distance of 10 map units separates two loci on an

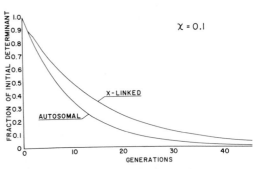

Fig. 25. Rate of Equilibration of Coupling and Repulsion Phases for Autosomal and X-linked Loci, Given, in Each Case, a Recombination Fraction of 0.10

autosome, then about 29 generations are required to reduce the departure from equilibrium from 1.0 (the maximum value) to 0.05. For two X-linked loci separated by the same distance about 43 generations are required.[7] A formal treatment of the approach to equilibrium with X–linked loci as compared to autosomal loci will be presented elsewhere. In Israel when Jewish sub-populations in which there are a high frequency of G6PD–deficiency and a relatively low frequency of color blindness mix with other Jewish sub-populations which have virtually no G6PD–deficiency but a much higher frequency of color blindness, a negative association between the two traits can be expected for many generations, since the linkage of the two traits appears to be a close one (Adam, 1961). In fact, such a negative association has been found; most families with both traits have shown repulsion phase (Adam, 1961) in doubly heterozygous females. In Sardinia (Siniscalco, et al., 1961) the situation is exactly the reverse; the two traits have been observed usually in coupling phase.

Possibly linkage is an explanation for the occurrence of mental deficiency and microphthalmia together (see No. A44) in some families and separately in others (No. A31). Mental deficiency is also a striking feature of the Börjeson syndrome (No. A32). One might wonder whether linkage is responsible for the occurrence of myopia in association with night blindness (No.

A51) and in association with external ophthalmoplegia (No. A43). Linkage seems unlikely, however, because to my knowledge myopia, external ophthalmoplegia and night blindness have not occurred independently as isolated X–linked traits. Pleiotropism is a much more likely basis for these two syndromes with myopia as a component.

A positive correlation between the past prevalence of malaria and the present prevalence of G6PD–deficiency has been demonstrated in Sardinia (Siniscalco, et al., 1961). Furthermore, Siniscalco and his colleagues (1961) write that "the incidence of colour-blindness itself is positively correlated with the past incidence of malaria and therefore with the frequency of the enzyme deficiency. The situation is interpreted as an example of the selection of a neutral gene through the close linkage with a highly adaptive one." Although this is an intriguing suggestion, other interpretations of the data are possible.

At this writing, active work is in progress exploiting the advantage to linkage studies of the newly discovered X–linked blood group system. In the next year or two a fairly detailed genetic map of the X chromosome may become available. More X–linked marker traits are needed, however, since the X chromosome is relatively long. The correlation of cytogenetic information (p. 68), such as, that which at present suggests that the color-vision locus is on the short arm and may be rather far removed from the kinetochore, will provide physical basis for the genetic map.

[7] In Figure 25 attainment of equilibrium for autosomal loci and X-linked loci, separated in each case by a distance corresponding to 10% recombination is compared (Murphy, et al., 1963). Both loci are assumed to have two alleles only.

V · CYTOGENETIC DATA ON THE CONSTITUTION OF THE X CHROMOSOMES OF MAN

T HE *mitotic X chromosome* (Harnden, 1961a; Robinson, 1960; Hamerton, 1961) is medium-sized, with submedian kinetochore (Fig. 26). It is the sixth or seventh longest chromosome and falls in the Denver Group III with autosomes 6–12. (Levan and Hsu (1959), Ferguson-Smith (1961a) and others place the sixth chromosome pair in Group II with the fourth and fifth pairs, as shown in Figure 26.) The sex chromosome constitution in a given individual can be determined from the number of chromosomes in Groups III and VII. In males there is one fewer in Group III (fifteen by the Denver system) and one more (five) in Group VII (chromosomes 21 and 22 plus the Y). The ratio of long arm to short arm for the X chromosome has been found to fall in the range of 1.6 to 2.8. The mean X chromosome centromere index (per cent of total length represented by the short arm) has fallen in the range of 32 to 38 in the measurements of various workers. The X chromosome is found to represent between 5.1 and 5.9

per cent of the total length of a haploid set containing an X (22A + X). (The above figures are from the compilation by Harnden (1961a).) The normal female with two X chromosomes has about 4 per cent more chromosomal material than the male with one X chromosome and a Y.

Sandberg and colleagues (1960) found that in cells cultured from the bone marrow the human X chromosome tends to be heteropycnotic and allocyclic, features useful in its identification. Morishima, Grumbach, and Taylor (1962) and German (1962a, b) showed that one chromosome of the normal female, an X, undergoes late replication, as indicated by studies using tritium-labelled thymidine (Lima-de-Faria, 1959). In general, however, the X chromosome is specifically identified with difficulty, especially in the female, and is hard to distinguish from chromosomes 6 and 7 (Patau, 1960). A large part of the difficulty is probably the factor pointed out by Boyes (1961). The length of the chromosomes is influenced by colchicine, heat, fixatives, and other features of the preparatory process. Boyes has shown that as a function of its heterochromatic property the X chromosome varies less with such preparatory procedures than does the rest of the complement, so that its relative length is inversely proportional to the total complement length. For example, Boyes found the X chromosome of the housefly to represent about 15 per cent of long complements and about 20 per cent of short complements. Furthermore, if there is a difference in the heterochromaticity of the two arms of the X chromosome the arm ratio may vary according to the total complement length. In the female there is even the possibility that one X chromosome will behave differently from its homolog in relation to preparatory procedures. Boyes made a plea for the inclusion of data on total complement length in any report of karyotyping studies which purport to be quantitative.

Muldal and Ockey (1961) suggest that chromosome 6, an autosome, can often be positively identified by the presence of a narrow secondary constriction in the short arm. Moreover, in their experience one X chromosome in both the male and the female often can be seen to have a large pale gap in its long arm immediately adjacent to the kinetochore (centromere). They found that in males the unpaired chromosome of group III (the X) was the most variable, a finding possibly supporting Boyes' suspicions (see above). Ferguson-Smith (1962) also is of the opinion that the X chromosome can usually be distinguished from both 6 and 7, by the secondary constriction in 6 and the smaller size of 7.

In practice, especially in the analysis of cases of sex anomalies, determination at least of the number of X chromosomes has been assisted by the number of Barr bodies in the buccal smear. Failure to make use of this approach or to interpret properly the results led several groups of workers (De Carli, et al., 1960; Fraccaro, Kaijser, and Lindsten, 1960a, b; Sandberg, Crosswhite, and Gordy, 1960) to report as trisomy of one of the large autosomes cases which, in the opinion of most (Ferguson-Smith, 1961a; Jacobs, et al., 1960a), represented in fact instances of X-polysomy.

Is there chiasma formation by the X and Y chromosomes to suggest homologous segments? In man and in other mammals the X and Y

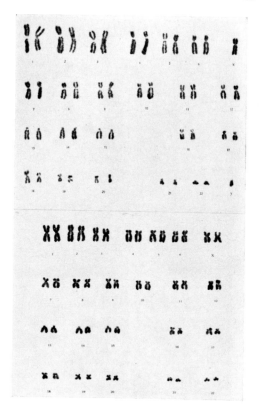

FIG. 26. KARYOTYPE OF NORMAL MALE AND NORMAL FEMALE
Courtesy of M. A. Ferguson-Smith

chromosomes form a unique type of meiotic bivalent. The short arm of the Y is attached to the tip of the short arm of the X (Fig. 27a). In man such was illustrated clearly in 1932 by Shiwago and Andres (1932) and has been further studied by Ford and Hamerton (1956), Kodani (1957), Ohno and colleagues (1957a, 1959c) and Ferguson-Smith (1961b) among others. Furthermore, early separation of the X and Y chromosome has been demonstrated (Fig. 27b). On this basis it is clear, therefore, that partial, or incomplete, sex linkage is unlikely. If it occurs at all (the very fact of synapsis, even terminal, of the X and Y may indicate limited homology), it would be expected to apply to few traits. Matthey (1951, 1957) surveyed the possible cytologic basis for partial sex linkage in all mammals and concluded there is none. He made a caustic comment: "It would be desirable if geneticists would have more confidence in the results of pure cytologists rather than in the work of cyto-

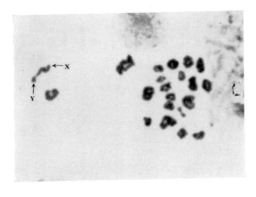

a

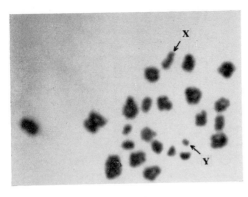

b

Fig. 27. End-to-end Synapsis of X and Y Sex Chromosome Bivalent at First Meiotic Metaphase in
the Normal Male and Precocious Disjunction of
the Sex Chromosomes at First Meiotic Metaphase
in the Normal Male

a. One autosomal bivalent is not seen in this
plate. Feulgen, ×4000. b. Feulgen, ×4000. Courtesy
of M. A. Ferguson-Smith.

geneticists who wish to find an explanation for
every genetic hypothesis."

In his discussion of the evolution of the sex
chromosome, Swanson (1957) points out that
the accumulation of differential sex-determining
factors in the X and in the Y has been accompanied by guarantees of sexual isolation
through restriction of crossing over between
them. It seems logical to presume that sex-determining factors are scattered throughout the
X chromosome and that the lack of crossing
over between X and Y preserves the uniqueness
of the sexes. Ohno and colleagues (1957a, 1957b)
point out that precocious condensation of the
sex pair during synaptic stages of meiosis in the
heterogametic sex limits chiasma formation and
therefore, genetic crossing over.

Kodani (1957) and Stern (1959a) suggest
that in the meiotic XY bivalent, three segments
of the long arm of the X chromosome (desig-
nated the right arm) can be identified by points
of angulation.

*Role of the X chromosome in sex determina-
tion as indicated by sex anomalies.* The female-
determining properties of the X chromosome
and the specific male-determining properties
of the Y chromosome are indicated by the
correlations of karyotype with sex phenotype in
the XO Turner syndrome (Fig. 28a, b), the
XXY Klinefelter syndrome (Fig. 28c, d), and
in more bizarre derangements (Fig. 36; Table
7). With rare exceptions (which may be exceptions only because of incomplete information
or imperfect understanding of the cases), including especially true hermaphrodites with 2A
+ XX karyotype (Ferguson-Smith, Johnston,
and Weinberg, 1960; Harnden and Armstrong,
1959; de Assis, et al., 1960; Hungerford, et al.,
1959; Sasaki and Makino, 1960), the presence of
the Y chromosome is always associated with testes
and conversely testes are not present in the absence of a Y chromosome. Herein man (and
mouse) differ from *Drosophila* in which the
Y chromosome is a "dud" in sex determination,
although essential for male fertility. (Obviously
the Y chromosome cannot be completely func-
tionless in *Drosophila*; if it were it would be
rather quickly lost in evolution.) The mechanism
of sex determination in man and the mouse is
essentially identical to that in the plant *Melandrium* in which the Y chromosome determines
maleness regardless of how many X chromosomes
are also present (Westergaard, 1948).

Fraccaro and his colleagues (1962) described
a true hermaphrodite with XX/XXY/XXYYY
sex chromosome mosaicism. They suggest that
testicular tissue develops only in the presence of
the Y chromosome and that all true hermaphrodites are chromosomal mosaics. "The cytological investigations of the apparent exceptions
so far reported in the literature (intersexes
with XX sex chromosomes) have been confined
to a single tissue specimen." The statement is
no longer true since multiple tissues were investigated in the three sibs with true hermaphroditism reported by Rosenberg, Clayton,
and Hsu (1963). (This may be a special case of
hermaphroditism due to homozygosity of a recessive gene. The authors (personal communication) found no paternal consanguinity, however.)

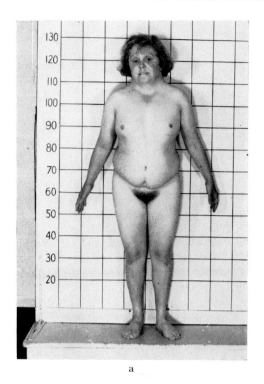

a

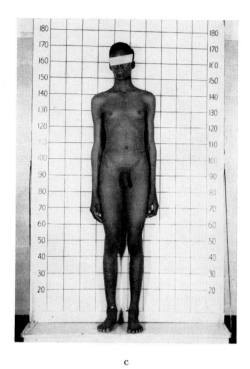

c

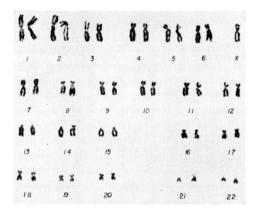

b

d

FIG. 28. CHROMATIN-NEGATIVE TURNER SYNDROME AND CHROMATIN-POSITIVE KLINEFELTER SYNDROME

a. Now 37 years old, M. H. (270068) demonstrates classic features of gonadal aplasia: short stature, low-set ears, characteristically hypoplastic jaw, web neck, shield-like chest with wide-set nipples, coarctation of the aorta (note scar of operation for resection of same), primary amenorrhea, infantile uterus, and "streak gonads." This is the chromatin-negative *Turner syndrome*. b. Karyotype of patient with chromatin-negative *Turner syndrome*. c. J.V.D. (856375), an 18 year old Negro male, came to the hospital because of enlarged breasts. He also demonstrated underdevelopment of body hair and very small testes and prostate. He had never shaved. Li-

bido was average. He had no difficulty in maintaining an erection and engaged in heterosexual relations about once monthly. The IQ was 76. The 24-hour urine excretion of 17-ketosteroids was reduced (9.92 mg.). The testis at biopsy was little larger than a lima bean. Histologically the majority of the seminiferous tubules were completely atrophic and many were represented merely by shrunken, hyalinized "ghosts." A few small tubules lined exclusively by Sertoli cells persisted among large masses of Leydig cells. No germinal cells were identified. This is the chromatin-positive *Klinefelter syndrome*. d. Karotype of patient with chromatin-positive *Klinefelter syndrome*.

The female phenotype of the XO Turner syndrome indicates that the autosomes and/or X chromosome contain female-determining factors. In Jost's classic experiments (1947), removal of the testis (determined by the Y chromosome) in the male fetus of the rabbit permitted expression of these female-determining potentialities. The Turner syndrome seems to be an analogous situation. To what extent the autosomes determine femaleness is not clear. A nullo–X state would answer the question but is almost certainly inconsistent with life. That poly–X cases do not have enhanced femaleness can scarcely be used as evidence that female-determining factors are *not* concentrated in the X chromosome since the Lyon hypothesis (p. 59) would permit the view that at least partial inactivity of the extra X chromosomes

obtains. For completely normal sexual development in the human female, two X chromosomes are necessary. (However, the XO female mouse is fertile.) Three X chromosomes (Fig. 36a, b) are consistent with little derangement of female sexual development and function (Johnston, et al., 1961).

(A different, so-called triheterosomic scheme of sex determination in mammals is suggested by Yerganian and his colleagues (1957; 1960), but it appears to have little to support it.)

Most cases of chromatin-positive gonadal aplasia (the Turner syndrome) show (Ferguson-Smith, 1962, personal communication, Glasgow) 1) XX/XO or similar mosaicism, or 2) deletion of part of one X chromosome and a diminished size of the Barr body (Barr and Carr, 1960; Jacobs, et al., 1961), or 3) an "isochromosome"

TABLE 7

Some abnormal sex chromosome patterns in man

Chromosome Number	Sex Chromosome Constitution	Sex Chromatin	Phenotype	Reference
45	XO	−	Turner syndrome	Ford et al. (1959)
45, 46	XO/XX	+	Turner syndrome	Sandberg et al. (1960)
45, 47	XO/XXX	+	Turner syndrome	Jacobs et al. (1960)
47	XXX	++	Triple-X female*	Jacobs et al. (1959)
48	XXXX	+++	Tetra-X female*	Carr, Barr (1961)
46	XX	+ (large)	Turner syndrome	Ferguson-Smith (1962)
46	XX/Xx	+	Oligomenorrhea	de Grouchy et al. (1961)
46	XX/XX	+ (large)	Turner syndrome	Fraccaro et al. (1960)
45, 47	XO/XYY	−	Turner syndrome	Cooper et al. (1962)
46	Xx	+ (small)	Turner syndrome	Jacobs et al. (1961)
45, 46	XO/Xx	+ (small)	Turner syndrome	de la Chapelle (1962)
47	XXY	+	Klinefelter syndrome	Jacobs et al. (1959)
47	XYY	−	Normal male	Hauschka et al. (1962)
46, 47	XX/XXY	+	Klinefelter syndrome	Ford et al. (1959)
48	XXYY	+	Klinefelter syndrome	Muldal, Ockley (1960)
48	XXXY	++	Triple X–Y Klinefelter syndrome	Ferguson-Smith et al. (1960)
47, 48	XXxY/XXY	+	Klinefelter syndrome	Crawfurd (1961)
49	XXXXY	+++	Tetra X–Y Klinefelter syndrome	Miller et al. (1961)
46	XX	+	True hermaphrodite	Harnden, Armstrong (1959) Hungerford et al. (1959) de Assis et al. (1960)
45, 46	XO/XY	−	True hermaphrodite	Hirschhorn et al. (1960)
45, 46, 47	XO/XX/XXX	+	True hermaphrodite	Ferguson-Smith et al. (1960)
46+	XX + fragment	+	True hermaphrodite	Ferguson-Smith et al. (1960)
46	XX/XY	+	True hermaphrodite	Waxman et al. (1962)

* A penta-X female has been observed by Dr. Paul V. Wooley Jr., Detroit, Mich., and studied by Grumbach, Morishima, and Taylor (1963).

(Ferguson-Smith, 1962; Fraccaro, et al., 1960b; Jacobs, et al., 1960b, 1961; Lindsten, 1961) composed of the long arm of one X chromosome in duplicate and an enlarged Barr body (Fig. 33d, 35). An isochromosome is thought to result through the transverse rather than longitudinal cleavage of the centromere. The "isochromosome" observed in some cases of the Turner syndrome could have a normal long arm and an abnormal arm made up of a duplicated short arm rather than being a true isochromosome of the long arm (Jacobs, et al., 1960a). However, such is much less likely because it would not fit well with observations of X chromosome *deficiency* in relation to most cases of the Turner syndrome. It must be emphasized, nonetheless, that positive identification of an isochromosome is possible only through the study of synaptic behavior. Lacking such proof, which will be difficult to obtain in cases of chromatin-positive Turner syndrome suspected of having an isochromosome–X, one must keep prominently in mind the fact that the observed large chromosome is only *assumed* to be an isochromosome.

There can, however, be little doubt that the so-called isochromosome X is indeed an isochromosome of the long arm. Muldal and colleagues (1963), Giannelli (1963), Lee and Bowen (1963), and others find that the two arms of the anomalous chromosome label in an identical pattern in autoradiography, the pattern being that of the long arm of a late-labelling X chromosome (Fig. 42). Admittedly, an autosome/X translocation might show the same labelling pattern. The only means of distinguishing translocation and isochromosome is by study of the synaptic behavior at meiosis, as has been done for cert in autosomal aberrations (e.g., Hamerton, et al., 1961). Such studies are not possible in the X X female.

Polani (1961) commented on the rather high frequency of the long-arm isochromosome-X form of the chromatin-positive Turner syndrome and the apparent rarity of an isochromosome-X involving the short arm. He referred to a single possible case, which is unpublished. The rarity of the short-arm form may, he suggested, be a matter of case selection. Such patients may not be of short stature. They might have only primary amenorrhea.

A ring X chromosome has also been described

in a mosaic case of chromatin-positive Turner syndrome (Lindsten and Tillinger, 1962).

Another structural abnormality of the X chromosome (described in a patient with the Klinefelter syndrome) probably consists of fusion of part of two X chromosomes. Elves and Israëls (1962) reported a case in which they plausibly interpret the karyotype in this way. The patient was chromatin-negative and had 46 chromosomes. What was considered the X chromosome was larger than any other in the complement. In general the clinical features were those of the Klinefelter syndrome, but the hypogonadism and eunuchoidism were more striking than in the usual Klinefelter syndrome. It is noteworthy that although excess X chromosome material was present there was no Barr body. The observations are consistent with the

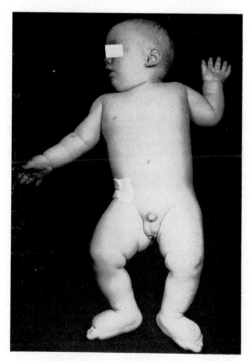

FIG. 29. MALE TURNER SYNDROME

D.H.B. (874339) had lymphedema of the extremities at birth. The neck was short with redundant skin folds. There were bilateral epicanthal folds. The nipples were widely spaced as in the usual Turner syndrome. The toenails were hypoplastic. Both testis were descended and grossly normal. Histologically, also, they were judged to be normal. The chromosome complement in the bone marrow was 46 (XY) and the patient was chromatin negative. No evidence of cardiovascular or renal malformation was found.

current views that one X chromosome in its entirety remains euchromatic and only separate X chromosomes in excess of one become heterochromatic, probably in their entirety. The exaggerated features of the Klinefelter syndrome are explicable because unlike the usual case all the extra X chromosomal material is euchromatic. It appears that either the short arm or a large part of the long arm was fused to the long arm of a full X chromosome. The patient was of average intelligence. He also had hemophilia. The implications for cytogenetic mapping are discussed on p. 69.

How genes (including those of the X chromosome) function in *sex determination* is almost totally unknown. Is the sex-determining genetic material on the X and Y chromosomes of the same nature as that which we conceive for other genes? If so, do mutations occur in it? Some sort of change must have taken place to account for the evolution of sex. Experience with the Turner syndrome would suggest that sex-determining genes are scattered throughout the X chromosome, a conclusion arrived at also from study of *Drosophila*. The comparison of cases with deletion of the short arm with those with deletion of the long arm might suggest that the short arm may carry a larger number of, or "more important", sex genes (de Grouchy, et al., 1961; Jacobs et al., 1960a). Some progress in understanding the embryologic basis of sex determination has been made, but nothing is known of the chemical means by which genes operate in sex determination.

In the second and third types of chromatin-positive Turner syndrome mentioned on page 42 (deletion of part of one X chromosome and "isochromosome" of the long arm of one X) bimodality in the size of the Barr bodies is not observed (Ferguson-Smith, 1962). One interpretation of these observations is the following:

1) Loss of part or all of one X chromosome results, in the absence of a Y chromosome or of more than one other X chromosome, in the Turner syndrome.

2) When one X chromosome is partially absent then only the aberrant X chromosome displays heterochromatic behavior and "inactivity," leaving the intact X chromosome active in each cell. Or possibly selection at the cellular level is a factor with loss of those cells in which the incomplete X chromosome is the active one.

3) Probably it is loss of all or part of the *short* arm of the X chromosome which is critical to the development of the Turner syndrome (Jacobs, et al., 1961). Patients with deletion of part of the long arm have primary amenorrhea or severe oligomenorrhea but have normal stature and none of the stigmata, such as webbed neck, of the Turner syndrome (Jacobs, et al., 1960b; de Grouchy, et al., 1961).

The origins of X chromosome aneuploidy. It is estimated (Polani, 1963) that one in every 200 newborn infants has a chromosomal aberration identifiable by present techniques and that two-thirds of these involve the sex chromosomes. The mechanism by which they arise and the causative factors are matters of practical as well as theoretical significance.

Theoretically (Stewart, 1962) sex chromosome aneuploidy can result from nondisjunction in gametogenesis in either parent and at either of the two stages of meiosis, with passage of two (or more) sex chromosomes or no sex chromosome into the gametes (Fig. 30). Also chromosome loss, from anaphase lagging, for example, can result in daughter cells without a sex chromosome. In addition, chromosome loss can occur between fertilization and the first cleavage, and both nondisjunction and loss of part or all of one or more chromosomes can occur in the first or other early cleavage stages.

Bearing on the question of the mechanism of origin of the aneuploid states involving the X chromosome of man are 1) the findings in studies of X chromosome marker-traits in the cases and their parents and other close relatives, 2) the relative frequency of the several types, 3) the precise type of aneuploidy, 4) the relative frequency of mosaicism, 5) parental age at conception of the aneuploid individual, 6) the differences between spermatogenesis and oögenesis in time-scale and in a number of other details, and 7) the occurrence of double aneuploidy in a frequency greater than expected and of various aneuploid states in more than one member of the same family. Parallel investigations in the mouse are also pertinent.

Before information on sex chromosome constitution was available, color blindness was used by Polani and colleagues (1956) to predict (or to strengthen previous suspicions of) the presence of only one X chromosome in cases of chromatin-negative Turner syndrome. Color blindness has also been used as a marker to identify

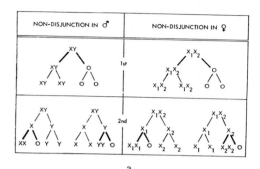

a

b

FIG. 30. THEORETICAL EXPECTATION CONCERNING NON-DISJUNCTION IN MEIOSIS AND FIRST CLEAVAGE EVENTS THAT CAN RESULT IN SEX-CHROMOSOME ANOMALIES

a. The cell division in which non-disjunction occurs is indicated by heavy lines. From L. B. Russell (1961). b. Lost chromosomes or chromatids are encircled. In the case of non-disjunction, the possible groupings of one and three chromosomes, respectively, are indicated by divisions of the squares. Mosaic, mos.; hermaphrodites, combined symbols for male and female. A wavy line separates the two genotypes in mosaics. From L. B. Russell (1961).

in which parent the meiotic accident (e.g., non-disjunction) responsible for chromosome aberrations occurred (Nowakowski and Lenz, 1961). In four cases of chromatin-negative Turner syndrome with color blindness the father had normal color vision (Bishop, Lessof, and Polani, 1960; Lennox, 1961; Lenz, 1957; Polani, et al., 1958; Polani and Hamerton, 1961; Walls, 1959), findings indicating that the anomalous event may have occurred in the father, who produced a sperm without a sex chromosome. An alternative possibility is that the loss of the paternal sex chromosome occurred between fertilization and first cleavage or at first cleavage.

In populations with a high frequency of the gene for glucose–6–phosphate dehydrogenase deficiency this trait can be used for investigating the question of origin of the XO Turner syndrome. Gartler, Vullo, and Gandini (1962) ob-

served G6PD–deficiency in an XO individual born from a mating of G6PD⁺/G6PD⁻ × G6PD⁺/ Y, indicating that the one X chromosome of the offspring was derived from the mother (so-called X^MO, matriclinous). (Welshons and Russell (1959) found an excess of X^MO cases in the mouse.) We have recently identified three further cases of chromatin-negative Turner syndrome to be of the X^MO type. In one, a Negro, this was accomplished by use of the X–linked electrophoretic variant of glucose–6–phosphate dehydrogenase (Boyer, Porter, and Weilbacher, 1962). In the other two the X–linked blood group antigen (Xg^a) was used. Boyer (personal communication, 1962) demonstrated the X^MO state (matriclinous) in a Negro with the Turner syndrome using the X-linked electrophoretic variant of glucose–6–phosphate dehydrogenase. Few instances of X^PO Turner syndrome have been identified in man (v. infra). However, the Xg system is the only one which gives conclusive evidence (Boyer, Porter and Weilbaecher, 1962).

In collaboration with Race and Sanger, four groups of workers (Lindsten, et al., 1963) determined the Xg^a blood group in 56 complete mother/father/XO-daughter combinations. The constellation of findings showed that the single X of the daughter was paternal in one, maternal in 20, and undisclosed in 35. In another family in which the father was dead the X chromosome was apparently of paternal origin. In an XO case reported by Frey (1961) the X chromosome was probably of paternal origin because both the father and the XO daughter were color-blind; the mother may have been a carrier, however. (See Fig. 31.) When they allowed for the greater difficulty in demonstrating the X^PO status (Table 9), Lindsten and colleagues (1963) concluded that their data did not indicate that the paternal X is contributed to the XO individual either more often or less often than either of the two maternal X's.

Another case of X^PO has probably been dem-

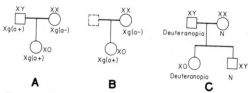

FIG. 31. THREE CASES OF X^PO TURNER SYNDROME A,B. From Lindsten, et al. (1963). C. From Frey (1961).

TABLE 8

Relative frequency of zygotes resulting from non-disjunction of sex chromosomes, assuming equal probability in both sexes and in both meiotic divisions

A

Non-disjunction in male

	In first stage		In second stage				
Gametes from male	4XY	4 O	XX	2 O	2Y	2X	YY
Gametes from female X	$8X^MX^PY$	$8X^MO$	$2X^PX^PX^M$	$4X^MO$	4XY	4XX	2XYY

Non-disjunction in female

	In first stage		In second stage		
Gametes from female	4XX	4 OO	2XX	2 O	4X
Gametes from male X	$4X^MX^MX^P$	$4X^PO$	$2X^MX^MX^P$	$2X^PO$	4XX
Gametes from male Y	$4X^MX^MY$	4YO	$2X^MX^MY$	2YO	4XY

B

Zygotes		Relative frequency	
XO	$\begin{cases} X^MO \\ X^PO \end{cases}$	$\left.\begin{matrix} 16 \\ 2 \end{matrix}\right\}$	18
XXY	$\begin{cases} X^MX^PY \\ X^MX^MY \end{cases}$	$\left.\begin{matrix} 8 \\ 6 \end{matrix}\right\}$	14
XXX	$\begin{cases} X^MX^MX^P \\ X^MX^PX^P \end{cases}$	$\left.\begin{matrix} 6 \\ 2 \end{matrix}\right\}$	8
XX			8
XY			8
YO (lethal)			6
XYY			2
			——
			64

onstrated by Lejeune (1962) using a different approach. He observed a sibship in which one child had ordinary trisomy-21 Down's syndrome and one had the XO Turner syndrome. The mother, phenotypically normal, had 45 chromosomes with fusion of chromosomes 2 and 22 ("balanced translocation"). In *Drosophila* it is well established that aberrations such as were present in this mother predispose to meiotic errors. Presumably an ovum without an X chromosome was fertilized by a normal X-bearing sperm to result in the X^PO Turner syndrome.

Benirschke and his colleagues (1962) described a family in which a mother with apparently normal karyotype had three children, each by a different husband. The first had the XXY Klinefelter syndrome, the second was normal and the third had Down's syndrome with a 21-21 fusion chromosome. Here is strong presumptive evidence that the Klinefelter case is $X^M X^M Y$.

The fact (p. 69) that several cases of chromatin-positive Turner syndrome with what is presumed to be an isochromosome of the long arm of one X chromosome have been associated with color blindness, with normal color-vision in both parents, suggests that in this situation also the normal X chromosome is maternal in origin and the anomalous one paternal.

Unlike the Klinefelter syndrome (see below), parental age is not increased in the Turner syndrome (Boyer, Ferguson-Smith, and Grumbach, 1961) and birth order is not different from the expected. Possibly this indicates that, unlike the Klinefelter syndrome, the XO Turner syndrome usually results, not from an accident of gametogenesis, but rather from loss of a paternal sex chromosome before or during the first cleavage. Polani (1962) pointed out that the distribution curve for maternal ages shows a small tail to the right, i.e., to higher ages, which may be abnormal and which is found in both XO and mosaic cases of the Turner syndrome. Possibly the latter fact indicates a similar mechanism, namely zygotic nondisjunction. A maternal age effect might be present in a rare form of the Turner syndrome, e.g., $X^P O$, and be detected only in a larger body of data than is now available.

In the Klinefelter syndrome interpreting the results of color blindness studies in terms of origin of the aneuploid state is rather more complicated than in the Turner syndrome. In an initial survey, Polani and colleagues in London, Glasgow and Zurich (1958) found no color blindness in 55 patients with chromatin positive Klinefelter syndrome. However, Nowakowski, Lenz, and Parada (1959) found three instances of color blindness in 34 cases. In none of the three was the father color-blind. In one the mother was color-blind, so that nondisjunction of the two maternal X's seems a straight-forward explanation. In the other two instances it is necessary to assume (Nowakowski and Lenz, 1961) one of two other accidents of maternal meiosis: 1) that homozygous X chromosomes resulted from equational nondisjunction (a combination of crossing-over and non-disjunction during oogenesis), as schematized in Figure 32; or 2) that nondisjunction of two color blindness-bearing X chromosomes occurs in the second stage of meiosis. (On the basis of the first possibility which requires crossing over Stern (1959b) suggested that the locus for color blindness is rather far from the kinetochore. See p. 69.)

Thus, in all instances of the Klinefelter syndrome, in which analysis was possible, abnormal *maternal* gametogenesis can be incriminated. This finding correlates with the finding that the average age of mothers of Klinefelter offspring is raised (Ferguson-Smith, 1961b; Lenz,

TABLE 9
Deductions on origin of sex chromosome aneuploidy in man

Father	Mother	Proband	Conclusion	Approx. frequency of parental mating in Northern Europeans
$X^{cb+}Y$	$X^{cb+}X^{cb-}$	$X^{cb-}O$	$X^M O$	.14
$XX^{Xg(a-)}Y$	$XX^{Xg(a+)}$__	$XX^{Xg(a+)}O$	$X^M O$	.33
$X^{G6PD-A}Y$	X^{G6PD-B}__	$X^{G6PD-B}O$	$X^M O$	—
$X^{G6PD+}Y$	$X^{G6PD+}X^{G6PD-}$	$X^{G6PD+}O$	$X^M O$	—
$X^{cb+}Y$	$X^{cb+}X^{cb-}$	X^{cb-} X	$X^M X^P$	.14
$X^{cb+}Y$	$X^{cb+}X^{cb-}$	$X^{cb-}X^{cb-}Y$	$X^M X^M Y$	.14
$XX^{Xg(a+)}Y$	$XX^{Xg(a-)}XX^{Xg(a-)}$	$XX^{Xg(a-)}XX^{Xg(a-)}Y$	$X^M X^M Y$	.07

Not yet observed in man*

Father	Mother	Proband	Conclusion	Approx. frequency
$XX^{Xg(a+)}Y$	$XX^{Xg(a-)}XX^{Xg(a-)}$**	$XX^{Xg(a+)}O$	$X^P O$	.07
$XX^{Xg(a+)}Y$	$XX^{Xg(a-)}XX^{Xg(a-)}$	$XX^{Xg(a-)}XX^{Xg(a+)}Y$	$X^M X^P Y$	.07

* Cases of $X^P O$ have now been observed using the Xg[a] marker (see text, p. 45).

** Occasional Xg(a−) female might be actually heterozygous, although no such case has been proved.

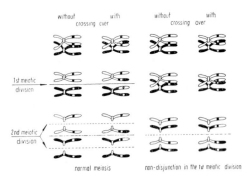

FIG. 32. THROUGH CROSSING OVER AND NONDISJUNC-
TION IN THE FIRST MEOITIC DIVISION IT IS POSSIBLE
FOR AN XX EGG HOMOZYGOUS FOR COLOR BLINDNESS
TO BE PRODUCED BY A HETEROZYGOUS MOTHER

This is one explanation for the occurrence of
color blindness in patients with the Klinefelter syndrome whose parents both have normal color vision.
(Another explanation involves simply nondisjunction of a noncrossover, color blindness-bearing X
chromosome in the second stage of meiosis in oogenesis.) From Nowakowski and Lenz (1961).

1959). The paternal age is probably also increased; the number of cases is not sufficient to
permit separate analysis.

A quite different explanation for the occurrence of the X^MX^MY Klinefelter syndrome involves mis-segregation in an XY zygote with formation of an XXY cell and a YO cell which dies
(Russell, 1961). (See Fig. 30b.) The high primary
sex ratio (see p. 62) with an excess of male zygotes could, through this mechanism, contribute
to the excess of XXY cases as compared to XO
cases.

If one assumes equal probability of nondisjunction in the two stages of meiosis and in the
two sexes the relative frequencies of various
forms of X chromosome aneuploidy would be as
indicated in Table 8. Actual observed frequencies are quite different. Tentative estimates
of the prevalence of XO chromatin-negative
Turner syndrome are 0.2 (Polani, 1960) and 0.3
per 1000 females (Maclean, Harnden, and
Brown, 1961). Recognized instances of chromatin-positive Turner syndrome are about one-
fourth or one-fifth as frequent. Based on sex-
chromatin surveys of newborns, the prevalence
of XXY males is more reliably estimated (Maclean, Harnden, and Brown, 1961) at 2.65 per
1000 male births (95% confidence limits of 1.43
and 3.87 per 1000). The XXX double-sex-chro-
matin female is rather frequent, about 0.8 per
1000 female births, and more frequent than the

XO Turner syndrome. (In mice the XO state
appears to be considerably more frequent than
the XXY state, the opposite of the situation in
man.)

The relative proportions of various aneuploid
states observed at birth is not a necessary indication of the relative frequency in zygotes. Intra-
uterine selection is intense (Hamerton, 1961),
with loss of 15 per cent or more of all concep-
tions. Differential selection is likely, furthermore. For example, the XXY fetus may fare
better than the XO fetus, since major congenital
malformations are rarely associated with the
Klinefelter syndrome but are frequent in the
Turner syndrome. Strong intrauterine selection
against the XO embryo is suggested by the finding of 3 XO cases among 56 spontaneous by
aborted concepti (Carr, 1963). No instance of
XXY karyotype was encountered.

Also demonstrated by Table 8 is the fact that
under the assumptions on which it is based one
would expect XO cases of the X^MO type to be
twice as frequent as those of the X^PO type. As
noted earlier, almost all instances capable of
analysis in man have been of the X^MO type.
The expected frequencies of X^MX^PY and
X^MX^MY Klinefelter syndrome are about equal;
however, all cases capable of analysis in man
have been of the X^MX^MY. (In the mouse Russell
and Chu (1961) identified an X^MX^PY mouse, the
first critical demonstration in a mammal that
non-disjunction can occur in the first meiotic
division in the male. In man, an Xg(a+) case of
XXY Klinefelter syndrome from an Xg(a+)
father and an Xg(a−) mother would provide
the necessary evidence.) Evidence that the YO
state is lethal before birth is available in the
mouse.

The probability of detecting X^PO and X^MX^PY
cases is much less than that of detecting X^MO
and X^MX^MY cases, because of the relative frequencies of the informative matings. Using
color blindness, all cv$^+$/cv$^-$ x cv$^+$/Y or cv$^-$/Y
matings (about 15 per cent of all matings) may reveal the X^MO Turner whereas no type of mating
gives incontrovertible evidence of the X^PO state
(except possibly the rare cv$^-$/cv$^-$ x cv$^+$/Y mating). In the Klinefelter syndrome again using
color blindness, the cv$+$/cv$^-$ x cv$^+$/Y mating
with a frequency of about 14 per cent can permit
detection of the X^MX^MY case but no mating gives
critical evidence on the X^MX^PY case. Using the

Xg^a blood group the mating Xg(a+) female x Xg(a−) male (about 33%) can indicate the X^{M}O cases whereas the mating Xg(a−) female x Xg(a+) male (about 7%) is required for detection of X^{P}O and X^{M}X^{P}Y cases. See Table 8.

In the mouse, no instance of spontaneously occurring X^{P}O state has been observed although a few examples were observed when female mice were irradiated between the time of sperm entry and the first cleavage (Russell, Russell, and Gower, 1959) and X^{P}O mice have been observed from XO x XY matings (Russell, 1961), which are possible in mice where the XO female is fertile. (Cattanach (1961b) may have observed the occurrence of an X^{P}O female from XX and XY parents.) In general, there was no spontaneous occurrence of a mouse either lacking the maternal X chromosome or with two maternal X chromosomes. For example, the X^{M}X^{M}Y state, frequent in man, has not been observed in the mouse. These and other chromosomal aberrations in mice are reviewed by Russell (1962).

Although nondisjunction can in some instances, be localized to maternal or paternal gametogenesis, no critical information is yet available to permit further pinpointing of the accident to the first or second meiotic division. The last type of family constellation listed in Table 8 would place nondisjunction in the first stage of spermatogenesis, but no such case has yet been identified in man.

In the mouse evidence that many XO cases occur through loss of an X chromosome, usually that of paternal origin, between sperm entry and the first cleavage is provided by the following observations: Multiple litter mates occasionally have the XO state, without XXX or XXY individuals represented (Russell, 1961). Irradiation of female mice during this stage results in an increased frequency of XO offspring (Russell and Saylors, 1960). Ohno, Kaplan, and Kinosita (1959d) found no secondary meiotic spermatocytes without a sex chromosome; 1460 cells were examined. Preferential loss of the paternal X chromosome is, as Russell (1961) indicates, probably not surprising since the male-contributed nuclear material (the male pronucleus) must undergo much more reorganization in the process of fertilization. Russell and Saylors (1962) demonstrated that irradiation of mouse spermatozoa resulted in as many as 1.2 per cent of female progeny being hemizygous for X–borne markers of the mother. However, the sperm is less sensitive to these effects than is the male pronucleus of the zygote.

The type of aneuploidy present is also a clue to the possible time of occurrence of the nondisjunctional accident. For example, cases of XXX/XO mosaicism (Jacobs, et al., 1959b) and of XO/XYY mosaicism (Cooper, et al., 1962) are most readily explained by non-disjunction at the first cleavage in a female and a male zygote, respectively. Similarly, the XXXXY state (Miller, et al., 1961) may be accounted for most easily on the basis of nondisjunction at successive meiotic divisions in oögenesis. The XYY state (Hauschka, et al., 1962) may arise through nondisjunction at the second meiotic division of spermatogenesis. Such conclusions are, of course, only unproved inferences.

A variety of mosaic states have been discovered as indicated in Table 7. Jacobs and her colleagues (1961) concluded that as many as 30 per cent of women with gonadal dysgenesis have some form of X chromosome mosaicism. These findings suggest that some of the non-mosaic aneuploid states may also be the result of chromosomal loss in the early stages of development, even before the first cleavage. Harnden and Jacobs (1961) suggested that deletion of part of one X chromosome and other morphologic abnormalities probably occur only as an accident of gametogenesis. However, de Grouchy and colleagues (1961) have described a case of XO/Xx mosaicism indicating the possibility that such accidents can also occur in early cleavage stages. Alternatively, the anomalous X chromosome may have been lost in some cells of the developing embryo, the primary accident having occurred in gametogenesis. The latter possibility exists for some of the other mosaic states as well.

The XYY/XO case of Cooper and his colleagues (1962) is particularly instructive. Clinically many of the features were quite typical of the chromatin-negative Turner syndrome. All cells cultured from the peripheral blood had 47 chromosomes and an XYY sex chromosome constitution. Almost all cells cultured from the skin had 45 chromosomes and an XO sex chromosome constitution. Anaphase lag with retention of both Y chromosomes in one daughter cell probably occurred in an early mitotic division, perhaps the first. Presumably the gonadal tissues were derived exclusively or principally from the XO cell line.

Gartler, Waxman, and Giblett (1962) presented evidence for yet another mechanism of mosaicism of all chromosomes including the sex chromosomes, namely double fertilization. An XX/XY true hermaphrodite had heterochromia iridis and blood groups indicating that both alleles of the father were contributed to the proband in the case of at least two systems, MNS and rhesus.

The origin of even more complex sex chromo-some aneuploidy, e.g., the triple X–Y syndrome (Ferguson-Smith, Johnston, and Handmaker, 1960), tetra X syndrome (Barr and Carr, 1960; Carr and Barr, 1961), tetra X–Y syndrome (Fraccaro, Kaijser, and Lindsten, 1960), and XXYY syndrome (Carr, Barr, and Plunkett, 1961; Ellis, et al., 1961; Motulsky, 1962, personal communication, Seattle), is more uncertain. Meiotic non-disjunction in both parents is a possible explanation, for the triple X–Y syndrome, for example. However, more likely in these other complex anomalies are repeated abnormalities of X chro-

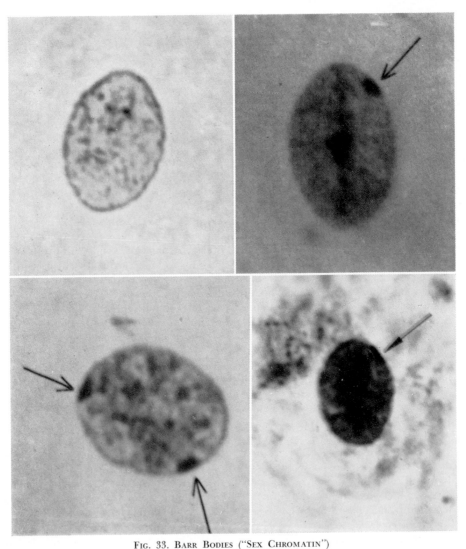

FIG. 33. BARR BODIES ("SEX CHROMATIN")

a. Normal male. b. Normal female. c. Double sex chromatin of XXXY and XXX individuals (see Fig. 34). d. Large Barr body in patient with presumed isochromosome of long arm of X (see Fig. 35). Courtesy of M. A. Ferguson-Smith.

mosome replication and segregation in *one* parent and/or the early zygote ("successive nondisjunction"). Breakey (1961) observed color blindness in an XXXY male. Since the mother showed "slight defects with the Ishihara charts" whereas the father and six sibs had normal color vision, he postulated double nondisjunction in oögenesis.

In the human female (and in many other female mammals), germ-cell multiplication is intense during the latter half of intra-uterine development. By the time of birth the oögonia have already differentiated into primary oöcytes in which the nuclei are in the initial stage of prophase of the first meiotic division, the unique dictyate stage or dictyotene which may persist for as long as 50 years (Ohno, Klinger, and Atkins, 1962). The female infant possesses the full stock of oöcytes which must last for her entire reproductive life (Parkes, 1956; Pinkerton, et al., 1961). Inventories of this stock in man have arrived at estimates of about 750,000 (Block, 1953). However, a large proportion of these degenerate at various stages of oögenesis and at various times in the life of the female. (See the detailed discussion by Austin, 1961.) By age 40 to 45 years the stock of ova has fallen to about 8,000 (Block, 1952).

The oöcyte nucleus normally contains a tetraploid amount of DNA throughout the prolonged dictyotene (Van de Kerckhore, 1959). The two X chromosomes are isopycnotic throughout oögenesis (Ohno, Kaplan, and Kinosita, 1960) and both cytologic and genetic evidence indicates free crossingover between them.

The first meiotic division is not completed until about the time of ovulation. The second meiotic division proceeds after the entry of sperm into the egg. When the chromosome groups in the male and female pronuclei come together, fertilization is considered complete and the cell is called a zygote. The process of fertilization takes place usually in the ampulla of the Fallopian tube. Implantation of the early human embryo occurs at six to seven days.

Spermatogenesis (Roosen-Runge, 1962) differs from oögenesis in the following respects, among others: 1) The production of sperm is extraordinarily profligate and the total number produced in the life-time of the male is astronomical. Proliferation of spermatogonia continues from puberty throughout the life of the male and is not confined to the fetal period as in the female. 2) Four spermatids are produced from each spermatogonium rather than one; no polar bodies are produced. 3) The time for the complete process of spermatogenesis is of the order of 64 days rather than 12–50 years as in oögenesis. 4) The X and Y chromosomes are positively heteropycnotic in the spermatocytes—a mechanism which probably evolved to ensure isolation of the male- and the female-determining chromosomes.

The pertinence of these differences between spermatogenesis and oögenesis to the origin of sex chromosome (and other) aneuploidy in man must be considerable although the details are, for the most part, still unknown.

The relatively frequent occurrence of "double trisomy" suggests that rather specific factors are responsible for aneuploidy rather than random accidents of gametogenesis. A historic case reported by Ford, Jones, Miller, et al. (1959) had both the XXY Klinefelter syndrome and the trisomy-21 Down's syndrome. This combination has been the type of double trisomy most often found (Harnden, Miller, and Penrose, 1960; Lehmann and Forssman, 1960; Lanman, et al., 1960; Hamerton, Jagiello, and Kirman, 1962). Although its frequency cannot be stated precisely, it would appear to be considerably more frequent than the product of the individual frequencies. Uchida and her colleagues (Uchida and Bowman, 1961; Uchida, et al., 1962) have described a case combining trisomy-18 and the triple-X syndrome. (Some might prefer to call the first example "double aneuploidy" not considering XXY a trisomy strictly speaking.)

The concentration in families (Hauschka, et

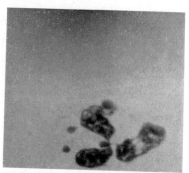

FIG. 34. THREE DRUMSTICKS IN A POLYMORPHONUCLEAR LEUKOCYTE OF A PATIENT WITH THE PENTA-X SYNDROME

Courtesy of Dr. Paul V. Woolley, Jr., Detroit.

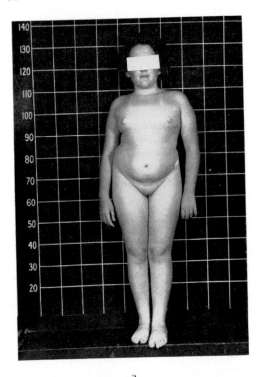

FIG. 35b.

a

FIG. 35. CHROMATIN-POSITIVE TURNER SYNDROME,
"ISOCHROMOSOME"-TYPE

a. The patient (847338), 17 year old, was 52 inches
tall, had no secondary sex characteristics, and had
spinal curvature and multiple pigmented moles, but
no webbing of the neck. She had been on estrogen at
the time of this photograph. Buccal smear was chromatin-positive with large Barr bodies (Fig. 33d). The
karyotype showed 46 chromosomes. On pairing of
the chromosome (b) one normal X was thought to
be present and in addition a large chromosome
matching the third pair of autosomes in length and
arm ratio. This was considered to be an isochromosome of the long arm of the X chromosome. Courtesy of M. A. Ferguson-Smith (1962). c. Giant drumstick in leukocyte of same patient. d. Autoradiograph
of cell from same patient showing late-labelling of
the isochromosome. The late-labelling chromosome
is peripherally located and is bent on itself. e. Xg^a
blood groups in this patient and her parents. That
the mother may be heterozygous is supported by
the finding of Xg(a–) brothers. The isochromosome is presumably of paternal origin. Conclusion
as to the possible location of the Xg locus on the
short arm is probably invalidated by the apparent
inactivation of the anomalous chromosome in all
cells (see text). Courtesy of Dr. Catherine S. N. Lee.

al., 1962; Miller, et al., 1961; Therman, et al.,
1961) of aneuploid conditions involving the
sex chromosomes and other chromosomes is
further evidence of the nonrandom nature of
these chromosomal aberrations.[8] Johnston and

———

[8] Breg and colleagues (1962) found two families in which the
triple X syndrome and mongolism occurred together.

Petrakis (1963) observed T21 mongolism and
the XO Turner syndrome in the same sibship.

For the possible application of preventive
measures, the cause of the cause, that is, the cause
of the chromosomal aberration underlying these
syndromes, must be sought. Forbes and Engel
(1963) have been impressed with the high frequency of *diabetes mellitus* in these families
and suggest "that some fault of the prediabetic
state leads to faults in meiosis or mitosis." Parental age was discussed above.

See Fraser (1963) and Lindsten (1963) for
further discussion of X chromosome aneuploidy.

Origin of the Barr body and "drumstick."
Some 20 per cent or more of cells in the buccal
smear of the normal female show a chromatin
mass adjacent to the nuclear membrane—the
so-called sex chromatin or, for its discoverer
(Barr and Bertram, 1949), the Barr body (Fig.
33). None of the cells of the normal male shows
the Barr body. (See Symposium, 1962.) Probably essentially all cells of the female have a
Barr body. That it cannot be identified in many
cells is probably because it is not in profile, because it is not in its characteristic position subjacent to the nuclear membrane, or because of
other technical factors. On the basis of mathe-
matic and geometric considerations Levij and
Meulendijk (1962) concluded that, assuming
that all cells of the buccal mucosa possess a
Barr body, one would not expect more than
about 50 per cent of Barr bodies to be in profile
and clearly subjacent to the nuclear membrane.
Therefore, they suggested that this is in fact
the location of the Barr body in all cells. In
cases of the triple–X or tetra–X syndrome, which

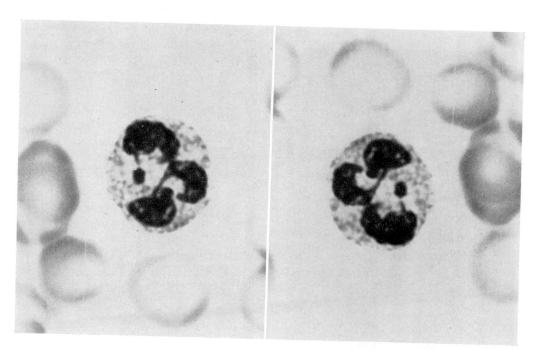

Fig. 35c.

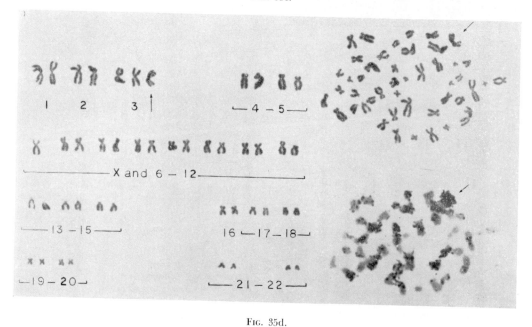

Fig. 35d.

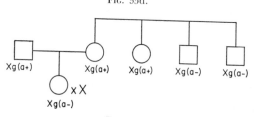

Fig. 35e.

53

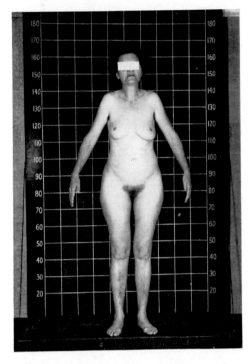

a

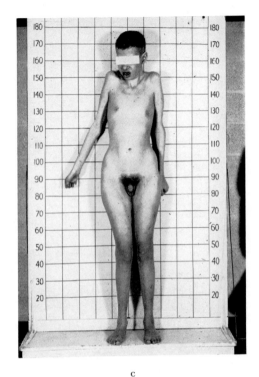

c

b

d

FIG. 36. DISORDERS ASSOCIATED WITH DOUBLE SEX CHROMATIN

a. *Triple X syndrome.* G.H. (946661) born in 1921, was institutionalized in 1936. She menstruates regularly. Examination in 1960 revealed an intelligence quotient less than 31 and the behavior of a four-year-old child. The external genitalia, breasts, pubic and axillary hair, and manual pelvic findings were all normal for an adult female. On laparotomy the uterus was found to be small but tubes were normal in size. The ovaries may have a normal appearance or may be cystic and small. Maturing Graffian follicles were identified histologically although their number is reduced. (Reproduction has been successfully accomplished by patients with the triple-X constitution. Of at least nine children born of such mothers all have had a normal sex chromosome constitution.) b. Karyotype in the *triple X syndrome.* Courtesy of A. W. Johnston and M. A. Ferguson-Smith. (Part of one normal chromosome 21 was obscured in reproduction.) c. *Triple X–Y syndrome.* M.G. (178523), age 22, of Polish-Russian-Austrian ancestry, was noted at an early age to be mentally retarded. He has been institutionalized from the age of 9 years with an estimated intelligence quotient below 20. The pelvis is broad. There is bilateral gynecomastia. The testes and prostate are very small. The testis measured 18 mm. in length at biopsy. Histologically it showed the changes typical of the Klinefelter syndrome. d. Karyotype in the *triple X–Y syndrome.*

show two or three Barr bodies in many cells, at least one Barr body may be identified in as many as 95 per cent of cells (Johnston, et al., 1961; Carr and Barr, 1961; Carr, Barr, and Plunkett, 1961); when two Barr bodies are present the chances that at least one will be in profile is increased. There remains a possibility that a small proportion of female cells have no Barr body. Ohno and Hauschka (1960) found that no heterochromatic chromosome was present in some cells in prophase. In more recent studies Ohno (1962, personal communication, Duarte, Calif.) finds that after implantation about 97 per cent of cells at prophase have one X chromosome heterochromatic and the remaining 3 per cent have no heterochromatic X. (See page 66 for another suggestion of why rapidly growing tissues might have a lower proportion of nuclei with a Barr body than slowly growing tissues.)

The Barr body was previously thought to be produced through the fusion of the heterochromatic portions of two X chromosomes. More recently this theory has been abandoned, and the conclusion that a Barr body is constituted from *one* X chromosome (or part thereof) has been forced by the the following observations:

1) Findings in normal individuals (XY, XX) and in individuals with XO, XXYY, XXX, XXY, XXXX, XXXXY and even more complex sex chromosome constitutions lead to the generalization (Barr and Carr, 1960; Stewart, 1960) that the maximum number of Barr bodies in any one diploid cell is one less than the number of X chromosomes (the n–1 rule).

2) In the rat Ohno, Kaplan and Kinosita (1959b) and in man Ohno and Makino (1961) find that during prophase, cells of the female show heteropycnosis of *one* chromosome (almost certainly one X chromosome), whereas the male shows no such phenomenon.[9] The heteropycnotic chromosome is often bent acutely at its center and resembles in shape the sex chromatin body seen in intermitotic nuclei. This may explain the fact that the Barr body sometimes looks double, leading to an erroneous view that it arises from two X chromosomes. That the X chromosomes show asynchronous incor-

poration of tritiated thymidine (German, 1962a, b; Morishima, Grumbach, and Taylor, 1962; Taylor, 1960) is evidence along this same line. In the XXY Klinefelter syndrome one X chromosome is late-labelling; in the XXXY syndrome there are two; in the XXXXY syndrome there are three (Rowley, et al., 1962).

Grumbach (1962, personal communication, New York) points out that the late DNA-synthesizing X chromosome tends to be peripheral in the mitotic spreads, as one might expect if it is the one constituting the Barr body.

Gilbert and his colleagues (1962) also demonstrated the late duplication of one X chromosome of the female. They emphasize the fact that the entirety of that one X chromosome synthesizes DNA late and that it tends to be peripherally located in the spreads with a bent configuration which could account for the seeming bifid nature of the Barr body in some preparations. No other pair of chromosomes showed comparable heterozygosity in pattern of incorporation of tritium-labelled thymidine.

As a third piece of evidence that the Barr body is formed from one X chromosome, Stewart and Sanderson (1961) presented their finding of what they interpreted as a Barr body in cells of the normal human testis. However, spermatogonia show the sex vesicle comprising the heteropycnotic X–Y bivalent and this vesicle was almost certainly confused for sex chromatin. The sex vesicle was recognized in man by Painter in the 1920's and Sachs in 1954 and has been studied also in the mouse and rat by Ohno, Kaplan, and Kinosita (1956, 1957a).

The findings in polyploidy do not necessarily require a modification in the n–1 rule. The triploid male patient of Böök and Santesson (1960) had 69 chromosomes (3A + XXY) and was chromatin negative. Recent information indicates (Böök and Santesson, 1961) that the patient is in fact a mosaic. Penrose's group (Delhanty, Ellis, and Rowley, 1961; Penrose and Delhanty, 1961) observed two instances of 3A + XXY abortuses and one studied from this point of view was chromatin positive (Mittwoch and Delhanty, 1961). The Barr bodies may have been unusually small in this case (Mittwoch, 1961, personal communication, London). Harnden (1961b) showed that octoploid and tetraploid cells of an XXXY individual have 12 and six X chromosomes and eight and four Barr bod-

[9] Sandberg and colleagues (1960) had observed heteropycnosis and allocycly of one X chromosome in the normal human female. By special techniques of fixation and staining, differentiation of the two X chromosomes can be demonstrated in mitotic metaphase plates (Saksela and Moorhead, 1962).

ies, respectively. Atkin (1960) found that tetraploid male cells are chromatin negative despite the presence of two X's and that tetraploid female cells have only two Barr bodies despite the presence of four X's. Harnden (1961b) suggested a modification of the n–1 rule to allow that one diploid set of autosomes suppresses heterochromaticity in one X chromosome. He formulated the modified rule as follows: $B = X - (p/2)$, where B is the number of Barr bodies, X is the number of X chromosomes, and p is the ploidy.

The Harnden formula does not predict the findings in the triploid cases. Moreover, assuming for the moment the validity of the Lyon hypothesis (p. 59 ff), the Harnden modification of the n–1 rule is not necessary to account for the findings in polyploidy. All the polyploid states cited as examples probably arise or may have arisen after the chromatin status of the parent cells was decided upon. Therefore, the number of Barr bodies in tetraploid and octoploid cells would be expected to be simple multiples of that in the parent cell.

Schuster and Motulsky (1962) have described a remarkable case of XX/XY/XO mosaicism in an individual with male pseudohermaphroditism. The XX cells contained no Barr body. The cultures of blood cells showed XY and XO types but none of the XX type, whereas skin cultures showed XX as well as XO karyotypes. The authors suggested that the XX cells arose by non-disjunction in an XO cell sometime after the "time of decision" postulated in the Lyon hypothesis. The findings and conclusion are consistent with those of polyploidy.

A possible exception to the n–1 rule—a case of chromatin-positive Turner syndrome with supposed XO sex chromosome constitution (Grumbach, Morishima, and Chu, 1960) may not be an exception if, as the most recent information indicates (Grumbach and Morishima, 1962), the patient is in fact an XO/XX/XXX mosaic. If one assumes that "fixed differentiation" of one X in XX cells before the origin of the XO and XXX lines, it is plausible that the XO cell line might have a Barr body. The fact that in birds, such as the domestic fowl (Kosin and Ishizaki, 1959; Ohno,

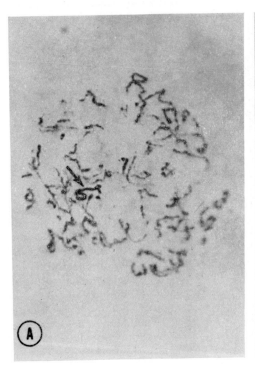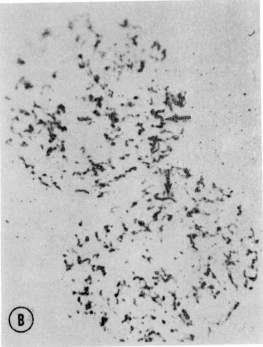

FIG. 37. HETEROPYCNOSIS OF ONE X CHROMOSOME IN LATE PROPHASE AND IN TELOPHASE
a. Late prophase. b. Telophase. The telophase chromosome is smaller since the cell has divided. Courtesy of Dr. S. Ohno (1963).

1961b; Ohno, Kaplan, and Kinosita, 1959a), the female is the heterogametic sex, yet is chromatin-positive, presents an interesting problem but possibly has no direct bearing on the question of the origin of the Barr body in man and other mammals.

Earlier Ohno and colleagues (1959b) suggested that which of the two X chromosomes forms the Barr body might be a function of the company each keeps or has previously kept, that is, that the X chromosome of paternal origin regularly constitutes the Barr body. However, as was discussed earlier (p. 47), in cases of the XXY Klinefelter syndrome both X chromosomes seem to come from the mother, yet the subject shows a Barr body. For this and other reasons, Ohno and Hauschka (1960) later wrote as follows: "More probably, heteropyknosis alternates between the two X's in a female somatic nucleus regardless of their parental derivation. Depending on stage of DNA synthesis

and degree of overlapping in the replication of the two X chromosomes, one may often discern one X, sometimes no X, or, rarely, two X's [which are heteropyknotic]."

The above considerations by no means exclude the possibility that only part of one X chromosome, possibly part of the long arm, goes to form the Barr body in the normal female. Maclean (1962) suggested that certain observations on the frequency and size of leukocyte drumsticks in cases of partial deletion of one X chromosome are best explained if part of the short arm is always euchromatic and does not participate in the formation of the sex appendage (or Barr body). Ohno (1962) considers this highly improbable, however, since the entire X chromosome is heterochromatic in early prophase preparations. In summary, the weight of evidence supports the view that the Barr body represents the heterochromatin portion of one X chromosome and is formed by a process which

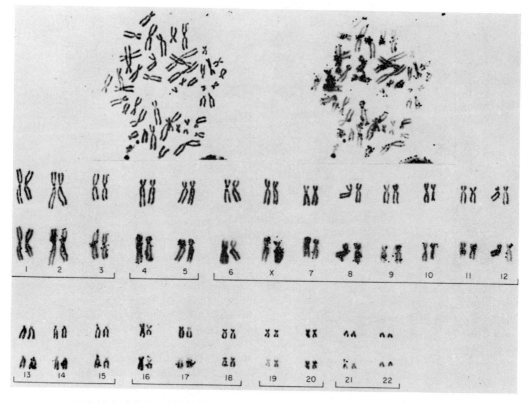

FIG. 38. AUTORADIOGRAPH, WITH TRITIUM-LABELLED THYMIDINE, SHOWING LATE-LABELLING OF ONE X CHROMOSOME

Several workers have noted that the late-labelling X chromosome is shorter than its homolog. Courtesy of Dr. James L. German, II.

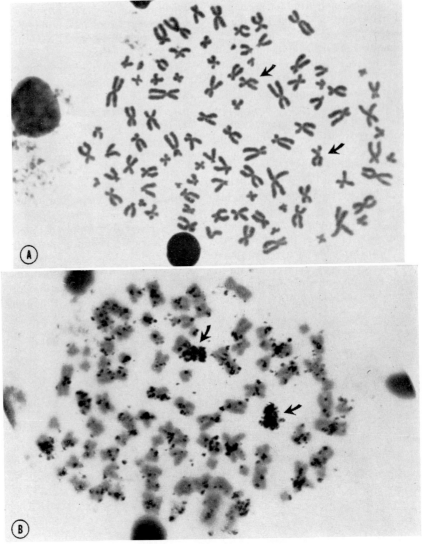

FIG. 39. AUTORADIOGRAPH OF TETRAPLOID CELL, SHOWING LATE-LABELLING
OF TWO X CHROMOSOMES

Courtesy of Bowen and Lee (1963) and *Bull. Johns Hopkins Hosp.*

Morishima, Grumbach, and Taylor (1962) call "fixed differentiation".

Modifications on the suggestion that in the normal female one entire X chromosome of all cells constitutes the Barr body include several combinations of the following: 1) only part of one X chromosome might be heterochromatic; 2) the heterochromatic behavior of one X chromosome might be limited to certain cells or certain tissue; 3) one X chromosome might be heterochromatic during only part of interphase.

The entirety of one X chromosome of the female synthesizes DNA late (see p. 55). Furthermore one *entire* X chromosome of every prophase and telophase figure of rapidly multiplying populations of female somatic cells is condensed. Ohno finds that the condensed X seen at prophase appears much larger than most of the sex chromatin bodies present in neighboring interphase nuclei whereas the size of the condensed X in each daughter nucleus of telophase corresponds quite well. He suggests that replication has taken place (in late interphase) to account for the larger size of the prophase X chromosome. Thus possibility one, above, seems unlikely.

Studying living human cells by phase microscopy through cycles of cell division, DeMars (1962) could identify an unequivocal Barr body only in late interphase in the few hours before the next cell division. However, at the earlier stages small condensations of chromatin material were present. Therkelsen and Peterson (1962) studied the frequency of Barr-positive cells in cultures of human tissues. A minimum of 60 per cent were Barr-positive during the logarithmic growth phase and almost 100 per cent were Barr-positive in the post-logarithmic phase. Thus the possibility that both X chromosomes are euchromatic during part of interphase cannot be excluded.

Ohno (1962) points out that heterochromatin still continues some activities, e.g., nucleolus organization. The Barr body was first found adjacent to the nucleolus in nerve cell nuclei of the female cat. Furthermore, in mice in which the X chromosome carries a nucleolus-organizer the condensed X was found in association with the nucleolus in 30 per cent of the female prophase figures (Ohno, Kaplan, and Kinosita, 1957b).

It would seem that in those cases in which two X chromosomes are present but one is partially deleted it is always the anomalous X chromosome which forms the Barr body. In simple deleted-X cases (Xx) *all* Barr bodies are small. In cases of what is interpreted as an isochromosome of the long arm with deleted short arm (XX), all Barr bodies are unusually large. Furthermore, assuming that the Lyon hypothesis (p. 59) is correct in its suggestion that the X chromosome which forms the Barr body is genetically inactive, then a cell with a deleted X chromosome as the only active one would be expected to die.

The "drumstick" of the leukocytes, described by Davidson and Smith (1954), was of uncertain origin (Davidson, 1960; Davidson and Flute, 1962). Ashley and Jones (1958) concluded that it is not an equivalent of the Barr body since they thought both structures can sometimes be identified in the same neutrophiles. For this reason they have suggested that the "drumstick" is a secondary sex characteristic at the nuclear level. However, that the "drumstick" is somehow related fairly directly to the X chromosomes is

suggested by 1) the demonstration of leukocytes with two "drumsticks" in cases of the XXXY syndrome (Harnden and Jacobs, 1961) and 2) the observation of large "drumsticks" in some subjects with one abnormally large X chromosome (Engel and Forbes, 1961; Jacobs et al., 1961). The extensive studies by Maclean (1962) of the "drumsticks" in cases with abnormalities in the number and structure of X chromosomes leave no room for question that the Barr body and the leukocyte appendage are of equivalent significance.

The functional significance (or insignificance) of the Barr body. Although apparently it occurred to several persons (e.g., Stewart, 1960, 1962; Ohno, 1961a; Beutler, Yeh, and Fairbanks, 1962; Grumbach and Morishima, 1962) at about the same time so that assigning priority, always a hazardous as well as useless task, is particularly difficult, Dr. Mary Lyon of Harwell, England, was among the first to expound what will be referred to as the *Lyon hypothesis* (Fig. 40): that only one X chromosome per cell is genetically active during interphase, the other in the normal female retaining its heterochromatic properties. In early embryogenesis each somatic cell of the female, it is postulated, reaches a "time of decision" when the die is cast as to whether X^P or X^M shall be the active one in that particular cell. Descendants of each cell abide by the decision originally made. The decision may be reached as early as the time of implantation and probably

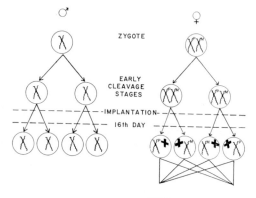

MOSAIC OF ADULT FEMALE

Fig. 40. The Lyon Hypothesis: A Schematic Portrayal

Implantation occurs 6½–7 days after fertilization. The postulated X chromosome differentiation is thought to occur at that time or no later than about the 16th day.

no later than the time of first appearance of the Barr body, which in this hypothesis represents the genetically inactive X chromosome. (As Platt (1961), writing in a different context, puts it: "...biologically you are nothing but a lot of clones.") The Lyon hypothesis suggests that it is a random proposition which of the two X chromosomes is "active" and which plays "dummy" in any particular somatic cell of the normal female, although the possibility of partial nonrandomness is not excluded by the hypothesis. All the X chromosomes of the normal male are presumably active. The germ cell line in the female probably does not participate in this process of X chromosome differentiation (see p. 51). As will also be discussed later, the term *inactivation* may be less appropriate than one such as *suppression, modification,* or *differentiation.*

Cytologic support for the Lyon hypothesis of X chromosome differentiation is provided by the observation of heteropycnosis in a single X chromosome of prophase cells from the normal female (p. 55). Taylor (1960), moreover, found asynchronous incorporation of tritium-labelled thymidine into X chromosome DNA in the Chinese hamster. German (1962a, b) and Morishima, Grumbach, and Taylor (1962) have evidence of the same in man (also, see Gilbert, et al., 1962).

Ohno, Weiler, and Stenius (1961) have described another example of different functioning of two chromosomes of a pair. In the guinea pig they consistently found in all somatic and germ cells that only one of the largest autosomal pair demonstrates a secondary constriction and participates in organization of the nucleolus. They suggested that in mammals many homologous regions of chromosome pairs within the same diploid nucleus do not function synchronously. They stated, furthermore, that in man although all 10 acrocentric autosomes of man exhibit nucleolar satellites at one time or another (Ferguson-Smith and Handmaker, 1961), they could find no more than six associated with nucleoli at any one time. Lima-de-Faria, Reitalu, and Bergman (1961) emphasized the asynchrony in DNA synthesis in the human chromosomes, between homologs, between separate chromosomes, and between the two arms of the same chromosome.

Necessary *genetic* consequences of the Lyon hypothesis (which can be used in testing the hypothesis) are the following:

1. There should be no dosage effect of the two X chromosomes in the female as compared with the male.

2. As a group females heterozygous for X–linked traits should show wide variability.

3. With X–linked traits which can be identified and studied at the cellular level, two populations of cells should be found in most heterozygous females: one population with the mutant phenotype, one with the wild phenotype.

4. In the case of multifactorial traits to whose genetic background the X chromosome contributes, monozygotic female twins should show greater intrapair differences than male monozygotic twins.

Each of these aspects will be discussed.

The female has, in the Lyon hypothesis, no greater number of *active* X chromosomes than does the male. The Lyon hypothesis is not in conflict with the facts of X–linked recessive inheritance; the heterozygous female has in all no more active X chromosomes than the hemizygous male but on the average half her active X chromosomes are mutant in type rather than all of them as in the hemizygous "affected" male. The Lyon hypothesis suggests a mechanism for what Muller (1947–1948) called "dosage compensation," that is, the reason that the homozygous normal female with two X chromosomes has no more (Stern, 1960a) of certain proteins determined by sex-linked genes than does the normal male with one X chromosome. In the case of autosomal loci dosage effects are familiar from many examples in which heterozygotes, with one dose of a particular gene, have roughly half as much protein product of the said gene as do the homozygotes: hypocatalasemia (Nishimura, et al. 1959), congenital methemoglobinemia due to diaphorase deficiency (Scott, 1960); PTA deficiency (Rapaport, Procter, Patch, and Yettra, 1961), nonspherocytic congenital hemolytic anemia due to deficiency of pyruvic kinase (Valenine, Tanaka, and Miwa, 1961; Tanaka, Valentine, and Miwa, 1962), rhesus antigen (Masouredis, 1960), galactosemia (Kirkman and Bynum, 1959), the variant hemoglobins, and others. In the case of X–linked loci such gene dosage effects have not been observed in comparisons of persons homozygous (XX) and hemizygous (XY) for specific wild–type alleles;

see below for possible exceptions. The normal XX female has no higher glucose–6–phosphate dehydrogenase activity than does the normal XY male and the same is true for the normal male and female in regard to the clotting factors, antihemophilic globulin and PTC. In the case of the X–linked blood group (Xg^a), Mann and his colleagues (1962) found that the Xg^aY male individual reacts more strongly than the heterozygous Xg^aXg female and that the Xg^aXg^a homozygotes react as strongly as hemizygotes and more strongly than heterozygotes—all findings consistent with the Lyon hypothesis. Furthermore, persons with three or four X chromosomes react no more strongly in the Xg^a system than do hemizygotes (Race and Sanger, 1962, personal communication, London). At least four laboratories have, to my knowledge, assayed the level of erythrocyte glucose–6–phosphate dehydrogenase in persons with three or four X chromosomes and found it not elevated (Grumbach, Marks, and Morishima, 1962). (In one patient studied by Grumbach, Marks, and Morishima (1962) the XXXX sex chromosome constitution was associated with elevated G6PD in the red cells. However, the possibility that the red cell population was on the average younger than normal was not investigated.)

Although no completely convincing example of an X chromosome dosage effect, distinguishing the "normal" male and female, has been observed, it is necessary to be cautious in drawing conclusions since few products of X chromosome gene action lend themselves well to this study. Furthermore, it is a general physiologic principle that conditions of stress are more likely to render differences evident. Childs and colleagues (1962) have focused their attention on the normal alleles for two X–linked mutants, that for vitamin D resistant rickets, and that for renal diabetes insipidus. Stressing the normal mechanisms which are postulated to be under X–linked control (e.g., water diuresis) might bring out a difference between the normal homozygous female and the normal hemizygous male. Indeed, a suggestion of greater response to antidiuretic hormones in the normal female was found (Childs, Cantolino, and Dyke, 1962). (This might, of course, have its basis in the different make-up of the female with regard to other hormones.) Furthermore, Childs and colleagues (1962) suggest that the present occurrence of vitamin D *deficiency* rickets predominantly in males may be evidence of dosage effect for the wild-type allele of the mutant responsible for vitamin D resistant rickets.

Part and parcel of the question of dosage compensation in the X chromosomes is the matter of degree of severity in homozygous affected females as compared with the hemizygous affected males. Suffice it to say that in the seven known examples (p. 16) the homozygous affected female is no more severely affected than the hemizygous affected male, an observation consistent with, indeed supporting, the Lyon hypothesis.

In conditions of X–polysomy the somatic and sexual phenotypes are perhaps not as drastically altered as one would anticipate if all the X chromosomes were genetically active. For example, the triple–X female is often fertile (Johnston, et al., 1961) and although mild mental retardation is usually present physical effects are not striking. Furthermore, no matter how many X chromosomes are present in combination with a Y chromosome the phenotype remains male (Table 7); the male-determining property of the Y chromosome is not overwhelmed. Here may be evidence supporting at least partial inactivation of all but one X chromosome with regard to sex determining properties as well as others.

By the Lyon hypothesis, should one not expect the XO and XXX females to be phenotypically identical to the normal XX female, and the XXXY Klinefelter male to be phenotypically identical to the XXY Klinefelter male? The fact that the XXX and XXXY states are distinguished from the XX and XXY states, respectively, by the presence of greater mental deficiency and somatic malformations suggests some dosage effect in these polysomic states. Fraser and colleagues (1961a) emphasize the occurrence of even more pronounced abnormalities in the XXXXY Klinefelter syndrome. Furthermore, cases of the XXY Klinefelter syndrome show, on the average, lower intelligence than normal XY males. (The criticism that the methods for ascertaining cases of the Klinefelter syndrome, e.g., by screening of special institutions, accounts for the low average intelligence does not pertain to some recent studies (Raboch and Sipova, 1961). Surveys of institutions for the mental defectives (Maclean, et al., 1962) reveal frequencies of the XXY state about three times that in the general population and the frequency of the XXX state is increased to about the same extent over the general prevalence. The XO state probably has no increased frequency in such institutions.) On the other hand, an alternative possibility is that important effects of the polysomic–X states antedate the "time of decision" when the Barr body is formed. The fact that no heterochromatic X chromosome is found in oögonia or oöcytes (Ohno, Kaplan, and Kinosita, 1960) may indicate that two active X chromosomes are essential to normal ovarian development, thus explaining the "streak gonads" of the Turner syndrome. Finally, as pointed out by Mittwoch (1961), it may not be fair to compare the function of the genetic material in sex determination and perhaps some other traits with its function in the monogenic traits with which the Lyon hypothesis is concerned.

Sex chromatin has not been observed in oöcytes and the XX bivalent of oöcytes is isopycnotic (Ohno, Kaplan, and Kinosita, 1960; 1961; Ohno and Weiler, 1961), observations suggesting that with gametogenesis a "new hand is dealt" insofar as differentiation of the X chromosome is concerned. In fact, the germ cell line probably does not participate in the X chromosome differentiation postulated for somatic cells.

The decision as to which particular X chromosome of the pair in a particular cell is to be inactive and "play dummy during the rest of the hand" may be made rather early in development, when the total number of cells in the organism is relatively small. Ohno (1961, personal communication, Duarte, Calif.) finds one X chromosome heterochromatic at the time of implantation (sixth to seventh day) and suggests that the decision may be made at that stage. The Barr body can be identified as early as the sixteenth day in the human embryo and somewhat earlier in the trophoblast (Park, 1957). Thus, the probable limits on the time of decision postulated by Lyon are the sixth day and the sixteenth day. From study of the two earliest embryos (Nos. 7762 and 7802) in the Carnegie collection in which Park (1957) identified sex chromatin, Ebert and Böving (1962, personal communication, Baltimore) estimated that the 16-day-old human fetus (germinal disc stage; Streeter's Horizon vii) has between 2800 and 4000 cells (excluding extraembryonic and tro-

phoblastic elements). Of these the ectoderm comprises 2000–2400 cells, the mesoderm 400 to 800 cells and the endoderm 400 to 800 cells. Of the cells destined to become, for example, the cells producing antihemophilic globulin in the adult, only a few, perhaps 10–20, may be present at this early stage.

Because of the small size of the pertinent cellular population it is likely that a population of females will fall, with regard to the proportion of cells which have a particular X chromosome as the active one, into a frequency distribution with a large variance (Fig. 41a). The anticipated consequence is that females heterozygous for X–linked genes will describe a normal distribution with a wide range of variability, with regard to the expression of said gene. Such has indeed been found for glucose–6–phosphate dehydrogenase, for antihemophilic globulin (Githens and Wilcox, 1962; Rapaport, Patch, and Moore, 1960), for PTC (Barrow, Bullock, and Graham, 1960) and for the Xg^a blood group. See Figure 41b. One would anticipate occasional full expression of X–linked recessive traits in the heterozygous female, and indeed such is observed. Rapaport and his colleagues (1960) estimated that 2 per cent of females heterozygous for the gene for hemophilia A have AHG levels sufficiently low to result in clinical hemophilia. McGovern and Steinberg (1958) presented a case of hemophilia A in a presumably heterozygous female and offered this explanation. The cases of de la Chapelle and colleagues (1961), of Taylor and Biggs (1961), and of Mellman and colleagues (1961a) may be of the same type. Trujillo and colleagues (1961) described a G6PD–deficient Sephardic Jewish female who must be heterozygous since she had two normal sons. The woman had no detectable enzyme activity in her erythrocytes and each spring for many years had suffered from severe hemolytic anemia upon ingestion of fava beans. The karyotype was normal. Gross and colleagues (1958) described a similar case. Niléhn and Nilsson (1962) described severe hemophilia B with very low Factor IX level in a female with a normal father and a carrier mother. Again the karyotype was normal.

Studying females heterozygous for the electrophoretic variant of G6PD, Boyer (1962, personal communication, Baltimore) finds that although most have essentially identical proportions of types A and B in red cells and white

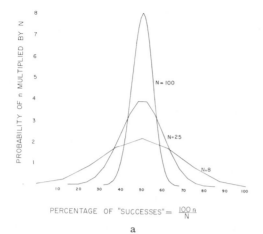

a

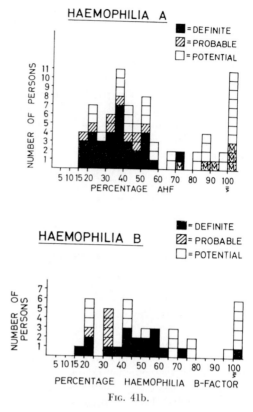

Fig. 41b.

Fig. 41. Frequency Distribution (Binomial Distribution) and Level of Clotting Factors in Females
Heterozygous for Hemophilia A or B

a. Frequency distribution (binomial distribution),
given various numbers of pertinent cells in females
heterozygous for an X–borne recessive gene and assuming an equal chance ($P = 0.5$) that in any particular cell the mutant chromosome or the wild
type X chromosome will be the "active" one. With
smaller numbers of cells, such as might obtain in
early embryonic life in specific pertinent tissues at
the "time of decision" on active vs inactive X chromosome, the variance (spread) of the distribution
would be greater. b. The level of antihemophilic
globulin (AHF in the terminology of these workers)
was low in 40 of 47 definite and probable carriers of
hemophilia A. Of seven carriers with normal AHF
values six were past the menopause. The level of
PTC (factor IX or hemophilia B factor) was low in 20
of 23 definite or probable carriers and in seven of 18
potential carriers. From Nilsson and colleagues
(1962).

cells, occasional subjects show a preponderance
of one type in red cells and of the other in
white cells. Furthermore, a deficiency of AB females and the occurrence of both A sons and B
sons from some females typed A, find possible
explanation in the Lyon hypothesis.

Manifesting heterozygotes for Duchenne muscular dystrophy have been referred to by Morton
and Chung (1959) and Fraser (1963), among
others, and described in detail by Emery (1963).

Genetic evidence in support of the Lyon
hypothesis has been assembled from mice (Lyon
1961a; Russell, 1961), in which mosaicism for
coat-color is observed in females heterozygous
for X–linked coat color genes. The mosaic phenotype in the "tortoise-shell" female cat is comparable to that in female mice heterozygous for
X–linked coat color genes. All the female offspring of a black female by yellow male cat are
"tortoise-shell." Two populations of pigment

cells would appear to exist: those with *yellow*-
bearing X chromosome active and those with
the non-*yellow*-bearing X chromosome active.
At least some of the male cats with tortoise-shell
coat have been found to have an XXY sex
chromosome constitution (Thuline and Norby,
1961). In 1953 Falconer commented on the mosaic phenotype in female mice heterozygous for
coat color mutations: "There is a curious point
of resemblance between the three sex-linked
genes described in this paper, which is shared
also by the sex-linked *yellow* in cats. All these
genes have mosaic heterozygotes, and no sex-
linked gene affecting the integument is known
that does not have a mosaic heterozygote. This
resemblance may be purely fortuitous but it is
nevertheless worth pointing out." The tabby
heterozygous mouse has areas of the coat identical to that of the black hemizygote and homozygote and other areas agouti like the wild type
(Falconer, 1953).

In man, evidence of this type (mosaicism in
heterozygotes) is more difficult to find. Lyon
(1961b and c) has, however, suggested that the
mottled appearance of the ocular fundus in

females heterozygous for the gene for ocular albinism (No. A42) might be such evidence. Roberts' pedigree of X–linked anhidrotic ectodermal dysplasia (Roberts, 1929) is of particular interest in this connection because of the following statement: "Three of the females were reported to have occasional 'patches' on the body which were smooth and in which the sweat glands did not function." Kline, Sidbury, and Richter (1959) studied a family with probable X–linked ectodermal dysplasia and demonstrated patchy skin involvement with maps of skin resistance. Demonstrating changes by starch-iodine mapping of sweating, Motulsky (1962, personal communication, Seattle) has had experience with patchy involvement in females presumably heterozygous for the X–linked disorder. In females who were heterozygous for glucose–6–phosphate dehydrogenase deficiency and showed intermediate levels of enzyme activity, Beutler, et al., (1962) studied in vitro the rate of disappearance of red cell glutathione in the presence of acetylphenylhydrazine and the rate of reduction of methemoglobin in the presence of Nile blue. He interpreted his findings as indicating two populations of erythrocytes, one with normal levels and one with very low levels of G6PD. However, by in vivo studies of erythrocyte survival by the DFP[32]–labelling method, Brewer, Tarlov, and Powell (1962) could demonstrate in two heterozygous females no cells with a normal survival when primaquine was administered, findings refuting the Lyon hypothesis. Observations in more subjects are desirable. Davidson, Nitowsky, and Childs (1963) have found in cultures of skin cells from Caucasian females heterozygous for G6PD–deficiency and/or the A-B electrophoretic polymorphism of G6PD (Boyer, et al., 1962), that some clones have normal enzyme level whereas others have very low enzyme level, and clones have either A or B type enzyme, not both. If confirmed in further experiments, these findings will constitue strong support for the Lyon hypothesis.

Gorman and his colleagues (1963) found that the red cells of females heterozygous for Xg^a blood group behave differently from an artificial mixture of Xg(a+) and Xg(a–) cells from males. They concluded that two populations of red cells do not exist in such heterozygous females. Studies in which the red cells of females heterozygous for both Xg^a blood group and G6PD–deficiency supported this conclusion. If the Xg^a antigen were not intrinsic to the red cell but rather a serum factor adsorbed on the red cell like the Lewis antigen, mosaicism would not be expected. However, it is unlikely that Xg^a is like Lewis because no trace of Xg^a antigen is found in the saliva or plasma and Xg(a–) cells incubated in plasma from Xg(a+) persons do not become Xg(a+) (Sanger and Race, 1962).

A crucial genetic test of the Lyon theory might be possible in mice. Females doubly heterozygous with reference to two X–borne recessive mutants affecting the same trait would be of two types, depending on whether the mutant alleles were in coupling or in repulsion: if in coupling the phenotype would be expected to be mosaic; if in repulsion no wild-type patches would be expected. Unfortunately many X–linked mutations thus far identified in mice are lethal in the hemizygous male (Russell, 1961). However, the prediction of complete mutant phenotype in the repulsion double heterozygote has been realized (Lyon, 1962a) using a coat color gene on one X chromosome and a hair-structure gene on the other. Either one or the other acted in all parts of the coat but never both. Also supporting the hypothesis is the observation of Searle (1962) that when the locus for *tabby* is transferred to an autosome through translocation, the gene behaves as an ordinary recessive.

In *Drosophila* and *Oenothera* (Lewis, 1950) and in the mouse (Russell, 1961) position effects of the variegated type (V–type) occur when part of an autosome is translocated or inverted to bring loci into the vicinity of heterochromatin. *Variegated* is the term applied because the phenotype is mosaic, only some cells showing the aberrant phenotype. When a piece of autosome containing loci bearing the wild-type allele comes to lie near a heterochromatic portion of its own or any other chromosome including the X chromosome then its dominance is suppressed or rendered *uncertain* so that if the allele on the other chromosome is mutant it is expressed in the heterozygote even though it is ordinarily recessive. *In the mouse* (Russell, 1961; Russell and Bangham, 1961) only a heterochromatic X chromosome seems capable of changing recessive-dominance relationships of the autosomal locus through the V-type position

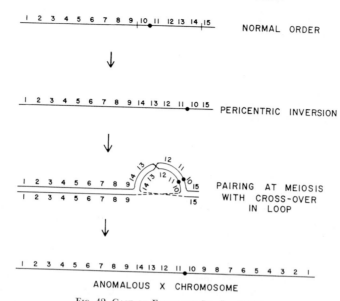

FIG. 42. CASE OF ELVES AND ISRAËLS (1962)

Possible mechanism by which a long metacentric X chromosome with partial duplication and with deletion of the AHG locus *might* have arisen during meiosis in the mother, who is considered to carry a pericentric inversion of one X chromosome.

effect (when an autosome/X chromosome translocation occurs). Only in the *female* mouse is an X chromosome heterochromatic; the variegated phenotype ordinarily occurs only in the female, or in the XXY male mouse (Cattanach, 1961). By the Lyon hypothesis only a proportion of the cells of the female mouse, ordinarily about half, show the anomalous phenotype, because it is a random matter whether the X chromosome which participated in the translocation or its ordinary mate is the one which becomes heterochromatic and inactive. The interpretation of the *variegated* phenotype advanced by Russell (1961) fits nicely with the Lyon hypothesis. (*Drosophila* apparently differs from the mouse in that variegation from X–linked translocations is expressed (Lewis, 1950) in flies with only one X chromosome; cytologically the distribution of heterochromatin seems to be different in the X chromosomes of *Drosophila* as compared with mammals.)

The variegated type of position effect has not been identified in man. No certain autosome/X chromosome translocation has been identified. Study of meiotic material is necessary for positive demonstration of translocations. Hamerton and colleagues (1961) have identified translocation figures in testicular material from cases of Down's syndrome of the translocation type. The expected consequence of some such X–autosome translocations would be a variegated phenotype corresponding to an autosomal recessive phenotype and occurring only in females. Albinism is an autosomal recessive trait which in the heterozygous female with the appropriate autosome/X chromosome translocation might have a variegated phenotype.

On the basis of the Lyon hypothesis one might anticipate greater intrapair variability, with regard to some metrical characters, in the case of female monozygotic twins than in male monozygotic twins. The prediction is based on the presumption that in the genetic determination of many multifactorial traits X–borne genes play a role. Because the random decision as to which X chromosome is to be the genetically active one is probably made at a time when relatively few anlage cells are present, the possibility for chance deviations between two female MZ co-twins exists. In male twins there can be no genetic variation between male MZ twins from this source. Although it was thought that for many traits female monozygotic twins indeed show more intrapair variability than do male monozygotic twins (Vandenberg, McKusick, and McKusick, 1962), errors in the study have come to light. On re-examination of the data no excess female twin variability interpretable as support for the Lyon hypothesis is found.

The Lyon hypothesis involves one of the few instances in which a large portion of chromosomal material can behave at times as heterochromatin, at times as euchromatin. Heterochromatin, as contrasted to euchromatin, has long been viewed as relatively or totally inactive genetically. As has been pointed out by Cooper (1959) in a review of the theory of "heterochromatin," it is not proper to consider heterochromatic chromosomal material as totally without function. Reference to the Barr body (and the X chromosome which forms it) as genetically inactive should not be construed as indicating that it has no function whatever. Its function is probably of more general and less specific nature than that of the genes whose effects can be analyzed in a Mendelian manner. V–type position effects are evidence of such influences of heterochromatin. The findings in X–polysomic states referred to earlier (p. 61) may be examples of other non-specific influence by the "inactive" X chromosome. Grumbach's term "fixed differentiation" (p. 60) clearly has advantages over "genetic inactivation."

A number of differences between men and women do not seem easily explicable on the basis of hormonal differences: e.g., the branching of the coronary arteries (James, 1960; Schlessinger, 1940) and the thickness of the coronary intima (Dock, 1946). Sex difference is observed in the frequency of congenital malformations of the heart and other structures. The ostium secundum type of atrial septal defect and patent ductus arteriosus occur more often in females; congenital aortic stenosis and coarctation of the aorta occur more often in males. Hare lip with cleft palate is more frequent in males; cleft palate alone is more frequent in females. Anencephaly is much more frequent in females: bilateral agenesis of the kidneys is more frequent in males. The superior viability of the female has been reviewed by others (Montagu, 1953; Shettles, 1958). Such differences, if not due to hormonal differences, may be heterochromatin effects and/or heterotic effects in the female. They need not contradict the Lyon hypothesis. Even upon the Lyon hypothesis the relative heterozygosity of the fe-

male as compared with the hemizygous male obtains. The biological superiority of the female may in part have its basis in this heterozygosity.

Commenting on the compelling evidence that the Barr body has its origin in one X chromosome, Ferguson-Smith (1962) wrote as follows: "The major implication of these studies is that the two X chromosomes in female somatic nuclei have different properties. One can only speculate how such differentiation could occur." Ample precedent for chromosomal differentiation is available (Markert, 1961). Evidence that some genes are active only at some stages of the life cycle of the organism and only in some cells of the organism has been provided by both cytologic and genetic studies. Possibly X–chromosome differentiation is a consequence of asynchrony of function as indicated by many observations such as those of Taylor (1960) and his colleagues (Morishima, Grumbach, and Taylor, 1962) referred to on p. 55. Possibly one X chromosome gets the lead and through feedback mechanisms the function of the other is repressed. This suggested mechanism would allow for the activity of both X chromosomes in some cells because of synchronous performance at the "time of decision." The X chromosome which synthesizes DNA late is thought to be the one which forms the Barr body. Heterochromatin is probably coiled differently than euchromatin, thus accounting for its different staining properties. In accordance with the Lyon hypothesis, only extended threadlike euchromatic chromosomal material is capable of producing "messenger RNA" and thereby performing the usual genetic functions. On p. 55 the question of whether all interphase cells of the normal female in fact have a Barr body or its equivalent was discussed. Grumbach, Marks, and Morishima (1962) suggested that many cells in rapidly growing tissues may lack a demonstrable Barr body because of uncoiling of the DNA preparatory to replication and cell division. The high proportion of female nuclei with the Barr body in tissues with low mitotic activity, e.g., those of the nervous system, and the low proportion in rapidly growing tissues and cell cultures are observations consistent with the suggestion.

Possibly implantion in some way initiates the process by which activation of one, but only one, X chromosome occurs, since a temporal relationship seems to exist. Grumbach, Morishima, and Taylor (1963) suggested that activation results from the effects on the X chromosome of an episome-like material and that the activated X chromosome then produces a substance which blocks activation of the other X chromosomes.

The theory of X chromosome differentiation elaborated by Grumbach, Morishima, and Taylor (1963) draws an analogy to systems in bacteria as elaborated by Jacob and Monod (1961). They postulate that an episomal factor prevents the X chromosome to which it becomes attached from producing a substance which is responsible for heterochromatinization of itself and at the same time initiates production of a substance which neutralizes other unincorporated factor of similar nature. The other X chromosomes, therefore, do produce a substance leading to heterochromatization. The properties of this postulated substance is that 1) RNA synthesis is prevented or hindered, 2) DNA synthesis is permitted to occur, 3) it does not diffuse beyond the limits of the one chromosome.

One might expect that evolution would favor the development of the mechanism of dosage compensation postulated by the Lyon hypothesis. From observations with reference to the autosomes, one concludes (p. 68) that monosomy and trisomy are severely disrupting and even lethal derangements. To permit the quantitative genic disparity that normally exists between the two sexes in the presence of an XX–XY sex-determining mechanism, evolution might have chosen an alternative to the Lyon mechanism: Mendelian factors might be eliminated from, or reduced to a minimum in, the X chromosome. But obviously this has not taken place, witness the long list of X–linked traits.

In summary, the Lyon hypothesis is attractive because it provides an explanation for many genetic and cytologic observations with regard to the X chromosome. At this writing, the evidence is as yet incomplete on some of the necessary consequences of the hypothesis as listed on p. 60. Argument against the theory are 1) the absence of precedence for unilateral (or heterozygous) chromosomal differentiation in sub-mammalian species, 2) the suggestion in the work of Childs and colleagues (1962) that there may be a dosage effect of two X chromosomes in the normal female as compared to the one

present in the normal male (p. 61), 3) the failure to find any erythrocytes with a normal survival with primaquine administration in females (Brewer, Tarlov, and Powell, 1962) heterozygous for G6PD-deficiency (p. 64), 4) the fact that not only have no Xg(a−) daughters of Xg(a+) fathers been observed (by the Lyon hypothesis occasional heterozygous females should react as Xg(a−) persons), but there is an excess of Xg(a+) females in the general population compared with that expected on the basis of the frequency of Xg(a+) in males (Race and Sanger, 1962, personal communications, London), and 5) the failure of Gorman and colleagues (1963) to find two populations of red cells in the Xg heterozygotes.

Although in man, at least, altered genetic functions related to heterochromatic properties and delayed synthesis of DNA may at present be more amenable to investigation in the X chromosome, a comparable mechanism may operate in the autosomes—in limited segments of some pairs in some tissues at some stages of development.[10] The possible significance to a central question about differentiation and development, why some genes function only at certain times and in certain tissues, should be kept in mind.

Indirect gauges of the relative amount of genetic material in the X chromosome. In terms of cytologic length the X chromosome represents 5 per cent or more of the haploid chromosome complement of man (22A+X). Assuming that about 60 separate X–linked loci are represented by the catalog (Table I) and that the rest of the chromosomes contain the same number of loci relative to length, then one might conclude that there are at least 1200 loci in the total human genome. Assuming that man has about the same number of genes per physical length of mitotic chromosome as does *Drosophila*, Spuhler (1948) estimated that the total number of genes in man is about 42,000, with at least 2000 on the X chromosome. Attention is directed to Herskowitz's (1950) estimate of 726 as the number of loci on the X chromosome of *Drosophila*. See p.

---

[10] Martensson (1963) points out, for example, that the essentially malignant clones of plasma cells in multiple myeloma produce 7S gammaglobulin which is either Gm(a+b−) or Gm(a−b+) in the heterozygous Gm(a+b+) person. There are other suggestions that normally only one type of Gm specificity is produced by a given clone of plasma cells.

73 for a further discussion of the number of genes on the X chromosome.

From considerations of the Lyon hypothesis and of the adaptation to X chromosome monosomy (of the normal male) which one would expect to have occurred in evolution it is unlikely that the relative gravity of the effects of trisomy or monosomy of the X chromosome and of autosomes can be used as an indirect gauge of the relative amount of genetic information in the X chromosome. Trisomy and monosomy of the X chromosome are compatible with life and result in only moderately severe somatic abnormality. On the other hand, no trisomy of the large autosomes 1–12 has been observed to date. Furthermore, no unequivocal instance of autosomal monosomy comparable to the X chromosome monosomy of the Turner syndrome has been described. Contrast the drastic consequences of trisomy of one of the smallest autosomes, No. 21, in Down's syndrome (the recommended new terminology for Mongoloid idiocy (Allen, et al., 1961)), with the relatively minor effects of X chromosome trisomy and of even more bizarre combinations of extra sex chromosomes. Striking as the contrast is, it is evidence probably not of lesser amounts of genetic information in the X chromosome, but rather of a potent mechanism of dosage compensation which has developed for the X chromosome.

Since Morgan and his colleagues put forward the hypothesis that each chiasma observed in meiotic material represents a genetic crossover, evidence both for and against (Cooper, 1949) it has accumulated. Recently Rhoades (1961) wrote as follows: "The relation of chiasmata to genetic crossing over was a controversial issue in the 1930's, but today it is widely held that in most organisms a chiasma represents a genetic crossover... Sturtevant's dictum that it is no longer permissible to equate a cytologically observed chiasma with a genetic crossover should be restricted for the present, at least, to *Drosophila*." The mouse is the only mammalian species in which both chiasma counts and estimates of the genetic length of the chromosomes from linkage data are available for correlation: Slizynski (1955) estimated a length of 19.2 morgans from chiasma counts, and Carter (1955) estimated a length of 16.2 morgans from linkage data.

Assuming that the hypothesis of correlation between chiasma formation and genetic linkage is indeed true in man and taking one chiasma as equivalent to 50 centimorgans, one can use counts of chiasmata for making an estimate of the total genetic length of the human chromosome complement. Ford and Hamerton (1956) are, to our knowledge, the only workers who have published chiasma counts in man. They found a mean chiasma count per cell of 55.9 and estimated that the total genetic length of the autosomes was 27.9 morgans. Taking the cytologic length of the X chromosomes as about one-fifteenth of that of the total autosome set and assuming uniform distribution of chiasmata in autosomes and X chromosomes, Ford and Hamerton estimated a genetic length of almost one morgan for the X chromosome. It follows that independent segregation of X–borne traits can easily occur, a conclusion supported by the experience with linkage of color blindness and night blindness (p. 31), and of color blindness and hemophilia B (p. 30). Parenthetically it should be commented that further studies of meiosis in man are badly needed. The chromosomes in prophase of meiosis afford the best possibilities for detailed cytologic mapping. Translocations and inversions can be identified and important features such as chiasma counts and the frequency of accidents of spermatogenesis, e.g., nondisjunction, can be determined. Slizynski (1961) predicts that the pachytene chromosomes of the human spermatocytes will be mapped within the next few years.

Another indirect estimation of the minimum number of loci on the X chromosome was made by Spuhler (1948) on the basis of the number of mutations necessary to reduce the primary sex ratio to the secondary sex ratio. See p. 73, where Goldschmidt's views (1955) on such estimates are also presented.

Cytogenetic mapping of the X chromosome. Further proof of the X-linkage (Lennox, 1961) of color blindness, pseudohypertrophic muscular dystrophy, and glucose–6–phosphate dehydrogenase deficiency—if such is needed—is provided by the description of cases of the XO type of chromatin-negative Turner syndrome affected by one or another of these traits (Gartler, et al., 1962; Polani, et al., 1958; Walton, 1956 and 1957). Cases in which only part of one X chromosome is missing should be even more illuminating as to the precise constitution of the X chromosome. Already this seems to have been shown: Stewart (1961) points to chromatin-positive Turner syndrome cases, which now number at least three (Lindsten, 1961), in which color blindness has been present and in which it was thought that the short arm of the X chromosome was missing and the long arm was duplicated in the form of an isochromosome (see p. 43). Both parents had normal color vision but the mother was presumably heterozygous for color blindness. Stewart suggests the tentative conclusion that the color blindness locus is on the short arm of the X chromosome. Polani and Hamerton (1961) point out that the two arms of an isochromosome are by definition isologous but may not be isoallelic. If the color blindness locus is on the long arm of the X chromosome, if the arms of the isochromosome in a given case were isoallelic for the color blindness locus, and if two mutant genes out of three resulted in expression of color blindness, then the findings would be explained. Findings with the Xg^a blood group marker yield results which are susceptible to identical interpretation but also have the same objections as the color blindness data. Lindsten and colleagues (1963) found an Xg(a−) case of isochromosome-X syndrome with both parents Xg(a+); the Turner syndrome daughter was, however, a mosaic of X X and XO cells. Lee and Bowen (1963, unpublished observations) find that the non-mosaic case of X X shown in Figure 35 is Xg(a−) whereas both parents are Xg(a+).

There is a more serious objection to Stewart's interpretation. If the isochromosome X is in all cells the one which forms the Barr body and is relatively inactive, then color blindness might occur in the situation discussed above regardless of the site of the color blindness locus. Studies by several groups (Muldal, et al., 1963; Giannelli, 1963; Lee and Bowen, 1963) indicate that the isochromosome is in all cells late-labelling (Fig. 35d). This finding is consistent with the finding that all Barr bodies in these cases are large.

On the basis of the relatively large number of possible cross over events in connection with color blindness and the Klinefelter syndrome (p. 47), Stern (1959b) suggested that the color blindness locus (or loci) may be rather far re-

moved from the kinetochore. If, as suggested on p. 48, an appreciable proportion of Klinefelter cases arise by mis-segregation in an X^{M}Y zygote (resulting in an X^{M}X^{M}Y zygote plus a YO zygote which dies), then the finding of color-blind Klinefelter cases is readily accounted for and Stern's deduction is not justified.

Elves and Israëls (1962) described a patient with features of the Klinefelter syndrome and with hemophilia A. Chromosome study showed 46 chromosomes with the X chromosome replaced by a metacentric chromosome longer than any autosome (see p. 43). The father was nonhemophilic and no hemophilia was known in the mother's family. In light of the Klinefelter features at least part of the X chromosome would appear to have been present in duplicate. Smith (1962) suggested that the most plausible explanation is inversion crossing over with deletion of the AHG locus in the process. Figure 42 schematizes such a process. Assuming this mechanism, one is led to the conclusion that the hemophilia A locus is on the *long* arm of the X chromosome, but it must be emphasized that the construction pictured is only one of several equally plausible ones.

At this point it is not clear what one can deduce about the constitution of the X chromosomes from the somatic abnormalities which occur in the XO type of Turner syndrome (Fig. 28), e.g., webbed neck, coarctation of the aorta, angiomata in the bowel, dwarfism, short metacarpals, characteristic facial malformation, mental retardation, pigmented nevi, etc. (de la Chapelle, 1962b). Jacobs and colleagues (1961) suggested that since gonadal dysgenesis cases with deletion of the long arm have no dwarfism whereas those with deletion of the short arm of the X chromosome invariably do, there are probably genes affecting height on the short arm. However, we know of no X–linked recessive form of dwarfism like that in the Turner syndrome nor of any of the other associated malformations. Schwarz and Walter (1962) suggested that the fact that patients with the XO Turner syndrome and those with pseudo-pseudo-hypoparathyroidism (see appendix No. B16) have features in common, e.g., short stature and shortened fourth metacarpals and fourth metatarsals, is evidence that pseudo-pseudohypoparathyroidism is an X–linked disorder. However, it is difficult to see how this follows from mere phenotypic similarities.

Coarctation of the aorta is several times more frequent in males than in females. Lewis (1933) found a ratio of 8 to 1; others find a less striking male preponderance. This fact and the high frequency of coarctation of the aorta in the Turner syndrome were partly responsible for the interest of Polani and his colleagues (1956) in testing for color blindness in patients with the Turner syndrome. However, coarctation is almost certainly not the direct result of an X–borne gene; modest familial aggregation is observed, but male-to-male transmission has been encountered (Gough, 1961; McAulley, 1961, personal communication, Bermuda; Niell, 1961, personal communication, Baltimore) in a number of instances.

The impressive frequency of Hashimoto's thyroiditis in association with the Turner syndrome especially that of the isochromosome-X type (Sparks and Motulsky, 1963; Engel, et al., 1963) likewise demands explanation.

In considering this question of the mechanism of the phenotypic findings in the XO Turner syndrome, Nowakowski and Lenz (1961) wrote as follows: "The XO genotype . . . can be thought of as an unfavorable milieu in which various genes of a usually latent pathogenic nature manifest themselves." Of course, one possibility still not excluded is that there is a short pairing segment of the X chromosome which could contain a fair amount of genetic material. Monosomy in the XO Turner syndrome could explain the abnormal features in these cases and in males with the same somatic features loss of the pairing segment either from the X chromosome or from the Y chromosome might be an explanation. It must be emphasized that neither the genetic nor the cytologic data sited earlier explode the existence of a short pairing segment.

Also not clear is what deductions should be drawn from the occurrence of some of the same somatic anomalies in phenotypic males (Futterweit, et al., 1961), often with testes that are hypoplastic and in some undescended (the so-called male Turner syndrome). (See Fig. 29.) Karyotypic analysis has shown a chromosomal constitution indistinguishable from that of the normal male (Futterweit, et al., 1961; Morishima and Grumbach, 1962; Steicker, et al., 1961).

A dimorphism of sperm? One might expect discernible differences between the X–bearing and Y–bearing sperms since the mass of the chromosomes which constitute most of the sperm head is appreciably greater in the former case. Shettles (1960a, b, and c) has indeed claimed that dried, unstained human spermatozoa show two distinct populations by phase contrast microscopy. The distinguishing features he describes relate to head and nuclear size, shape, and diffraction of light. He concludes that the X–bearing sperms are those with larger heads. Shettles (1961) studied the sperm of men in families in which all children for many generations had been male; almost all spermatozoa had small, round heads and were presumably Y–bearing. He claims that all men have a preponderance of sperms with small, round heads and that this is the explanation for the male preponderance in the primary sex ratio.

Strong skepticism of the reality of this alleged dimorphism has been expressed by Bishop (1960), van Duijn (1960), and Rothschild (1960). The last writer reviewed all the methods which have been tried for separating X and Y spermatozoa—pH, immunologic means, electrophoresis, size and shape of head—and concluded that "there is so far no evidence that physical differences have been found between X and Y spermatozoa." Bishop (1960) pointed to "the compounded artefacts of air-dried shrinkage and phase-contrast optical aberrations." Van Duijn (1960) likewise stated, "In my opinion there cannot be the slightest doubt that Shettles has misinterpreted a number of physical artefacts." He proceeded to explain Shettles' finding on the basis of physical optics and also gave cytologic reasons for questioning Shettles' observations.

VI · OTHER CONSIDERA-TIONS PERTINENT TO THE CONSTITUTION OF THE X CHROMO-SOME

STIMATES of *mutation rate* in man are probably inexact for many reasons (Glass, 1954; Penrose, 1961; Crow, 1961). For X–linked recessive traits, the mutation rate is estimated by an indirect method, as elaborated by Haldane (1935). By determining the proportion of individuals affected sporadically by an X–linked mutation (X) and estimating mean effective fertility (f), the mutation rate (μ) is found as follows:

$$\mu = \frac{1}{3}(1 - f)X$$

Estimates thus arrived at are presented in Table 10. The figures are given in terms of number of mutations per gamete because it is in no case certain that only one locus is involved. The rates for X–linked traits are higher than most of those estimated for autosomal dominant traits (Penrose, 1961). Penrose (1961) suggested that "perhaps the X-chromosome is peculiar in that it has many complex loci or distinct loci with similar effects." For hemophilia there are indeed at least two separate loci involved in the estimate of mutation rate given in Table 10. For the autosomal recessive traits somewhat higher mutation rates are estimated than for autosomal dominant traits (Penrose, 1961).

Frota-Pessoa (1961b) suggested a method by which the mutation rate of X–linked loci can be determined more directly when a test for the heterozygous carrier state is available. He could find no existing data suitable for application of the method but urged the feasibility of collecting such data.

A theoretically possible factor responsible for inaccuracy in estimates of mutation rate is the occurrence of sectorials which if the female germ cells were involved could result in multiple affected sons from a mother who is not a carrier in the usual sense. The occurrence of sectorials in the autosomal dominant neurofibromatosis was investigated by Crow, Schull, and Neel (1956) and has been considered in connection with some pedigrees of split-hand (Graham and Badgley, 1955; Auerbach, 1956; Vogel, 1958).

71

Sectorials are probably rare and thus not an appreciable factor in misestimation of mutation rates.

The male-female differences in opportunity for mutation of X–linked genes is the basis of Morton's method (1962) for distinguishing X–linked recessive inheritance from male-limited autosomal dominant inheritance (see p. 13). Morton has derived the following expression for the expected proportion of sporadic cases among all affected persons: $m/(m + 1)$, if the trait is autosomal dominant, and $m\mu/(2\mu + v)$, if the trait is X–linked recessive, where m = selection coefficient against affected males (one, in the case of the testicular feminization syndrome); μ = mutation rate in the egg; v = mutation rate in sperm. It can be seen that half of cases of an autosomal dominant trait with *m* of one will be sporadic, whereas only about a third of cases of an X–linked recessive will be sporadic. If $v > \mu$ (n. infra), then even a smaller proportion of X–linked recessive cases will be sporadic. See Morton and Chung (1959) for an application of this approach to muscular dystrophy, for which their data fitted better the X–linked recessive hypothesis.

As suggested by Quick (1960), the relative frequencies of sporadic cases of hemophilia A and hemophilia B give information on the relative mutation rate of the two loci, provided one assumes that only one X–borne locus is involved in each of these two forms of hemophilia and takes into account the relative intensity of selection in the two disorders. Since hemophilia A is about five times more frequent than hemophilia B (Sjølin, 1961; Wilkinson, et al., 1961) and since a greater proportion of hemophilia A cases are sporadic, hemophilia B being on the average milder with a higher proportion of familial cases, the mutation rate for hemophilia A must be several times greater than that for hemophilia B. This conclusion also assumes, of course, that the sporadic cases of hemophilia B are detected as readily as sporadic cases of hemophilia A. The assumption is probably not true, since as just stated hemophilia B is, on the average, a milder disorder. Be this as it may, Ikkala (1960) arrived at an estimate of 3.2×10^{-5} for the mutation rate per X chromosome per generation for hemophilia A, and 0.2×10^{-5} for hemophilia B—values generally supporting Quick's prediction.

In *Drosophila melanogaster* Glass and Ritterhoff (1956) found that the mutation rate is higher in males than in females, i.e., higher in spermatogenesis than in oogenesis. In man X–linked traits provide a method for study of *the sex ratio of mutation rate*. If mutation occurs at a higher rate in females, then one should observe an excess of sporadic cases of an X–linked recessive trait as compared to familial cases, i.e., cases with affected brothers and/or maternal uncles and cousins. On the other hand, since a recessive mutation in the X chromosome of the male can result only in a carrier daughter, then an excess of familial cases will be observed if the mutation rate is greater in males. Using this approach Haldane (1947) concluded that the mutation rate for hemophilia may be about 10 times greater in the male than in the female and that a similar male excess occurs in muscular dystrophy (Haldane, 1956). The results may, however, have been biased by the methods of ascertainment; familial cases are more likely to be ascertained. Cheeseman and colleagues (1958) and Smith and Kilpatrick (1958) could

TABLE 10

Estimates of spontaneous mutation rates for some X–linked loci
(after Penrose 1961)

Trait	Mutation Rate per Million Gametes per Generation	Region	Author
Hemophilia	20	England	Haldane (1947)
Hemophilia	32	Denmark	Andreassen (1943)
Hemophilia	27	Switzerland and Denmark	Vogel (1955)
Duchenne muscular dystrophy	95	U.S.A.	Stephens, Tyler (1951)
Duchenne muscular dystrophy	60	Northern Ireland	Stevenson (1958)
Duchenne muscular dystrophy	43	England	Walton (1957)
Duchenne muscular dystrophy	47	England	Blyth, Pugh (1959)

find no evidence of sex difference for mutation rate in Duchenne type muscular dystrophy and the findings of others (Koskower, Christiansen, and Morton, 1962) have failed to support the suggested difference in hemophilia.

The sex ratio at fertilization (primary sex ratio) is not known but may be (Szontagh, Jakobovits, and Méhes, 1961) at least 1.22 (male/female); the secondary sex ratio (that at birth) is of the order of 1.06 in U. S. whites. The figure is said (Stern, 1960b, p. 424) to vary from 1.01 for Cuban Negroes to over 1.13 for natives of Greece and Korea. The preferential loss of male zygotes, embryos, and fetuses may be the result in part of lethal X–linked recessive genes. (As mentioned in another connection [p. 10], there are conditions [e.g., No. B2] which may be X–linked and result in death of affected males in utero.) To counteract the loss of genes which the theory assumes, new mutations would have to occur constantly and/or selective advantage of the heterozygous female is required. The superior viability of the female throughout the span from conception to death may be merely a special case of heterosis. One can visualize the sex-ratio as a balance between 1) a greater likelihood for fertilization of an ovum by a Y–bearing sperm than by an X–bearing sperm, and 2) a lesser viability of the XY organism at all stages.

On certain assumptions, the *minimum* number of genes on the X chromosome can be estimated from the number of X–linked recessive lethals necessary to reduce the primary sex ratio to the secondary sex ratio (Spuhler, 1948). The number of genes thus estimated by Spuhler is 1000–1500, a value of the same order of magnitude as that in *Drosophila melanogaster* for chromosomes of comparable length. It must be emphasized that the above approach probably gives only a minimal value. Recombination in the X chromosomes of the mother and in the autosomes in both parents probably results in different effects of X–borne genes in different individuals. Furthermore, since the value under consideration is a relative one, the ratio between males and females, heterozygous advantage of the female is a possible factor of importance. Possibly it is more accurate to think in terms of male lethal equivalents, in accordance with the method of Morton, Crow, and Muller (1956).

Frota-Pessoa (1961a) extended Spuhler's argument and using new data arrived at a lower estimate, namely 340 as the minimum number of X–borne loci which mutate to recessive lethals and detrimentals acting before birth.

Such estimates of number of loci were, in the view of Goldschmidt (1955, p. 107), suspect or even absurd:

> In discussions of my views on the non-existence of the corpuscular gene, the following argument is frequently heard. Many people have counted the number of genes and measured their size with nearly identical results. How can something not existing be counted and measured? The answer is that we can get any answer to questions if the proper elements are fed into the question. We can calculate the number of people on Mars if we assume that the canals are dug by people and that they accomplish as many man hours as we do in digging, that slave labor prevails on Mars, and so on.

The above criticism is now only of historical amusement because the gene has become (or is becoming) a physically defined unit (Demerec, 1961) with a chemical structure identified even to the level of the sequence of bases which encode the genetic information (Crick, Barnett, Brenner, and Watts-Tobin, 1961). In organisms more favorable for detailed genetic analysis than man it is possible (Demerec, 1961) to determine the limits of the *locus* and to enumerate the *sites* of which it is composed. (The site is the "subunit of the locus, at which mutation may occur but within which recombination has not been observed and presumably does not occur" (Demerec, 1961).)

It may be possible to arrive at an indirect estimate of the number of genes in man on the basis of the following information (Dintzis, 1962, personal communication, Baltimore): 1) the amount of DNA per cell nucleus, and 2) the amount of DNA required to encode one polypeptide of average length assuming a triplet code, or, alternatively, making use by extrapolation of the information on the amount of DNA which encodes one polypepetide in bacteria. The amount of DNA in all diploid cells of man is approximately 5.5×10^{-12} gm, (Vendrely, 1955). The calculation must take into account the weighty body of evidence indicating that the human chromosome is multistranded (Steffensen, 1959, 1961), that is, composed of a hierarchy of parallel and genetically identical DNA strands, probably 16 in number. The estimates arrived at, perhaps of the order of 20,000, are terribly crude but probably no cruder than those presented on p. 67.

Little and Gibbons (1921) proposed a test for *sex-linked lethal* genes in man, based on linkage with demonstrably X–borne genes. If in a family with hemophilia A lethal is closely linked with the normal allele of hemophilia then some nonhemophilic males will die in utero and a deficiency of normal brothers will be observed among the sibs of hemophiliacs. In data on hemophilia available to them in 1921, they found 551 observed hemophiliacs as compared to 457 expected among the brothers of hemophilic probands ($p = 10^{-9}$). For color blindness the figures were 106 and 90. Corrections for ascertainment bias, which might account for the observations, were not made. More important, there is a fallacy in the approach as originally stated. Females who are heterozygous carriers for hemophilia and also for the postulated X–linked lethal recessive would be of two types: those doubly heterozygous in repulsion and those doubly heterozygous in coupling. Females of the first type should have an excess of hemophilic sons whereas those of the second type should have an excess of normal sons. In a collection of sibships these distortions of segregation in opposite directions should balance each other if coupling and repulsion phases are equally frequent. Because of the uncertainties involved it is doubtful that this type of analysis is practicable in man, except possibly by using a very frequent X–linked polymorphism such as the Xg^a blood group.

Change in the secondary sex ratio among the offspring of exposed individuals can be used to evaluate mutational *effects of ionizing radiation*. Exposure of the male can probably be expected to cause an increase in the sex-ratio, if any change at all occurs. Exposure of the female can be expected to have a relatively greater effect on the sex-ratio of the offspring, a decrease. Using this approach Schull and Neel (1958) concluded that the atomic bombing of Hiroshima and Nagasaki produced a significant reduction in the sex-ratio of the offspring of exposed persons. Questionnaire studies of the offspring of Japanese (Tanaka and Ohkura, 1958) and American (Crow, 1955) radiologists and radiologic technicians and of French men and women (Turpin, Lejeune, and Rethore, 1956) who had received high gonadal doses of X-ray for medical reasons had similar results. However, failure of return of some questionnaires introduced uncertainties in studies of this last type.

Using the data of Stevenson and colleagues (1959) on abortions between the third week and birth, Frota-Pessoa and Saldanha (1960) extended the method of Spuhler (1948) to an estimation of the spontaneous rate of mutations for sex-linked detrimentals in man and of the doubling dose of radiation.

Another use of the sex-ratio to evaluate mutation rate has been proposed and applied by Cavalli-Sforza (1960). He is determining the sex-ratio of the progeny of women and correlating it with the age of their father at the time of their birth. If sex-linked recessive lethals accumulate in gametes with increasing age, the regression of the ratio males/females born alive to the woman, on the age of the woman's father at her birth, will be expected to have a negative slope. The same regression for the ratio among the stillborn should have a positive slope. Preliminary analyses yield results consistent with the hypothesis (Cavalli-Sforza, 1961).

Apparently, no study has been made of grandparental age in hemophilia or muscular dystrophy, which could be interpreted in relation to mutation rate, as Penrose (1955) has done for some autosomal disorders. The maternal grandfather's age at conception of the mother of the proband would be the value of interest, among others.

Selection with regard to X–linked genotypes should in principle be no different from selection operating on autosomal genotypes. Whatever differences exist are related to the hemizygous state of the male which excludes the occurrence of heterozygote advantage in this sex. With transient polymorphism of an X–linked character (indicated by asterisk), the several genotypes might bear the following relation to each other as to selection advantage:

$$X^*Y = X^*X^* > X^*X > XX = XY$$

or

$$X^*Y = X^*X^* > X^*X = XX = XY$$

or

$$X^*Y = X^*X^* = X^*X > XX = XY$$

A balanced polymorphism (Bennett, 1957, 1958) due to advantage of the heterozygous female can be represented thus:

$$X^*Y = X^*X^* < X^*X > XX = XY$$

The last situation may pertain to the polymorphism for glucose–6–phosphate dehydrogenase deficiency (Motulsky, 1960), which in the heterozygous female (and probably in the hemizygous affected male as well) appears to confer advantage with regard to falciparum malaria (Allison and Clyde, 1961; Harris and Giles, 1961; Siniscalco, Bernini, Latti, and Motulsky, 1961), whereas the hemizygous affected male and the homozygous affected female are prone to hemolytic anemia on exposure to chemical (e.g., fava bean) and possibly biological (e.g., viral) agents. Any advantage enjoyed by hemizygous enzyme-deficient males toward malaria is probably cancelled out (Motulsky, 1961) by their vulnerability to hemolytic anemia in the neonatal period (Doxiades, Fessas, and Vales, 1960; Weatherall, 1960). Balance in the polymorphism must have been maintained largely through the advantage of the heterozygous female, which probably obtains only in a malarious environment.

Kidson and Gorman (1962) point out that the low frequency of G6PD–deficiency in some groups, such as Malays, Indonesians and Armenians, and smaller groups such as the Tolai and Sause in Melanesia, which inhabit areas holoendemic for malaria including the falciparum form requires consideration of other factors with negative selective value vis-à-vis G6PD–deficiency. In some of these groups thalessemia is relatively frequent, as would be predicted from the malaria hypothesis. In the case of G6PD, viral infections, dietary habits, and social customs may create disadvantages of G6PD–deficiency which outweigh advantages toward malaria.

As indicated on p. 37, Siniscalco and his colleagues (1961) interpreted a positive correlation of color blindness with the past incidence of malaria (in Sardinia) as "an example of the selection of a neutral gene through the close linkage with a highly adaptive one." Boyer, Porter, and Weilbaecher (1962) have observed an electrophoretic variant of G6PD which is due either to a mutation in the same cistron as contains the mutation for G6PD–deficiency or to mutation at a very closely linked locus. The high frequency attained by the electrophoretic variant in Africans (about 34 per cent of American negro males show the variant) and the occurrence of enzyme deficiency almost only in persons of the variant type suggest that a similar mechanism may have been operative in this case.

In the large Swiss kindred of the Tenna district, Rosin, Moor-Jankowski, and Schneeberger (1958) found that females who were carriers for hemophilia B had more children than did non-carrier females. The fitness of male bleeders was estimated to be $f = 0.64$. The fitness of carrier females was estimated by three methods yielding values averaging about 1.22. They suggested that the selection against bleeders could be largely counter-balanced by the increased fertility of carrier females without invoking mutation as a mechanism.

Similar findings were reported by Simpson and Biggs (1962) working in Oxford, England, an area with an unusually high frequency of Christmas disease. (Biggs and colleagues first described this form of hemophilia in 1952, simultaneously with Aggeler and colleagues in this country.) They suggested that most of their cases distributed in 16 apparently unrelated kindred may have been derived from a single mutation many generations ago and that little movement out of the rural communities around Oxford occurred to scatter the gene. In the sons of sisters of affected males the proportion of affected was 36 per cent rather than the expected 25 per cent. Compensation on the part of those women with affected sons was suggested. Lewis and Li (1958) also found an excess of affected sons of sisters of Christmas disease patients (12/37). However, in both this study and that of the Oxford group no excess of affected males was observed in sons of daughters of affected males.

Carter (1962) suggested that the relatively high frequency of color blindness may be because of a selective *advantage* in hunting societies of the past. He pointed out that a color blind person is less confused by the protective camouflage of hunted animals. However, Post (1962) arrived at a quite different conclusion. Assembling data on the world distribution of color blindness he pointed out that aboriginal hunting populations such as those of Australia, Brazil, Fiji, and North America have the lowest frequency of color blindness, whereas "civilized" groups with an agricultural economy for several millenia (peoples of Europe and the Far East, including the Brahmins of India) have the highest rates. Post suggests that in hunting societies color blindness is disadvantageous and that in agricultural (and perhaps industrial) societies negative selection has been relaxed almost completely. Postulating that selection has been relaxed for 120 generations, during which time the protan allele frequency has gone from .005 to .02 and the deuteran frequency from .015 to .06, he estimated net mutation rates (disregarding reverse mutation) for all deficiency-producing alleles as follows:

For protans: .015 ÷ 120 = .000125, or 1.25 × 10^{-4} per locus per generation.
For deuterans; .045 ÷ 120 = .000375, or 3.75 × 10^{-4} per locus per generation.
If 160 generations are allowed, the mutation rates become 9.375 × 10^{-5} and 2.8125 × 10^{-4} respectively.

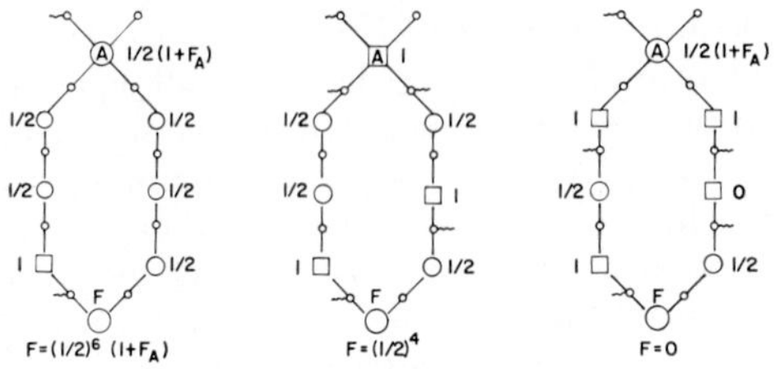

a

Neel and Post (1963) make a further suggestion that the relatively high frequency of color blindness in "civilized" peoples is due not merely to a relaxation of negative selection but that positive selection may have operated during a transitional period from a hunting-gathering culture to an agricultural culture. They suggest that the color-blind male, because of his disadvantage in hunting, was impelled to make the transition to agriculture more rapidly and that in the long run this was to his advantage.

Inbreeding does not alter the frequency of X–determined phenotypes in males, since the phenotype frequency in males and the gene frequency are identical and inbreeding *per se* does not influence gene frequency. However, in females homozygosity for X–linked loci results from inbreeding, probably with important effects, which have been little studied. Most attention in consanguinity studies has been focused on autosomal loci. Wright (1951) described the modification in his method of path coefficients to be used in calculating the coefficient of inbreeding with reference to X–linked loci (Fig. 43a).

The several types of first cousin marriages are not random in their occurrence (Morton, 1955) (Freire-Maia, 1957). Depending on the religious, social, and economic structure of the population, certain of the four possible types (Fig. 43b) occur in a frequency out of proportion to the expected 1 : 1 : 1 : 1 ratio. Types 2 and 4 are ob-

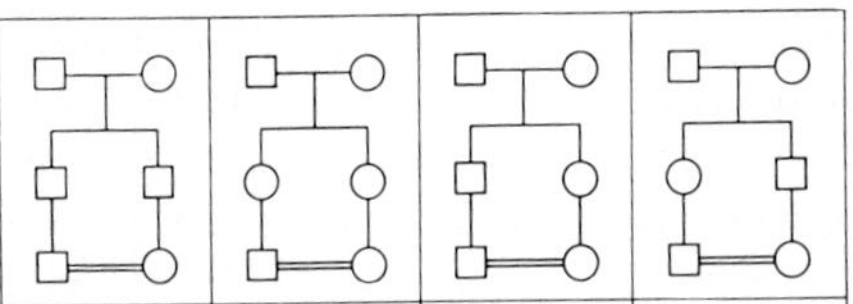

	TYPE 1	TYPE 2	TYPE 3	TYPE 4
JAPAN, 3 CITIES	149	229	127	184
AUSTRIA-GERMANY	430	656	472	591
U.S., CHICAGO	23	39	22	20
BRAZIL	55	46	53	57
INDIA	80	75	87	48
GREAT BRITAIN	12	32	17	14

□:MALE   ○:FEMALE   □═○:CONSANGUINEOUS MARRIAGE

b

FIG. 43. COEFFICIENT OF INBREEDING AND TYPES OF FIRST COUSIN MARRIAGES

a. Wright (1951) described the modification in his method of path coefficients for calculating the coefficient of inbreeding with reference to X–linked loci. F = coefficient of inbreeding; F_A = coefficient of inbreeding of common ancestor. In the examples shown here a single common ancestor is assumed in the first generation indicated, i.e., the two persons in the second generation are half-sibs. The figures by the symbols are the probabilities that a given X–borne gene will be transmitted to the next generation. For autosomal loci the coefficient of inbreeding is F = $(1/2)^7(1 + F_A)$ for all three cases. b. The nonrandomness in consanguineous marriages is indicated by the figures provided here. From Morton (1961). Types 2 and 4 are of particular pertinence to X–linkage (see Fig. 43a).

viously those pertinent to the study of consanguinity and X–linked loci. In some endogamous populations of India (Sanghvi, Varde, and Master, 1956) first cousin marriages of Type 4 occur very frequently (8 per cent or more of all marriages) and are, in fact, the most frequent form of close consanguineous mating. Uncle-niece matings between a man and the daughter of his sister are also frequent and obviously are also pertinent to X–linkage. A comparison of the results of such matings with those of other types of consanguineous and nonconsanguineous matings might be of interest. Schull and Neel (1963) are probably the only persons who have undertaken such a study. In an analysis of data from Japan they were unable to relate ten anthropometric measurements obtained on 853 daughters of first cousin spouses to the coefficient of inbreeding for X–linked genes.

Jacobs and her colleagues (1963) have shown that with *ageing* there is a progressive increase in the proportion of body cells which lack a chromosome. In males it appears to be the Y chromosome which is lost, whereas in females it is probably one X chromosome. In males the percentage of cells lacking the Y chromosome rose from 0.62 in the 0–14 age group to 3.26 in the 75+ age group. In females the percentage was 0.76 in the 0–24 age group and rose progressively to 7.58 in the 75+ age group. They suggested that the findings are explained "1) if there was special liability for cells to lose a sex chromosome, or 2) if all chromosomes were liable to be involved, but that the cells with an abnormal number of autosomes failed to survive, or 3) if both possibilities occurred together."

Evolution and the X chromosome. If sex-determining factors are scattered throughout the X and Y chromosomes, evolutionary advantage would accrue from isolation of the two chromosomes through restriction in crossing over between them. This point was already discussed (p. 39) in connection with the cytologic and genetic evidence on partial sex linkage. Kalmus and Smith (1960) analyzed the matter of the evolutionary origin of sex differentiation. Furthermore, they pointed out why and when a 1:1 sex ratio might be advantageous and the mechanism by which it might have arisen. The evolution of the morphology of the X chromosome is likely to become much better known through work such as that by Chu and Bender (1961, 1962) on primates. The gorilla, for example, has 48 chromosomes with remarkable similarities (Fig. 44) to the chromosomes of man. The major differences include the fact that in the gorilla the X chromosome is metacentric and the largest of the complement (Hamerton, et al., 1961). (The Barr body is also larger in the gorilla.) Darlington (1953) foresaw the value of the approach before the necessary techniques had been developed:

> Great institutions have been devoted to collecting and preserving, describing and naming the bony fragments of our ancesters and relatives and great bodies of literature have been brought forth by their labours. Rightly so. Yet at the cost of a few hundred cells and a few drops of blood, a few moments of discomfort to the animals and a few hours of work to the cytologist, the genetic record of human evolution could be laid bare.

Furthermore, when one notes the drastic effects of trisomy of even smaller autosomes and the fact that no monosomy of an autosome is known in man, whereas X chromosome aneuploidy is quite compatible with life despite the considerable amount of genetic information carried by the X chromosome, one is impressed with the likelihood that in evolution a mechanism has developed for compensating for the monosomic state of the X chromosome in the normal male, or viewed conversely, for the poly-

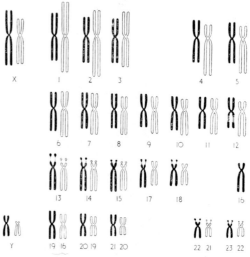

Fig. 44. Comparison of the Karyotypes of the Gorilla (Black Figures) and Man (Open Figures)
From Hamitan et al, 1961. The above arrangement is now known to be incorrect. (Hamitan, personal communication, June, 1963.) The gorilla X chromosome is actually number 5 or 6.

somic state of the X chromosome in the normal female.

The question of a disproportionately large number of ocular traits determined by genes on the X chromosome was raised on p. 23. Modern theories of the evolution of the genetic material through duplications and divergence by independent mutation (Ingram and Stretton, 1961) are consistent with the concentration of groups of traits in particular chromosomes, but as was pointed out (loc. cit.) no clear evidence of a clustering effect in the X chromosome is at hand.

Genetic counselling has fallen into ill repute with many geneticists and has in the view of some (Morton 1961) "received more encouragement than is altogether wise at the present state of development" of knowledge in the area. One aspect of genetic counselling, *genetic prognosis*, is a legitimate phase of medical practice. Clinical medicine resolves itself into three questions (Bradford Hill, 1961, personal communication, London): What is wrong with the patient? What can and should be done about it? What is going to happen? (A fourth question—why did it happen?—is also the physician's responsibility.) In genetic prognosis the question, what is going to happen, usually refers to the offspring of the person counselled. As with other types of medical problems, e.g., cancer, the matter of how much and what prognostic information should be given requires nice judgment of human nature and often demands more knowledge of the risks involved than is available. The objective of genetic counselling (in the restricted sense of genetic prognostication) is to no significant extent eugenic. Its purpose is rather to prevent, insofar as possible, physical suffering of affected individuals and emotional and economic burdens to their relatives and society.

Genetic counselling in regard to X–linked traits has certain special problems. What is to be told the sister of a male with sporadic hemophilia? What is the risk that the brother's disease is not the consequence of new mutation but rather that the mother was the new mutant and the sister a carrier? Binet, Sawers, and Watson (1957) addressed themselves to this matter and provided a mathematical treatment. Unfortunately, in the individual case the problem remains a difficult one.

VII · THE Y CHROMO-SOME OF MAN

EFORE concluding it might be noted parenthetically that the Y chromosome of man appears to carry little specific genetic information. It is not as complete a dummy as previously thought from analogy to *Drosophila*, since the male sex phenotype is dependent on its presence (p. 40). The unlikelihood that a part (at least, any significant part) of the Y chromosome is homologous to some part of the X chromosome has been commented on (p. 39). Traits previously thought to be determined by genes on the Y chromosome and present in all males in a direct line of descent, cases of so-called holandric inheritance (Fig. 45), have not stood up to intense scrutiny (Stern, 1957; Penrose and Stern, 1958). An exception (Fig. 46) may be the trait "hairy ears" (Dronamraju, 1961; Dronamraju and Haldane, 1962; Sarker, et al., 1961). In mice there appear to be histocompatibility genes on the Y chromosome (Hauschka, 1955); in some inbred strains skin grafts from males to females are rejected although the reciprocal graft is successful (Eichwald and Lustgraff, 1961; Eichwald, Silsmen, and Wheeler, 1957). In man the possibilities of testing for such genes in the Y chromosome are limited since two individuals genetically identical except for the presence or absence of the Y chromosome are required. Turpin and colleagues (1961) and Lejeune and Turpin (1961) have described identical twins, one of whom was a case of XO Turner syndrome and the other a normal XY male. Pre-

sumably the Y chromosome was lost in an early stage of cleavage in the cells which went to form the XO twin. Reciprocal grafts were in each case accepted satisfactorily. On the basis of this evidence alone no histocompatibility genes can be identified on the Y chromosome of man. On the other hand, histocompatibility genes are not excluded for the additional reason that interfetal circulatory connections are not rare in uniovular twins and might have led to induction of immune tolerance in this pair of twins.

Renkonen, Mäkelä, and Lehtovaara (1962) mentioned the possibility that the immunization of a certain number of mothers to Y chromosome-determined antigens might be responsible for the fact that the sex-ratio shows a decline with birth order. Szilard (1960) pointed out this phenomenon but suggested a different explanation.

That the Y chromosome contains little genetic information is further suggested by the observation (Hauschka, et al., 1962) of a fertile XYY male with average intelligence and no obvious defect related to the aneuploidy. On the other hand, the rarity of XO males (i.e., an XX–XO sex determining mechanism) in mammals (White, 1960) is evidence again of the vital importance of the Y chromosome to sex determination. Possibly the XX–XY sex mechanism is related to the viviparous state in mammals. Maintenance of distinctive differences through isolation of the genetic material into X and Y chromosomes would seem to be more important

79

to viviparity which probably demands greater reproductive specialization of the sexes than is necessary in nonviviparous species. Rather marked variability in the size of the Y chromosome without evident phenotypic influence also suggests relative genetic emptiness.

Although little specific information is borne by the Y chromosome, nonspecific properties of heterochromatin (see p. 64) and other observations would suggest that the Y chromosome does have functional significance in addition to that involved in sex determination. In part some of the male-female differences commented on earlier (p. 66) may have their basis in positive effects of the Y chromsome. Tanner and colleagues (1959) found that skeletal age in XXY males corresponds to that of XY males whereas skeletal age of XO females corresponds to that of XX females. From before birth until adulthood the female is ahead of the male in skeletal development and other features of physical development. These workers suggest that the double dose of the X chromosome is responsible for less mesomorphy in females through an in-

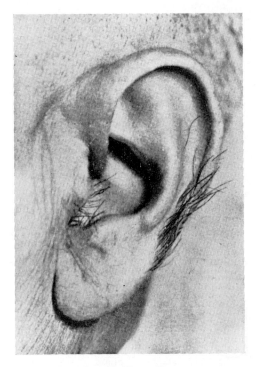

FIG. 46. HAIRY EARS
From Dronamraju (1961)

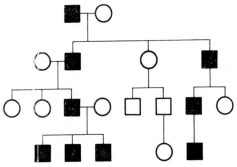

FIG. 45. IDEALIZED PEDIGREE PATTERN OF HOLANDRIC
(Y–LINKED) TRAIT

hibiting action on muscular differentiation and development. The effect of the Y chromosome in causing differentiation of the primitive gonad into a testis is evident at about 7 weeks of age. Retardation in the male as compared with the female becomes evident at about the same time. The growth phenomena may, therefore, be related to the differentiation of the testis which in turn is determined by presence of the Y chromosome.

APPENDIX ·
A CATALOG OF
X-BORNE MUTATIONS
IN MAN

X–LINKAGE of the traits listed in A is considered quite certain. X–linkage of those listed in B is less certain. Some will probably be proved not to be X–linked. Those listed in C have been shown quite clearly not to be X–linked. Discussion of them is included here, because X–linkage has been suggested and the traits are sometimes cited improperly in lists of X–linked traits.

The order in the listings is largely arbitrary. The only system used was to list more frequent traits first and to cluster traits by organ system to a considerable extent. It is suggested that the trait for which information is sought be found in the list in Table 1 (p. 7) which serves as a guide to the order of discussion in this catalog.

In addition to a "thumbnail" description of the trait, the information given in each case usually includes 1) some indication of frequency, 2) description of manifestations in heterozygous females, and 3) a statement on the existence of autosomal genocopies.

    A. Mutations for which X–linkage is considered proved or very likely.
      1. *Partial color blindness, deutan series.*[11]
        See text, pp. 30, 37, 75, etc.
        In Western Europeans about 8 per cent of

[11] Etymologically, *deuteran* is probably better than *deutan*.

males are color blind; of these about 75 per cent have a defect in the deutan series and about 25 per cent have a defect in the protan series.
      2. *Partial color blindness, protan series.*
        See text, p. 30.
        The two-locus hypothesis for color blindness is supported by three sets of observations:
        a. The relative frequency of color blindness in males and females is most consistent with the existence of two loci. Given a frequency of color-blind males of .08 and a total gene frequency for color blindness also of .08, then on a one-locus hypothesis the frequency of color-blind females should be $(.08)^2$ or .64 per cent. On a two-locus hypothesis, with the protan and deutan series representing 25 and 75 per cent, respectively, then the frequency of color-blind females should be less, assuming that doubly heterozygous females are normal:

Females color-blind for protan
  series — $.02 \times .02 =$ .04%
Females color-blind for deutan
  series — $.06 \times .06 =$ .36%

                               .4%
(The expected frequency of doubly hetero-

zygous females is the product of the frequencies of singly heterozygous females—$(2 \times .02 \times .98)$ $(2 \times .06 \times .94)$, or 0.0044.) In fact, the data on relative frequency of color blindness in males and females collected in Norway by Waaler and in Switzerland by von Planta agree with the values predicted by a two-locus theory.

PLANTA, P. VON. 1928. Die Häufigkeit der angeborenen Farbensinnstörungen bei Knaben und Mädchen und ihre Feststellung durch die üblichen klinischen Proben. *Graefes Arch. Ophthalmol.*, 120: 253–281.

WAALER, G. H. M. 1927. Über die Erblichkeitsverhältnisse der verschiedenen Arten von angeborener Rotgrünblindheit. *Z. Abstgs. Vererbgsl.*, 45: 279.

b. The two-locus theory is also supported by the fact that females who by the nature of the color-vision defect in their sons are known to carry genes for both types of color blindness usually do not show a defect in color-vision. This is essentially the complementarity test of allelism (p. 21). (As shown in Fig. 18B, the double heterozygotes in the pedigrees of Kondo and Brünner had normal color vision.)

Complementarity is also indicated by the findings in the families by Franceschetti and Klein (1956), as illustrated in Figure 47. It is possible, of course, that the mother in each family was a manifesting heterozygote. It is to be hoped that the presumably doubly heterozygous daughters shown in Figure 47 have a large number of sons and that the color-vision of these sons is tested in the future.

c. The pedigree of Vanderdonck and Verriest (p. 32) indicates independent assortment of deutan and protan genes among the offspring of a doubly heterozygous female.

The Nagel anomaloscope, used in determination of the type of color blindness, consists of a viewing tube with a circular bipartite field, one half illuminated with yellow and the other half with a mixture of green and red. The yellow half is not variable except in brightness. The other half can be varied continuously from red to green. The subject's color sense is tested by having him mix colors in the variable half-field until he achieves a subjective match to the yellow field. Certain color combinations are considered normal whereas specific differences from the normal indicate the type and degree of anomalous color-vision.

Ishihara plates alone are unreliable in distinguishing deutan and protan types. Although the Nagel anomaloscope is the "last court of appeal" in making the differentiation, it is expensive, time-consuming, difficult for unsophisticated subjects, and, of course, not usable "in the field." Two "book" tests, the Tokyo Medical College test and the AO–HRR (Hardy-Rand-Rittler) pseudoisochromatic plates, especially when used together, represent probably the methods which are both the easiest and the most reliable now available (Sloan, 1961).

Identification of a small proportion of deuteroheterozygotes is possible by means of the luminosity quotient, determined by a modification of the Nagel anomaloscope designed by Crone. Most cases of protoheterozygotes can be identified as such with a high degree of certainty using this method. (See Fig. 48.)

It appears (Nemoto and Murao, 1961) that the order of dominance in color blindness is normal > anomaly > anopia (Franceschetti's hypothesis).

CRONE, R. A. 1959. Spectral sensitivity in color-defective subjects and heterozygous carriers. *Am. J. Ophthalmol.*, 48: 231–238.

FRANCESCHETTI, A., and D. KLEIN. 1957. Two families with parents of different types of red-green blindness. *Acta genet. Statist. Med.*, 7: 255–259.

NEMOTO, H., and M. MURAO. 1961. A genetic study of color blindness. *Jap. J. Genetics*, 6: 165–173.

SCHMIDT, I. 1955. A sign of manifest heterozygosity in carriers of color deficiency. *Am. J. Optometry*, 32: 404.

SLOAN, L. L. 1961. Evaluation of the Tokyo Medical College Color Vision Test. *Am. J. Ophthalmol.*, 52: 650–659.

3. *Total color blindness*

Associated features are nystagmus, myopia, and astigmatism. Vision is best in dim light; squinting improves vision. Minor fundus changes are sometimes observed but would be discounted as normal variation if the defect in color-vision and visual acuity were not known. Total color blindness is probably more common than realized. There is good evidence that color-vision is sometimes normal in early life and lost later. Phenotypically there is no clear evidence of heterogeneity in the general category of achromatopsia. How-

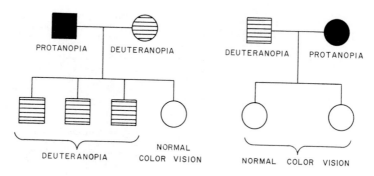

FRANCESCHETTI, KLEIN (1957)

Fig. 47. Support for the Two-locus Hypothesis for Color-blindness
(Franceschetti and Klein, 1957)

ever, genetically the finding of unmistakable X–linked inheritance in the family studied by Spivey and Opitz indicates heterogeneity; in most cases the disorder appears to be inherited as an autosomal recessive. Allelic relationship of the X–linked form with the varieties of partial color blindness is unknown.

François, J., G. Verriest, and A. DeRouck. 1955. L'achromatopsie congénitale. *Doc. Ophthalmol.*, 9: 338–424.

Opitz, J. M. 1961. Introduction to medical genetics. Part one. *J. Iowa State Med. Soc.*, 51: 393.

Sloane, L. L. 1954. Congenital achromatopsia; a report of 19 cases. *J. Opt. Soc. Am.*, 44: 117.

Spivey, B. E., Iowa City. Personal communication.

4. *Glucose–6–phosphate dehydrogenase deficiency*

There is reason to think that at least four X–linked mutations involving G6PD exist:

a. Primaquine-sensitivity (G6PD–deficiency) in Africans. In hemizygous affected males the enzyme level in erythrocytes and other tissues is not as markedly depressed as in the second type.

b. Favism (G6PD–deficiency) in Mediterranean peoples. Very low enzyme levels are observed in both erythrocytes and leucocytes of affected hemizygous males (Marks and Gross).

c. Non-spherocytic hemolytic anemia due to G6PD–deficiency. Anomalous properties of the enzyme have been identified (Kirkman, Riley, and Crowell).

Atypical electrophoretic mobility of the enzyme in a Caucasoid patient with G6PD-deficiency and non-spherocytic hemolytic

anemia was observed by Boyer (personal communication) who designates it the Eyssen phenotype.

d. Electrophoretic variants of G6PD have been identified by Boyer and colleagues, by Kirkman, and by Marks.

Although linkage studies in man cannot provide absolute proof of allelism, non-allelism can be demonstrated (p. 35). Linkage studies to date are consistent with the view that all four of these mutations are at the same genetic locus.

Yet further heterogeneity is suggested by

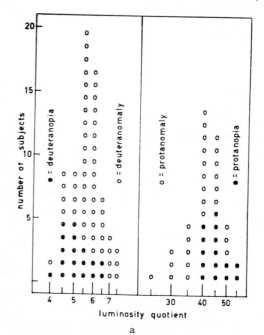

Fig. 48. The Luminosity Quotient

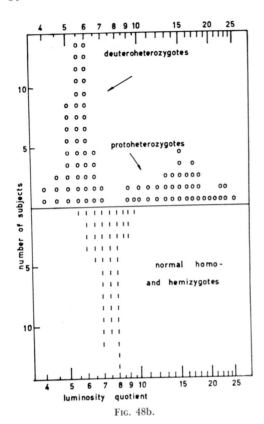

FIG. 48b.

The luminosity quotient as a method for distinguishing deutan and protan color blindness (a) and for identification of heterozygous carriers (b). The quotient is the ratio of the luminosity of green and red monochromatic light:

$$\frac{V(0.530 \ \mu)}{V(0.650 \ \mu)}$$

Most protan heterozygotes can be identified. A few deutan heterozygotes can be identified with some certainty. From Crone (1959).

findings with regard to "stromal activation." In Israel Rimon and co-workers (1960) presented data suggesting the absence of a stromal activator in patients with G6PD–deficiency. In the Melanesian population of New Guinea, Kidson and Phillips found heterogeneity. In the blood of 25 of 32 G6PD–deficient subjects activation occurred when normal erythrocyte stroma was added, whereas such did not occur in the remaining seven.

BOYER, S. H., IV, I. H. PORTER, and R. WEILBAECHER. 1962. Electrophoretic

heterogeneity of glucose-6-phosphate dehydrogenase and its relationship to enzyme deficiency in man. *Proc. Natl. Acad. Sci. U.S.*, 48: 1868–1876.

CHILDS, B., W. H. ZINKHAM, E. A. BROWNE, E. L. KIMBRO, and J. V. TORBERT. 1958. A genetic study of a defect in glutathione metabolism of the erythrocyte. *Bull. Johns Hopkins Hosp.*, 102:21–37.

KIDSON, C., and J. G. PHILLIPS. 1962. Mechanisms underlying glucose-6-phosphate dehydrogenase deficiency: heterogeneity of response to stromal activation in erythrocytes. *Biochem. Biophys. Res. Commun.*, 7: 268–271.

KIRKMAN, H. N. 1962. Electrophoretic differences of human erythrocytic glucose-6-phosphate (Abstract). *A.M.A. J. Diseases Children*, 104: 566.

——, H. D. RILEY, JR., and B. B. CROWELL. 1960. Different enzymic expressions of mutants of human glucose-6-phosphate dehydrogenase. *Proc. Natl. Acad. Sci. U. S.*, 46: 938–944.

MARKS, P. A., J. BANKS, and R. T. GROSS. 1962. Genetic heterogeneity of glucose-6-phosphate dehydrogenase deficiency. *Nature*, 194: 454–456.

——, and R. T. GROSS. 1959. Erythrocyte glucose-6-phosphate dehydrogenase deficiency; evidence of difference between Negroes and Caucasians with respect to this genetically determined trait. *J. Clin. Invest.*, 38: 2253–2262.

RIMON, A., I. ASKENAZI, B. RAMOT, and C. SHEBA. 1960. Activation of glucose-6-phosphate dehydrogenase of enzyme deficient subjects. I. Activation by stroma of normal erythrocytes. *Biochem. Biophys. Res. Commun.*, 2: 138–141.

SZEINBERG, A., C. SHEBA, and A. ADAM. 1958. Selective occurrence of glutathione instability in red blood corpuscles of the various Jewish tribes. *Blood*, 13: 1043–1053.

5. *The Xg blood group system*

The antigen called Xg^a behaves as an X-linked dominant. It was found in 89 per cent of 188 Caucasian females and in 62 per cent of 154 males. The antiserum was derived from a patient with hereditary hemorrhagic telangiectasia who had received many transfusions. The antigen is well developed at birth. In the few Negroes tested the phenotype frequencies seem to be about the same as in Caucasians. "Evidence is accumulating that homozygotes react as strongly as hemizygotes and more strongly than heterozygotes." The efficient estimate of the frequency of the Xg^a allele in Caucasians, making use of the data on females as well as males, is 0.651 (Sanger, et al., 1962).

The discovery of the Xg^a blood group is of great potential use to genetics especially for study of linkage and determination where non-disjunction occurs leading to X chromosome aneuploidy.

COOK, I. A., M. POLLEY, and P. L. MOLLISON. 1963. A second example of anti-Xgᵃ. *Lancet*, 1: 857–859.

MANN, J. D., A. CAHAN, A. G. GELB, N. FISHER, J. HAMPER, P. TIPPETT, R. SANGER, and R. R. RACE. 1962. A sex-linked blood group. *Lancet*, 1: 8–10.

SANGER, R., R. R. RACE, P. TIPPETT, J. HAMPER, J. GAVIN, and T. E. CLEGHORN. 1962. The X-linked blood group system Xg: more tests on unrelated people and on families. *Vox Sang.*, 7: 571–578.

6. Pseudohypertrophic progressive muscular dystrophy, Duchenne type

Usually the onset is before age six and the victim is chair-ridden by age 12 and dead by age 20. The myocardium is affected. An autosomal recessive form of muscular dystrophy can closely simulate the sex-linked form but the myocardium is probably not affected.

Chung, Morton, and Peters, among others, have concluded that a minority of heterozygous female carriers have an increase in serum aldolase and even fewer have physical disability and creatinuria. Leyburn, Thomson and Walton, on the other hand, could demonstrate no abnormality of creatine and creatinine excretion or of serum levels of aldolase and transaminases in carrier females. Serum phosphocreatine kinase (creatine phosphokinase) is elevated beyond the normal range in many female carriers, according to Shapiro and colleagues and Aebi and colleagues.

AEBI, U., R. RICHTERICH, J. P. COLOMBO, and E. ROSSI. 1961–1962. Progressive muscular dystrophy. II. Biochemical identification of the carrier state in the recessive sex-linked juvenile (Duchenne) type by serum creatine-phosphokinase determinations. *Enzymol. Biol. Clin.*, 1: 61–74; *Helv. Paediat. Acta*, 16: 543–564.

CHUNG, C. S., N. E. MORTON, and H. A. PETERS. 1960. Serum enzymes and genetic carriers in muscular dystrophy. *Am. J. Human Genet.*, 12: 52–66.

LEYBURN, P., W. H. S. THOMSON, and J. N. WALTON. 1961. An investigation of the carrier state in the Duchenne type of muscular dystrophy. *Ann. Human Genet.*, 25: 41–49.

MORTON, N. E., and C. A. CHUNG. 1959. Formal genetics of muscular dystrophy. *Am. J. Human Genet.*, 11: 360–379.

SCHAPIRO, E., J. C. DREYFUS, G. SCHAPIRA, and J. DEMOS. 1960. *Rev. franc. Etudes Clin. Biol.*, 5: 990–994.

SKYRING, A. P., and V. A. McKUSICK. 1961. Clinical, genetic and electrocardiographic studies of childhood muscular dystrophy. *Am. J. Med. Sci.*, 242: 534–547.

7. Progressive muscular dystrophy, tardive type of Becker

The onset is often in the 20's and 30's and survival to a relatively advanced age is frequent. Several affected males in Becker's large kindred had produced children in many instances and the resulting pedigree pattern was consistent with X-linked inheritance. Others (ref. below) have described such families. Allelism with the Duchenne type is possible. Linkage studies might establish non-allelism as in the case of hemophilias A and B (p. 30). There may be more than one form of X-linked late form of muscular dystrophy. Emery has restudied the family of Dreifuss and Hogan (1961) and found features different from those in the families reported by Becker.

BECKER, P. E. 1957. Neue Ergebnisse der Genetik der Muskeldystrophie. *Acta genet. Statist. Med.*, 7: 303–310.

——. 1955. Eine neue X-chromosomale Muskeldystrophie. *Acta Psychiat. Neurol. Scand.*, 193: 427.

——. 1962. Two new families of benign sex-linked recessive muscular dystrophy. *Rev. Canad. Biol.*, 21: 551–566.

BLYTH, H., and R. J. PUGH. 1959. Muscular dystrophy in childhood. *Ann. Human Genet.*, 23: 127–163.

DREIFUSS, F. E., and G. R. HOGAN. 1961. Survival in X-chromosomal muscular dystrophy. *Neurology*, 11: 734–741.

EMERY, A. E. H. 1962. Personal communication, Baltimore.

8. Hemophilia A

Classical hemophilia is the result of a hereditary defect in antihemophilic globulin (Factor VIII). A partial deficiency in heterozygous carriers has been demonstrated by the following workers, among several:

BIGGS, R., and J. M. MATTHEWS. 1963. The treatment of haemorrhage in von Willebrand's disease and the blood level of Factor VIII (AGH). *Brit. J. Hæmat.*, 9: 203–214.

CORNU, P., et al. 1963. Transfusion studies in von Willebrand's disease: effect on bleeding time and Factor VIII. *Brit. J. Hæmat.*, 9: 189–202.

RAPAPORT, S. I., M. J. PATCH, and F. J. MOORE. 1960. Antihemophilic globulin levels in carriers of hemophilia A. *J. Clin. Invest.*, 39: 1619–1625.

NILSSON, I. M., M. BLÖMBACK, O. RAMGREN, and I. v. FRANCKEN. 1962. Hæmophilia in Sweden. II. Carriers of hæmophilia A and B. *Acta Med. Scand.*, 171: 223–235.

Alexander and Goldstein (*J. Clin. Invest.*,

32: 551, 1953) first noted low levels of Factor VIII in cases of von Willebrand's disease ("vascular hemophilia"), an autosomally inherited disorder. This was confirmed by other workers including Nilsson and colleagues (*Acta med. scand.*, 159: 35, 1957), who studied von Willebrand's original family in the Åland Islands. Thus, an autosomal locus seems also involved in some way in Factor VIII formation. The situation is apparently complicated because the prolonged bleeding time in Willebrand's disease can be corrected by plasma lacking Factor VIII activity. Arrants, Jordon, and Newcomb (1962) are of the opinion that AHG is not deficient in Willibrand's disease but rather a separate clotting factor.

Several observations (Cornu, et al., 1963; Biggs and Matthews, 1963) are pertinent to the nature of the AHG defect in von Willebrand's disease. 1) Blood from a patient with hemophilia A will correct the clotting defect in von Willebrand's disease. 2) The converse is not true. Blood from a patient with von Willebrand's disease will not correct the clotting defect in hemophilia A. 3) The bleeding tendency in von Willebrand's disease is corrected promptly by hemophilia A blood. 4) after administration of hemophilia A blood to von Willebrand patients there is a delay of several hours before the level of AHG reaches normal. These observations are consistent with the following schema: At least two biochemical steps are involved in the synthesis of AHG. The first step under control of an autosomal locus produces the Willebrand factor which is concerned with platelet adhesiveness and therefore with vascular integrity. The Willebrand factor is also the substrate for the second step which is under X–chromosome control and which results in AHG. The above schema conceives, therefore, a chain of biochemical processes, each under separate genetic control—the type of system of which many instances have now been demonstrated.

The possible allelic relationship of mild Factor VIII deficiency is suggested by families such as that of Graham and collegues (*Am. J. Med. Sci.*, 225: 46–53, 1953) and that of Bond and colleagues (*New Engl. J. Med.*, 266: 220–223, 1962) in which the carrier females as well as hemizygous males showed depression of Factor VIII levels and sometimes clinical hemophilia, although the levels of Factor VIII were not as low as in hemizygous affected males. Sutton (in *Metabolic Basis of Inherited Disease*, Stanbury, et al., editors, 1960) and Woolf (*Nature*, 194: 609, 1962) have made the interesting suggestion that in man as in

bacteria feedback repression, operating at the level of the gene or at the level of RNA, may be involved in setting the rate of protein synthesis. Specifically, if a mutation is of a type in which no protein of a particular type is formed, then no abnormality in level would be expected in heterozygotes. On the other hand, if a "warped molecule" is synthesized as a result of the mutation, then feed-back repression might occur even though the molecule was defective in the performance of its physiologic function. Sutton and Woolf suggested that the findings in the heterozygote for mild hemophilia fit the latter model, whereas those of severe hemophilia may fit the first model. The concept is compatible with the Lyon hypothesis and quite independent of it.

9. *Hemophilia B*

Christmas disease is the result of a hereditary defect in Factor IX (PTC; plasma thromboplastic component). Linkage studies suggest that the genes responsible for hemophilias A and B are not allelic.

WHITTAKER, D. L., D. L. COPELAND, and J. B. GRAHAM. 1962. Linkage of color blindness with hemophilias A and B. *Am. J. Human Genet.*, 14: 149–158.

Blackburn and colleagues described two unrelated girls with Christmas disease (PTC deficiency) and a "primary" vascular abnormality. In both instances all other members of the family were normal. This may be a situation comparable to the combination of AHG and vascular defects in Willebrand's disease.

BLACKBURN, E. K., J. H. MONAGHAN, H. LEDERER, and J. M. MACFIE. 1962. Christmas disease associated with primary capillary abnormalities. *Brit. Med. J.*, 1: 154–156.

The combination of Factor IX with Factor VII deficiency in an X–linked pattern of inheritance was described by several workers (e.g., Nour-Eldin and Wilkinson). However, Verstraete, Vermylen and Vandenbroucke found Factor VII deficiency in all affected males of four families with Christmas disease and suggested that it is a consistent secondary phenomenon. By the latter view no separate mutation for the combined defect need be postulated.

DIDISHEIM, P., and R. L. E. VANDERVOORT. 1962. Detection of carriers for factor IX (PTC) deficiency. *Blood*, 20: 150–155.
NOUR-ELDIN, F., and J. F. WILKINSON. 1959. Factor-VII deficiency with Christmas dis-

ease in one family. *Lancet*, 1: 1173–1176.

VERSTRAETE, M., C. VERMYLEN, and J. VANDENBROUCKE. 1962. Hemophilia B associated with decreased factor VII activity. *Am. J. Med. Sci.*, 243: 20–26.

10. *Agammaglobulinemia*

Patients are unusually prone to bacterial infection but not to viral infection. A clinical picture resembling rheumatoid arthritis develops in many. Before antibiotics, death occurred in the first decade.

GARVIE, J. M., and A. C. KENDALL. 1961. Congenital agammaglobulinemia. *Brit. Med. J.*, 1: 548–550.

JANEWAY, C. A., L. APT, and D. GITLIN. 1953. Agammaglobulinemia. *Trans. Assoc. Am. Physicians*, 66: 200.

In the more usual X-linked form of the disease plasma cells are lacking. A rarer form of agammaglobulinemia (Hitzig and Willi, 1961), which appears to be inherited as an autosomal recessive, shows marked depression of the circulating lymphocytes and lymphocytes are absent from the lymphoid tissue. The alymphocytotic type is even more virulent than the X-linked form leading to death in the first 18 months after birth, from severe thrush, chronic diarrhea, and recurrent pulmonary infections.

HITZIG, W. H. and H. WILLI. 1961. Hereditäre lympho-plasmocytäre Dysgenesie ("Alymphocytose mit Agammaglobulinämie"). *Schweiz. Med. Wchnschr.* 91: 1625–1633.

11. *Hurler syndrome*

The form of the Hurler syndrome (gargoylism) which is sex-linked differs from the autosomal type in being on the average less severe and in not showing clouding of the cornea. (J. F. Van Pelt reports slight corneal opacities in a 3-year-old boy in a family in which 12 males in two generations were affected. Nijmegen thesis: "Gargoylism," 153 pp., 1960.) Features are dysostosis with dwarfism, grotesque facies, hepatosplenomegaly from mucopolysaccharide deposits, cardiovascular disorders from mucopolysaccharide deposits in the intima, mental retardation, deafness, excretion of large amounts of certain mucopolysaccharides in the urine.

MCKUSICK, V. A. 1960. *Heritable Disorders of Connective Tissue.* C. V. Mosby Co., St. Louis. (2nd edition.)

12. *Late spondylo-epiphyseal dysplasia*

This disorder has some similarities to the Brailsford-Morquio syndrome which in clas-

sic form is inherited as an autosomal recessive. The trunk is particularly short and the hips show degenerative disease. Changes in the spine and hips become evident between 10 and 14 years of age.

BARBER, H. S. 1960. An unusual form of familial osteodystrophy. *Lancet*, 1: 1220–1221; 2: 154–155.

HOBAEK, A. 1961. *Problems of Hereditary Chondrodystplasia.* Oslo University Press, Oslo, Norway.

JACOBSEN, A. W. 1939. Hereditary osteochondro-dystrophia deformans. A family with twenty members affected in five generations. *J. Am. Med. Assoc.*, 113: 121–124.

LAMY, M., and P. MAROTEAUX. 1960. *Les chondrodystrophies génotypiques.* L'Expansion. Paris. Pp. 67ff.

MAROTEAUX, P., M. LAMY, and J. BERNARD. 1957. La dysplasie spondylo-epiphysaire tardive. *Presse Méd.*, 65: 1205–1208.

13. *Aldrich syndrome*

The manifestations are eczema, thrombocytopenia, proneness to infection, and bloody diarrhea. Death occurs before age 10.

ALDRICH, R. A., A. G. STEINBERG, and D. C. CAMPBELL. 1954. Pedigree demonstrating a sex-linked recessive condition characterized by draining ears, eczematoid dermatitis and bloody diarrhea. *Pediatrics*, 13: 133–139.

GELZER, J., and C. GASSER. 1961. Wiskott-Aldrich-Syndrome. *Helv. Paediat. Acta*, 16: 17–39.

KRIVIT, W., and R. A. GOOD. 1959. Aldrich's syndrome (thrombocytopenia, eczema and infection in infants). *A.M.A. J. Diseases Children*, 97: 137–153.

STEINBERG, A. G. 1959. Methodology in human genetics. *J. Med. Educ.*, 34: 315–334.

14. *Hypophosphatemia*

Low serum phosphorus with vitamin D resistant rickets behaves as a sex-linked dominant trait. Heterozygous females have on the average less pronounced depression of serum phosphate and less severe skeletal change. Affected persons show a reduction in renal phosphate Tm to about 50 per cent of normal. Males and females are not significantly different in this respect. It is unsettled whether the basic defect concerns 1) renal resorption of phosphate, or 2) intestinal absorption of calcium with secondary hyperparathyroidism.

BLACKARD, W. G., R. R. ROBINSON, and J. E. WHITE. 1962. Familial hypophosphatemia: report of a case with observations regarding pathogenesis. *New Engl. J. Med.*, 266: 899–905.

WINTERS, R. W., J. B. GRAHAM, T. F. WIL-
LIAMS, V. W. McFALL, and C. H. BURNETT.
1958. A genetic study of familial hypophosphatemia and vitamin D resistant
rickets with a review of the literature.
Medicine, 37: 97–142.

15. *Hyperparathyroidism*

Peden's family showed neo-natal true idiopathic hypoparathyroidism. She suggested
that most familial cases of early onset are of
the X–linked type. The autosomal variety
has a later onset. No affected males reproduced in Peden's family and probably not in
others of the X–linked type.

> PEDEN, V. N. 1960. True idiopathic hypo-
> parathyroidism as a sex-linked recessive
> trait. *Am. J. Human Genet.*, 12: 323–
> 337.

16. *Nephrogenic diabetes insipidus*

The defect concerns the ability of the
renal tubule to respond to antidiuretic hormone. A partial defect is demonstrable in
females.

> CARTER, C. O., and M. J. SIMPKISS. 1956.
> The carrier state in sex-linked nephro-
> genic diabetes insipidus. *Lancet*, 2: 1069–
> 1072.

17. *Neurohypophyseal type of diabetes insipidus*

In addition to the X–linked forms of diabetes insipidus, autosomal dominant forms
also exist. Forssman had five families: two
probably autosomal and three X–linked. Of
the three X–linked families, one was of the
pitressin-resistant type, whereas the other two
families were susceptible. The latter two families presumably represent the neurohypophyseal type.

> FORSSMAN, H. 1955. Two different muta-
> tions of the X–chromosome causing dia-
> betes insipidus. *Am. J. Human Genet.*,
> 7: 21–27.
> ——. 1945. An hereditary diabetes in-
> sipidus. *Acta Med. Scand., Suppl.* 159.

18. *Lowe's oculo-cerebro-renal syndrome*

The features are hydrophthalmia, cataract,
mental retardation, vitamin D resistant rickets, aminoaciduria, and reduced ammonia
production by the kidney. Streiff and colleagues suggested X–linkage because all cases
are male and affected brothers have been
described. In one case two brothers and a
cousin (the mothers were sisters) were affected.

> AURICCHIO, S., W. FRISCHKNECHT, and D.
> SHMERLING. 1961. Primäre Tubulo-
> pathien. III. Ein Fall von oculo-cerebro-

renalem Syndrome (Lowe-Syndrom).
Helvet. Paediat. Acta, 16: 647–655.
LOWE, C. U., M. TERREY, and E. A. MAC-
LACHLAN. 1952. Organicaciduria, decreased renal ammonia production, hy-
drophthalmos, and mental retardation.
A.M.A. J. Disease Children, 83: 164–184.
——. 1960. Oculo-cerebro-renal syndrome. *Maandschr. Kindergeneesk.*, 28:
77.
STREIFF, E. B., W. STRAUB, and L. GOLAY.
1958. Les manifestations oculaire du syndrome de Lowe. *Ophthalmologia*, 135:
632–639.

19. *Hypochromic anemia*

This condition was first described by
Cooley, who also first described thalassemia.
He pointed out possible X–linkage in a family in which 19 males in five generations were
affected, with transmission through unaffected females. Rundles and Falls reported
two families, of which one was the same as
that reported by Cooley.

Hypochromic anemia has, of course, other
causes, notably iron deficiency. What is referred to here are the rare cases in which it
is hereditary. The condition is also known
as hereditary iron-loading anemia (Byrd and
Cooper). The features include: a) anemia detected first in childhood in some cases; b)
death from hemochromatosis at a relatively
young age, with the number of transfusions
inadequate to account for the hemochromatosis; c) hyperferricemia; and d) abundance
of siderocytes in peripheral blood after splenectomy. Somewhat enlarged spleens and
minor red cell abnormalities without anemia
were observed in female carriers by Rundles
and Falls.

Bishop and Bethell restudied an affected
male from Rundle and Falls' family and
found a partial correction of the anemia with
pyridoxine administration. However, they
concluded that transfusion hemosiderosis was
inhibiting hemesynthesis and that only this
acquired aspect of the anemia was corrected
by pyridoxine. It appears that in no instance
have sons of affected males been studied. The
possibility of male-limited autosomal dominant inheritance with the female partially
protected by blood losses in menstruation
should be considered.

> BISHOP, R. C., and F. H. BETHEL. 1959.
> Hereditary hypochromic anemia with
> transfusion hemosiderosis treated with
> pyridoxin. *New Engl. J. Med.*, 261: 486–
> 489.
> BYRD, R. B., and T. COOPER. 1961. Heredi-
> tary iron-loading anemia with secondary
> hemochromatosis. *Ann. Internal Med.*,
> 55: 103–123.
> COOLEY, T. B. 1945. Severe type of he-

reditary anemia with elliptocytosis; interesting sequence of splenectomy. *Am. J. Med. Sci.*, 209: 561–568.

RUNDLES, R. W., and H. F. FALLS. 1946. Hereditary (?sex-linked) anemia. *Am. J. Med. Sci.*, 211: 641–658.

20. *Diffuse angiokeratoma*

Skin lesions of vascular nature are the main basis of the name. Attacks of pain in the abdomen are often misdiagnosed appendicitis. Such pains and those elsewhere, such as in the extremities, probably have their basis in lipid changes in ganglion cells of the autonomic nervous system. Vascular lesions of lipid nature occur at other sites such as the ocular fundi and kidney. Renal failure is the usual cause of death. Heterozygous females almost never have skin lesions and survive longer despite renal involvement.

RAHMAN, A. N. and others. 1961. Angiokeratoma corporis diffusum universale. *Trans. Assoc. Am. Physicians*, 74: 366–377.

WISE, D. 1962. Angiokeratoma diffusum: a clinical study of eight affected families. *Quart. J. Med.*, 31: 177–206.

21. *Congenital dyskeratosis* (Zinsser–Cole–Engman syndrome)

The features are cutaneous pigmentation, dystrophy of the nails, leucoplakia of the oral mucosa, continuous lacrimation due to atresia of the lacrimal ducts, often thrombocytopenia, anemia, and in most cases testicular atrophy. Only males are affected in a pattern consistent with X–linked recessive inheritance.

GARB, J., and C. M. BUNCKE. 1958. Dyskeratosis congenita with pigmentation, dystrophia unguium and leukoplakia oris. *A.M.A. Arch. Dermatol.*, 77: 704–714.

KOSZEWSKI, B. J., and T. F. HUBBARD. 1956. Congenital anemia in hereditary ectodermal dysplasia. *A.M.A. Arch. Dermatol.*, 74: 159–166.

22. *Hereditary bullous dystrophy, macular type*

The features are formation of bullae without evident trauma, absence of all hair, hyperpigmentation, depigmentation, acrocyanosis, dwarfism, microcephaly, mental inferiority, short tapering fingers, sometimes anomalies of the nails. Most patients die before attaining adulthood. This disorder has been recognized only in a single kindred living in the Netherlands and described in three publications as listed below.

CAROL, W. L. L., and J. R. KOOI. 1936. Macular type of hereditary bullous dys-

trophy. *Maandschr. Kindergeneesk.*, 6: 39.

MENDES DA COSTA, S., and J. W. VAN DER VALK. 1908. Typus maculatus der bullösen hereditären Dystophie. *Arch. Dermatol. Syph.*, 91: 1–8.

WOERDEMANN, M. J. 1958. Dystrophia bullosa hereditaria, typus maculatus. *Ned. Tijdschr. Geneesk.*, 102: 111–116.

23. *Keratosis follicularis spinulosa decalvans cum ophiasi*

Affected men show thickening of the skin of the neck, ears, and extremities, especially the palms and soles, loss of eyebrows, eyelashes and beard, thickening of the eyelids with blepharitis and ectropion, and corneal degeneration. The term "cum ophiasi" means "with ophiasis," i.e., baldness in one or more winding streaks about the head. The term comes from the Greek for *snake*. *Decalvans* refers to the loss of hair. Autosomal dominant inheritance has also been described (Thelen: *Zentr. Haut. Geschlechtskr.* 65: 5, 1940).

In Siemens' publication pointing out X–linked inheritance, two families were described. In the one not observed personally by Siemens (described by Laméris, 1905, and by Rochat, 1906) the inheritance appeared to be X–linked recessive, whereas the other was an example of X–linked dominant (or intermediate) inheritance. The Laméris kindred was studied further by Jonkers (1950) and the pedigree was reproduced by Waardenburg, Francheschetti, and Klein (*Genetics and Ophthalmology*, vol. 1, 1961). Restudy indicates that the inheritance is the same as in Siemans' pedigree (see Fig. 49).

JONKERS, J. H. 1950. Hyperkeratosis follicularis and corneal degeneration. *Ophthalmologia*, 120: 365–367.

SENDI, H. 1957. *Quelques cas de keratosis follicularis spinolosa decalvans (Siemens).* M.D. thesis, Geneva.

SIEMENS, H. W. 1925. Ueber einen in der menschlichen Pathologie noch nicht beobachteten Vererbungsmodus: dominant-geschlechtsgebundene Vererbung. *Arch. Rass. Gesellsch.-Biol.*, 17: 47–61.

24. *Ichthyosis vulgaris*

Affected males show dry, scaly skin which in patches is often thick and keratotic. The extensor surfaces of the extremities are especially affected. Czörsz described a presumed homozygous, affected female. In 1929 Orel found in the literature 10 families with the X–linked form. Turpin and his colleagues (1945) described associated changes in the fundus oculi of affected males.

ARGÜELLES CASALS, D. 1948. Genetica y dermatologia. Ictiosis vulgar transmitio a por herencia recesiva sexual. *Inform. med.*, 12: 129.

COCKAYNE, E. A. 1933. *Inherited Abnormalities of the Skin and its Appendages.* Oxford University Press, London, p. 213.

CZÖRSZ, B. 1928. *Monatschr. Ungar. Mediz.,* 2: 180. Also *Zentr. Haut Geschlechtskrankh.* 26: 463.

HARRIS, H. 1947. A pedigree of sex-linked ichthyosis vulgaris. *Ann. Eugenics,* 14: 9.

OREL, H. 1929. Die Vererbung von Ichthyosis congenita und der Ichthyosis vulgaris. *Z. Kinderheilk.,* 47: 312–340. Orel found 10 families with the X–linked form.

TURPIN, DESVIGNES, and DEMASSIEUX. 1945. *Semaine Hôp. Paris,* 21: 343.

25. *Anhidrotic ectodermal dysplasia*

The affected males show absence of teeth, hypotrichosis, and absence of sweat glands. Heterozygous women may show reduction or malformation of teeth and mild abnormalities of sweat glands and breasts. In Robert's family, skin involvement in heterozygous females was patchy (p. 64). Sometimes the inheritance is autosomal dominant. Halperin and Curtis' case showed mental defect also, but this is not an invariable feature of cases, even in their family. This was the condition affecting the "toothless men of Sind," members of a Hindu kindred which resides in the vicinity of Hyderabad and was described by Darwin (1875) and by Thadoni (1934).

GRANT, R., and H. F. FALLS. 1944. Anodontia; report of a case associated with ectodermal dysplasia of anhydrotic type. *Am. J. Orthodontics,* 30: 661–672.

THADANI, K. I. 1934. The toothless men of Sind. *J. Heredity,* 25: 483–484.

HALPERIN, S. L., and G. M. CURTIS. 1942. Anhidrotic ectodermal dysplasia associated with mental deficiency. *Am. J. Mental Deficiency,* 46: 459–463.

ROBERTS, E. 1929. The inheritance of anhidrosis associated with anodontia. *J. Am. Med. Assoc.,* 93: 277–279.

DARWIN, C. 1875. *The Variation of Animals and Plants under Domestication.* 2nd edition. John Murray, London. II, p. 319.
"...I may give an analogous case, communicated to me by Mr. W. Wedderburn, of a Hindoo family in Scinde, in which ten men, in the course of four generations, were furnished, in both jaws taken together, with only four small and weak incisor teeth and with eight posterior molars. The men thus affected have very little hair on the body, and become bald early in life. They also suffer much during hot weather from excessive dryness of the skin. It is remarkable that no instance has occurred of a daughter being affected ... Though the daughters in the above family are never affected, they transmit the tendency to their sons; and no case has occurred of a son transmitting it to his sons. The affection thus appears only in alternate generations, or after long intervals ..."
(Hutt called attention to Darwin's description: *J. Heredity,* 26: 65–66, 1935.)

Singh, Jolly, and Kaur described a severe case in a 27-year-old Sikh woman in India. Two brothers had died of the disease. Whether this was a homozygous affected or a heterozygous manifesting female is uncertain, especially since no information was provided on whether the father was affected. Consanguineous matings of the types which are expected to result in homozygous affected females are frequent in some Indian groups (p. 77).

SINGH, A., S. S. JOLLY, and S. KAUR. 1962. Hereditary ectodermal dysplasia. *Brit. J. Dermatol.,* 74: 34–37.

26. *Amelogenesis imperfecta, hypomaturation type*

The enamel is opaque white, soft, and easily abraded but appears of normal thickness in unerupted teeth. The condition is inherited as an X–linked recessive.

WITKOP, C. J. 1957. Hereditary defects in enamel and dentin. *Acta Genet. Statist. Med.,* 7: 236.

27. *Amelogenesis imperfecta, hypoplastic type*

In this condition the enamel is very hard but is abnormally thin so that the teeth appear small. The surface is rough. This type is inherited as an X–linked dominant. Possible genetic relationship, e.g., allelism, with the factor for the hypomaturation type is unknown. Therefore the two have been listed as separate loci.

SCHULZE, C., and F. LENZ. 1952. Uber Zahnschmelzhypoplasie von unvollständig dominantem geschlechtsgebundenen Erbgang. *Z. Menschl. Vererb. Konstit. Lehre,* 31: 104–114.

———. 1957. Erbbedingte Structuranomalien menschlicher Zähne. *Acta Genet. Stastis. Med.,* 7: 231–235.

HALDANE, J. B. S. 1937. A probable new sex-linked dominant in man. *J. Heredity,* 28: 58–60.

28. *Absence of central incisors*

Huskins described an English family with affected members of at least three generations. He specifically stated that there was "no evidence of any other defective condition being associated with this dental anomaly." There was one affected female in the family. We know of no other report of X–linkage.

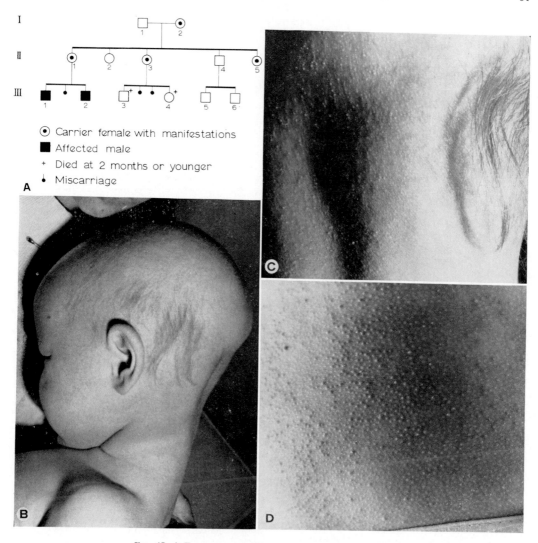

⊙ Carrier female with manifestations
■ Affected male
+ Died at 2 months or younger
• Miscarriage

Fig. 49. A Family with Keratosis Follicularis Spinulosa

a. The pedigree. The family, resident in Baltimore, originated in Germany. b, c. The alopecia and follicular keratosis in individual III 2, age 34 months, are shown. The child has photophobia, almost no eyebrows or eyelashes, and keratotic papules on the back of the neck, shoulders, knees and upper arms. d. An example of similar keratotic papules on the abdomen in a heterozygote, II 5. This and the other heterozygotes indicated in the pedigree chart also showed corneal changes by slit-lamp examination. Courtesy of Drs. A. E. H. Emery and David Wise.

Huskins, C. L. 1930. On the inheritance of an anomaly of human dentition. *J. Heredity*, 21: 279–282.

29. *Congenital deafness*

Probably about 1.5 per cent of genetic deafness is determined by an X–borne gene. The X–linked form of congenital deafness has been described from Missouri (Dow, Poynter), Japan (Mitsuda et al.), Belfast (Stevenson, cited by Deraemaeker), the Netherlands (Deraemaeker), Philadelphia (Sataloff et al.) and Australia (Parker). Fraser found several families in England. In the family reported by Dow and Poynter four affected males married deaf-mute women who probably had the autosomal recessive form of the disease because no children were affected.

Deraemaeker, R. 1958. Sex-linked congenital deafness. *Acta Genet. Statist. Med.*, 8: 228–231.

Dow, G. S., and C. I. Poynter. 1930. The Dar family. *Eugenical News*, 15: 128.

Fraser, G. R. 1962. Personal communication, Seattle.

Mitsuda, H., S. Inoue, and Y. Kazama. 1952. Eine Familie mit rezessiv geschlechtsgebundener Taubstummheit. *Japan J. Genetics*, 27: 142.

Parker, N. 1958. Congenital deafness due to a sex-linked recessive gene. *Am. J. Human Genet.*, 10: 196–200.

Richards, B. W. 1963. Sex-linked deafmutism. *Ann. Human Genet.*, 26: 195–199.

Sataloff, J., P. N. Pastore, and E. Bloom. 1955. Sex-linked hereditary deafness. *Am. J. Human Genet.*, 7: 201–203.

30. *Progressive deafness*

Sufficient hearing is present at first that speech develops normally, then deteriorates.

Mohr, J., and K. Mageroy. 1960. Sex-linked deafness of a possibly new type. *Acta Genet. Statis. Med.*, 10: 54–62.

31. *Mental deficiency*

Among the numerous types of mental deficiency an hereditary X–linked form exists. An apparently X–linked non-progressive form of mental deficiency without evident somatic malformation and without motor or sensory disfunction was described by Martin and Bell (1943) and possibly the same mutation was described by Allan and Herndon (1944). Priest and colleagues, as well as others, found more males in state institutions for mental defectives and found that affected sibs were more often male. However, males are probably more likely to be institutionalized. Furthermore, as is discussed in the text (p. 18), several autosomal conditions show a male preponderance which almost certainly has a basis other than X–linkage in a proportion of cases. Another kindred with convincingly X–linked mental retardation is reported by Renpenning and his colleagues.

Allan, W., C. N. Herndon, and F. C. Dudley. 1944. Some examples of the inheritance of mental deficiency; apparently sex-linked idiocy and microcephaly. *Am. J. Mental Deficiency*, 48: 325–334.

——, and C. N. Herndon. 1944. Retinitis pigmentosa and apparently sex-linked idiocy in a single sibship. *J. Heredity*, 35: 41–43.

Martin, J. P., and J. Bell. 1943. A pedigree of mental defect showing sex-linkage. *J. Neurol. Psychiat.*, 6: 154–157.

Priest, J. H., H. C. Thuline, G. D. LaVeck, and D. B. Jarvis. 1961. An approach to genetic factors in mental retardation. Studies of families containing at least two siblings admitted to a state institution for the retarded. *Am. J. Mental Deficiency*, 66: 42.

Rosanoff, A. J. 1931. Sex-linked inheritance in mental deficiency. *Am. J. Psychiat.*, 11: 289–297.

32. *Börjeson syndrome* (mental deficiency, epilepsy, endocrine disorders)

Features were severe mental defect, epilepsy, hypogonadism, hypometabolism, marked obesity, swelling of subcutaneous tissue of face, narrow palpebral fissure, large but not deformed ears. Three females who might be carriers had moderate mental retardation. This is a "new" syndrome described in a single kindred.

Börjeson, M., H. Forssman, and O. Lehmann. 1962. An X–linked, recessively inherited syndrome characterized by grave mental deficiency, epilepsy, and endocrine disorder. *Acta Med. Scand.*, 171: 13–21.

33. *Spinal ataxia*

A kindred with X–linked inheritance of what the authors thought was probably Friedreich's ataxia was reported by Turner and Roberts. Onset was at about five years and the victim was bedfast by about 20 years. The first carrier female in the kindred was of English extraction. In 1910 Brandenberg described four males with Friedreich's ataxia in three generations of a family, related through females in a pattern consistent with X–linkage.

Brandenberg, F. 1910. Kasuistische Beiträge zur gleichgeschlechtlichen Vererbung. *Arch. Rass. Ges. Biol.*, 7: 290–305.

Turner, E. V., and E. Roberts. 1938. A family with sex-linked hereditary ataxia. *J. Nervous Mental Disease*, 87: 74–80.

34. *Cerebellar ataxia with extrapyramidal involvement*

Malamud's family had an unusual form of neurologic disease in that the clinical picture dominated at the outset by cerebellar signs was later characterized by extrapyramidal signs. Anatomical changes involved both the cerebellar and the extrapyramidal systems.

Malamud, N. and P. Cohen. 1958. Unusual form of cerebellar ataxia with sex-linked inheritance. *Neurology*, 8: 261–271.

35. *Spastic paraplegia*

Spastic paraplegia is an autosomal dominant in many families, an autosomal recessive in many others. The family of Johnston and McKusick showed X–linked recessive in-

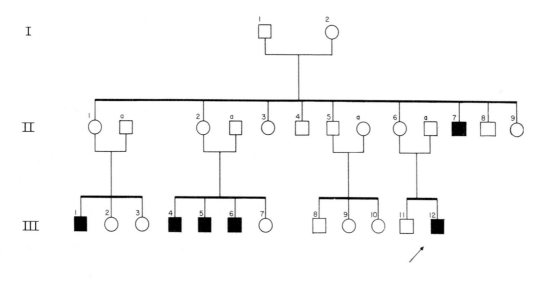

ICHTHYOSIS VULGARIS

a

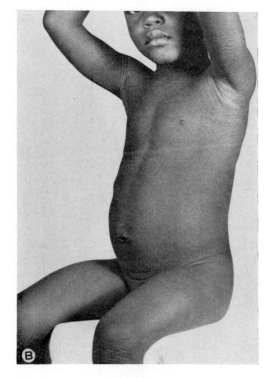

b

FIG. 50. A FAMILY WITH ICHTHYOSIS VULGARIS
a. The pedigree. b. The characteristic cutaneous changes as seen in the proband.

heritance. Wolfslast's family, with what he termed spastic diplegia, is another possible example. One affected male was living at age 50 and a second at age 20. Nystagmus was described in a female carrier. Prof. P. E. Becker of Göttingen is of the opinion, however, that Wolfslast's family suffered from the Pelizaeus-Merzbacher syndrome, and Verschuer in his textbook states the same opinion. A more likely case of X–linked spastic paraplegia is that of Blumel et al. Early onset, slow progression, and long survival with eventual involvement of the cerebellum, cerebral cortex and optic nerves are features of the X–linked form as observed by Johnston and McKusick.

BLUMEL, J., E. G. EVANS, and G. W. N. EGGERS. 1957. Hereditary cerebral palsy. A preliminary report. *J. Pediat.*, 50: 454–457.

JOHNSTON, A. W., and V. A. McKUSICK. 1962. Sex-linked recessive inheritance of spastic paraplegia. *Am. J. Human Genet.*, 14: 83–94.

WOLFSLAST, W. 1943. Eine Sippe mit rezessiver geschlechtsgebundener spastischer Diplegie. *Z. Menschl. Vereb.-Konst.-lehre*, 27: 189–198.

36. *Progressive bulbar paralysis.*

The disease apparently had the same clinical features as the autosomally transmitted forms. The proband was a 55-year-old Japanese farmer. Only this one X–linked family has been described.

TAKIKAWA, K. 1953. A pedigree of progressive bulbar paralysis appearing in sex-linked recessive inheritance. *Japan. J. Genetics*, 28: 116.

Same family referred to by:

MURAKAMI, U. 1957. Clinico-genetic study of hereditary disorders of the nervous system, especially on problems of pathogenesis. *Folia Psychiat. Neurol. Japan.* *Suppl. 1*, 1–209.

KURLAND, L. T. 1957. Epidemiologic investigations of amyotrophic lateral sclerosis. III. A genetic interpretation of incidence and geographic distribution. *Proc. Staff Meetings Mayo Clinic*, 32: 449–462. (Kurland mentions *two* such families seen by him in Japan.)

37. *Charcot–Marie–Tooth peroneal muscular atrophy*

This condition is essentially a degeneration of spinal nerve roots, especially the motor roots to the distal parts of the extremities. Autosomal dominant and recessive forms also exist.

ALLAN, W. 1939. Relation of hereditary pattern to clinical severity as illustrated by peroneal atrophy. *Arch. Internal Med.*, 63: 1123–1131.

38. *Diffuse cerebral sclerosis, Pelizaeus-Merzbacher form*

The diffuse cerebral sclerosis group rivals the spinocerebellar degeneration group in clinical, pathologic, and genetic confusion. It is currently under intense investigation and hopefully will be elucidated through biochemical characteristics in the not too distant future. Some, e.g., Ford, refer to the Pelizaeus-Merzbacher form as the chronic infantile type. It begins in infancy as early as the eighth day and usually no later than the third month and is very slowly progressive so that the victim may survive to middle age. One of Pelizaeus' patients lived to 52 years of age and in Tyler's Negro family an affected male was still living at age 51. At first, rotary movements of the head and eyes develop but curiously may later disappear. Affected children are known in these families as "head nodders" and "eye waggers." Spasticity of the legs and later the arms, cerebellar ataxia, dementia, and Parkinsonian symptoms are other features developing over the first decade or two of life. Some heterozygous females show the disorder. The brain of such a female in Merzbacher's family was studied by Spielmeyer (cited by Tyler) with demonstration of changes.

FORD, F. R. 1960. *Diseases of the Nervous System in Infancy, Childhood and Adolescence.* Charles C Thomas, Springfield. (4th ed.), pp 831–833.

TYLER, H. R. 1958. Pelizaeus-Merzbacher disease: a clinical study. *A.M.A. Arch. Neurol. Psychiat.*, 80: 162–169.

MERZBACHER, L. 1909. Gesetzmässigkeiten in der Vererbung und Verbrietung verschiedener hereditär-familiären Erkrankungen. *Arch. Rass. Ges. Biol.*, 6: 172–198.

PENROSE, L. S. 1954. *Biology of Mental Defect.* Sidgwick & Jackson Ltd., London, (2nd edition).

39. *Diffuse cerebral sclerosis, Scholz type*

Ford refers to this form as the subacute childhood type. It begins at age 8–10 years and is characterized by deafness, blindness, weakness and spasticity of the legs, and dementia. Survival is shorter after onset of symptoms. However, in Scholz' family, although the affected males in the youngest generation showed this picture, their maternal grandfathers, age 65 and 60, had the picture of spastic paraplegia (like No. A35).

Walsh described under the heading of Schilder's disease, or encephalitis periaxialis diffusa, a kindred in which four males, offspring of sisters, succumbed to an illness possibly of the type shown by Scholz' youngest patients.

Hoefnagel, van der Noort and Ingbar (1962) have described histologic changes in endocrine glands, especially the pituitary and adrenal, in cases of probable X-linked cerebral sclerosis.

BECKER, P. E. 1953. Andere neurologische Erbkrankheiten. *Handbuch der Inneren Medizin*, Springer, Berlin-Göttingen-Heidelberg. 4. Aufl. V/III: 1003.

HOEFNAGEL, D., S. VAN DER NOORT, and S. H. INGBAR. 1962. Diffuse cerebral sclerosis with endocrine abnormalities in young males. *Brain*, 85: 553–568.

SCHOLZ, W. 1925. Klinische, pathologisch-anatomische und erbbiologische Untersuchen bei familiärer, diffuser Hirnsklerose im Kindesalter. *Z. Neurol. Psychiat.*, 9: 651.

WALSH, F. B. 1957. *Clinical Neuro-Ophthalmology.* Williams and Wilkins Co., Baltimore, (2nd edition). p. 664.

40. *Hydrocephalus due to congenital stenosis of aqueduct of Sylvius*

The hydrocephalus may become arrested and the principal manifestations may be mental deficiency and spastic paraplegia. Hypoplasia and contracture of the thumb is characteristic (Edwards).

BICKERS, D. S. and R. D. ADAMS. 1949. Hereditary stenosis of the aqueduct of Sylvius as a cause of congenital hydrocephalus. *Brain*, 72: 246–262.

EDWARDS, J. H., R. M. NORMAN, and J. M. ROBERTS. 1961. Sex-linked hydrocephalus. *Arch. Disease Childhood,* 36: 481–499.

——. 1961. The syndrome of sex-linked hydrocephalus. *Arch. Disease Childhood,* 36: 486–493.

FANCONI, G. 1934. Zur Diagnose und Therapie hydrocephalischer und verwandter Zustände. *Schweiz. Med. Wochnschr.,* 64: 214–223.

41. *Parkinsonism*

Like some other traits listed here, Parkinsonism is only a symptom and has many causes. Cases of idiopathic paralysis agitans (that is, cases in which arteriosclerosis and encephalitis are considered unlikely causes) have been found to have family histories consistent with autosomal dominant inheritance. The Filipino kindred showing X–linked recessive inheritance (observed by McKusick and colleagues) appears to be unique. Onset of symptoms occurs at the age of about 40 years. (See Fig. 51.)

McKUSICK, V. A., A. W. JOHNSTON, C. N. LUTTRELL, and H. F. KLINEFELTER, JR. X–linked recessive inheritance of Parkinsonism. To be published.

42. *Ocular albinism*

In affected men the iris is only slightly pigmented and therefore diaphanous and the pupillary reflex is characteristic of albinism. The fundus is depigmented and the choroidal vessels stand out strikingly. Nystagmus, head nodding, and impaired vision also occur. Pigmentation is normal elsewhere than in the eye. The iris of carrier females is abnormally translucent and the fundus, especially that in the periphery, shows a mosaic of pigmentation, as first recognized by Vogt. Lyon feels that the fundus finding in heterozygous females supports her theory (p. 163).

Nystagmus is, as noted above, frequently an associated feature. In fact the ocular albinism has been commented on only obliquely or not at all in some reports of X–linked nystagmus in families which almost certainly had ocular albinism. Waardenburg and van den Bosch's family was earlier reported by Engelhard as a family with hereditary nystagmus.

Fundus drawings of heterozygous carriers are provided by Falls, François and Deweer, Ohrt, François (textbook), and by others. Theoretically one should be able to count the number of pigmented spots and arrive at an estimate of the number of anlage cells present at the "time of decision" postulated by Lyon. Unfortunately most of the available drawings are probably too crude to be relied

on for this use. Furthermore, the drawings suggest appreciable variation in the number and size of pigmented areas, a finding to be expected from the considerations of the Lyon hypothesis. (See frontispiece.)

ENGELHARD, C. F. 1915. Eine Familie mit hereditärem Nystagmus. *Z. Ges. Neurol. Psychiat.,* 28: 319–343.

FRANÇOIS, J., and J. P. DEWEER. 1953. Albinisme oculaire lié au sexe et alterations caracteristiques du fond d'oeil chez les femmes hétérozygotes. *Ophthalmologia,* 126: 209–221.

GILLESPIE, F. D. 1961. Ocular albinism with report of a family with female carriers. *Arch. Ophthalmol.,* 66: 774–776.

NEGRELLI, B. C. 1959. L'albinisme oculaire lié au sexe dans de cadre du dépistage des hétérozygotes en ophthalmologie. *J. génét. hum.,* 8: 108.

VOGT, A. 1942. Die Iris Albinismus solum bulbi. *Atlas Spalt-lampen-mikroskopie,* 3: 846.

WAARDENBURG, P. J., and J. VAN DEN BOSCH. 1956. X-chromosomal ocular albinism in Dutch family. *Ann. Human Genet.,* 21: 101–122.

Isolated albinism of the eye is inherited in the rabbit as an autosomal recessive.

MAGNUSSEN, K. Beitrag zur Genetik und Histologie eines isolierten Augenalbinismus beim Kaninchen. I–V. *Z. Morphol. Anthropol.,* 44: 127–135, 1952; 46: 24–29, 1954; 49: 306–311, 1959; 50: 103–120, 1959; 51: 81–88.

43. *External ophthalmoplegia and myopia*

In the probably unique family of Salleras and de Zárate, affected men showed bilateral ptosis, complete or partial ophthalmoplegia, abnormal shape or function of the pupil, myopia, and progressive degeneration of the retina and choroid. Often there was also absence of patellar and Achilles reflexes, spina bifida, and cardiac and other congenital malformation. Some carrier women showed absent deep tendon reflexes only. Hereditary ophthalmoplegia without myopia is frequently an autosomal dominant or recessive.

SALLERAS, A., and J. C. O. DE ZÁRATE. 1950. Recessive sex-linked inheritance of external ophthalmoplegia and myopia coincident with other dysplasias. *Brit. J. Ophthalmol.,* 34: 662–667.

44. *Microphthalmia*

In Stephen's cases white opacification of the cornea and blindness were present. Roberts' cases also had corneal change. Mental deficiency was present in some in Roberts' family, but intelligence was normal in at least two of six cases of microphthalmia examined. No

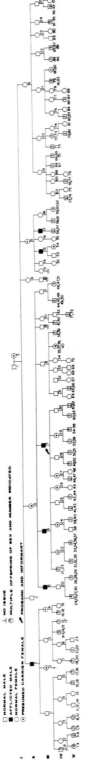

FIG. 51. APPARENTLY X-LINKED PARKINSONISM

Males in the fifth generation are too young to have developed the disorder. (McKusick, et al., to be published.)

mental defect was present except in microph-thalmia cases. On the other hand, Stephens' cases were of university level of intelligence. Sjögren and Larsson (*Acta Psychiat. Neurol. Scand., Suppl.* 56, pp. 1–103, 1949) described microphthalmia and oligophrenia behaving as an autosomal recessive syndrome.

Anophthalmia and microphthalmia are terms used interchangeably. The family reported by Hoefnagel, Keenan, and Allen was probably one of X–linked microphthalmia.

HOEFNAGEL, D., M. E. KEENAN, and F. H. ALLEN. 1963. Heredofamilial bilateral anophthalmia. *A.M.A. Arch. Ophthal.,* 69: 760–764.
ROBERTS, J. A. F. 1937. Sex-linked microphthalmia sometimes associated with mental defect. *Brit. Med. J.,* 2: 1213–1216. (Waardenburg, vol. 2, pp. 768–770, of textbook with Franceschetti and Klein, thinks this was an instance of pseudoglioma or of retinal dysplasia.)
STEPHENS, F. E. 1947. A case of sex-linked microphthalmia. *J. Heredity,* 38: 307–310.

45. *Microphthalmia or anophthalmos, with digital anomalies*

The eye anomaly was unilateral in some of the affected persons in Lenz's remarkable pedigree. Narrow shoulders, double thumbs, other skeletal anomalies, and dental, urogenital and cardiovascular malformations were observed. The mother of the proband, a 13-year-old boy born blind, had a deformity of the joints of the fifth finger, suggesting mild expression.

LENZ, W. 1955. Recessiv-geschlechtsgebundene Mikrophthalmie mit multiplen Missbildungen. *Z. Kinderhheilk.,* 77: 384. (See also, Waardenburg, Franceschetti, and Klein, *Genetics and Ophthalmology,* 1961.)

46. *Nystagmus*

Nystagmus is, of course, only a symptom and has many causes. In fact it occurs as part of the symptom complex in certain other sex-linked traits (e.g. Pelizaeus-Merzbacher, spastic paraplegia, ocular albinism, etc.). What is referred to here is a hereditary form which occurs alone and of which the neuro-anatomical basis is still unknown.

Autosomal dominant and recessive forms are less frequent than the X–linked form. Waardenburg (personal communication) feels there is no reason to separate an X–linked recessive from an X–linked dominant form as some have attempted. In some families the disorder is recessive in one line and dominant

in another (Hemmes (1924); Waardenburg, Franceschetti and Klein (textbook, 1961)). The explanation could be that the mutation is identical but that there is a series of "wild-type" isoalleles which have different effects on penetrance of the mutation in the heterozygous female.

RUCKER (1949) For references see text.
BILLINGS, M. L. 1942. Nystagmus through four generations. *J. Hereditary,* 33: 457.
COX, R. A. 1936. Congenital head-nodding and nystagmus; report of a case. *Arch. Ophthalmol.,* 15: 1032–1036.
CUENDET, J. F. and V. DELLA PORTA. 1949. Une famille de nystagmiques. *Ophthalmologia,* 117: 199–201.
HEMMES, G. C. 1924. *Over hereditairen Nystagmus.* Utrecht thesis.
WAARDENBURG, P. Z. 1953. Zum Kapitel des ausserokularen erblichen Nystagmus. *Acta Genet. Statist. Med.,* 4: 298–312.

47. *Megalocornea*

Affected males show large cornea as an isolated defect. Heterozygous women may show slight increase in corneal diameter (Riddell). Autosomal dominant inheritance is probably much rarer. Megalocornea occurs at times as part of the Marfan syndrome (inherited as an autosomal dominant).

RIDDELL, W. J. B. 1941. Uncomplicated hereditary megalocornea. *Ann. Eugenics,* 11: 102–107.
GRÖNHOLM, V. 1921. Ueber die Vererbung der Megalocornea nebst einem Beitrag zur Frage des genetischen zusammenhangen zwischen Megalokornea und Hydrophalmus. *Klin. Monatsbl. Augenh.,* 67: 1–15. (Two presumed homozygous females occurred in this family; see Fig. 52.)

Falls also had a family with X–linked megalocornea. (*Trans. Am. Ophthalmol. Soc.,* 50: 421–467, 1952.)

48. *Hypoplasia of iris with glaucoma*

Frank-Kamenetzki described this disorder in two Russian kindreds. The atrophy or hypoplasia of the iris seemed, from the findings in young family members, to be primary and glaucoma secondary. Makarow (cited by Waardenburg, Franceschetti, Klein, Textbook, 1961, p. 609) probably described the same disorder, also in Russia. No other families are known.

FRANK-KAMENETZKI, S. G. 1925. Eine eigenartige hereditäre Glaukomform mit Mangel des Irisstromas und geschlechtsgebundener Vererbung. *Klin. Monatsbl. Augenh.,* 74: 133–150.

49. *Congenital total cataract*

Stieren's family seems to be unique, although Halbertsma's cataract may be the same as Stieren's. In three generations only males to a total of 17 out of 37 were affected. Although there are many varieties of hereditary cataract, X–linked inheritance is uncommon. In Stieren's family the affected males were born blind and died in infancy. Some were hydrocephalic and some had convulsions.

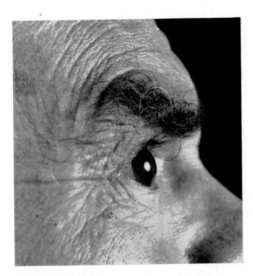

GRÖNHOLM (1921)   MEGALOCORNEA

a

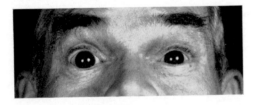

b

c

FIG. 52. MEGALOCORNEA

a. Grönholm's kindred in which two presumably homozygous affected females were observed. The degree of involvement was identical to that in hemizygous affected males. (b and c) Megalocornea in 54-year-old male (W.S., 709297).

STIEREN, E. 1907. A study in atavistic descent of congenital cataract through four generations. *Ophthalmol. Rec.*, 16: 234–238.

HALBERTSMA, K. T. A. 1934. Familiäre angeborene Katarakt. *Ned. Tijdschr. Geneesk.*, p. 1705–1709.

50. *Congenital cataract with microcornea or slight microphthalmia*

Waardenburg (loc. cit. p. 880) observed a family with clear X–linked recessive inheritance. Witkop-Oostenrijk (1956) described a family in which X–linked dominance (possibly with lethality in the affected hemizygote) might be the genetic mechanism. Autosomal dominant and autosomal recessive forms also exist.

WITKOP-OOSTENRIJK, G. A. 1956. Microphthalamus, microcornea en aangeboren cataract. *Ned. Tijdschr. Geneesk.*, 100: 2910–1913.

WAARDENBURG, FRANCESCHETTI and KLEIN. 1961. *Genetics and Ophthalmology*, Vol. 1.

51. *Congenital stationary night blindness with myopia*

Night blindness (hemeralopia) is a symptom of several chorioretinal degenerations (e.g., No. A52). The distinctive feature of the mutation listed here is the stationary nature of the night blindness. There is an autosomal dominant variety reported in many families of which the most famous is that descendant from Jean Nougaret, born in Provence in 1637, and studied by Cunier (1838), Nettleship (1907) and others. (An abnormal segregation ratio with fewer affected persons than anticipated has been suggested in this family, but other large pedigrees do not show this.) The X–linked form is distinguished from the autosomal form by the association of myopia.

Myopia has not been listed as a separate X–linked mutation because it is not completely certain that it indeed occurs with this mode of inheritance and independent of night blindness or ophthalmoplegia (A43). Worth (1906) reported four families with myopia which apparently were X–linked. At Nettleship's suggestion he looked for associated night blindness and found it in the affected members of only one of the families. In Oswald's family with myopia transmitted in a pattern otherwise consistent with X–linked inheritance apparent male-to-male transmission occurred in the first generation (see p. 14).

KLEINER, W. 1923. Ueber den grossen schweizerischen Stammbaum in dem mit

Kurzsichtigkeit kombinierte Nachtblindheit sich forterbt. *Arch. Rass. Ges. Biol.,* 15: 1–17.

NETTLESHIP, E. 1909. On some hereditary diseases of the eye (Bowman lecture). Retinitis pigmentosa, night blindness with myopia, ocular albinism. *Trans. Ophthalmol. Soc. U. K.,* 29: 57–148, 1912. A pedigree of congenital night blindness with myopia. *Trans. Ophthalmol. Soc. U. K.,* 32: 21–45.

WHITE, T. 1940. Linkage and crossing-over in the human chromosomes. *J. Genet.,* 40: 403–437.

WORTH, C. 1906. Hereditary influence in myopia. *Trans. Ophthalmol. Soc. U. K.,* 26: 141–144.

52. *Choroideremia* (progressive tapeto-choroidal dystrophy)

Affected males suffer progressive loss of vision (reduction of central vision, constriction of visual fields, night blindness) beginning at an early age, and the choroid and retina undergo complete atrophy. Heterozygous females show no visual defect but often show striking fundoscopic changes such as irregular pigmentation and atrophy around the optic disc.

The term choroidermia, which is comparable to irideremia and means absence of choroid, is inappropriate, since there is no congenital absence of the choroid. The condition is an abiotrophy beginning shortly after birth and progressing gradually. Waardenburg favors an alternative designation "tapeto-choroidal dystrophy" (Pameyer, et al.).

SORSBY, A., A. FRANCESCHETTI, R. JOSEPH, and J. B. DAVEY. 1952. Choroideremia. Clinical and genetic aspects. *Brit. J. Ophthalmol.,* 36: 547–581.

PAMEYER, J. K., P. J. WAARDENBURG, and H. E. HENKES. 1960. Choroideremia. *Brit. J. Ophthalmol.,* 44: 724–738.

53. *Retinitis pigmentosa*

The X–linked form is also called choroidoretinal degeneration, or pigmentary retinopathy. Affected males show typical "bone corpuscle" clumps of pigment on fundoscopic examination and progressive choroidal sclerosis leading to complete blindness. Heterozygous women may show a tapetoretinal reflex (brilliant, scintillating, golden hued, patchy appearance most striking around the macula) but no visual defect. Retinitis pigmentosa is sometimes autosomal dominant, sometimes autosomal recessive. In addition to these hereditary forms without associated manifestations, retinitis pigmentosa is one component of certain hereditary syndromes, notably the Laurence – Moon – Bardet – Biedl syndrome. Thus there may be at least seven or eight distinct genetic varieties of the phenotype. The X–linked form is one of the rarer. All families do not show the expression in female carriers described above. Thus, there seems to be a fully recessive and an intermediate X–linked form; their relation to each other is unknown. The gyrate choroidal atrophy described by Waardenburg (1932) as X–linked was found on further study to be retinitis pigmentosa (Waardenburg, Franceschetti and Klein, textbook, 1961, p. 799). As is reviewed by Jacobson and Stephens, there are some phenotypic differences between families reported; the genetic significance of these differences is unknown.

ALLAN, W. 1937. Eugenic significance of retinitis pigmentosa. *Arch. Ophthalmol.,* 18: 938–947.

FALLS, H. F. 1952. The role of the sex chromosome in hereditary ocular pathology. *Trans. Am. Ophthalmol. Soc.,* 50: 421–467.

JACOBSON, J. H., and G. STEPHENS. 1962. Hereditary choroidoretinal degeneration. Study of a family including electroretinography and adaptometry. *Arch. Ophthalmol.,* 67: 321–335.

McQUARRIE, M. D. 1935. Two pedigrees of hereditary blindness in man. *J. Genet.,* 30: 147–153.

USHER, C. H. 1935. Bowman Lecture: On a few hereditary eye affections. *Trans. Ophthalmol. Soc. U. K.,* 55: 164–245.

WAARDENBURG, P. J. 1932. *Das menschliche Auge und seine Erbanlagen.* Martinus Nijhoff, 's-Gravenhage.

54. *Macular dystrophy*

Halbertsma's pedigree is consistent with X–linked inheritance except for an instance of apparent father-to-son transmission in the first generation. Color blindness also was segregating in Halbertsma's family, but analysis in terms of linkage is impossible because in those males with macular dystrophy the retinal disease may have been responsible for the color blindness. Falls studied a family of X–linked macular dystrophy with affected identical male twins.

HALBERTSMA, K. T. A. 1928. Ueber eine erbliche familiäre Augenerkrankungen. I. Erbliche familiäre Entartung des gelben Fleckes (zusammen mit Farbenblindheit). *Klin. Monatsbl. Augenh.,* 80: 792–812.

FALLS, H. F. 1952. The role of the sex chromosome in hereditary ocular pathology. *Trans. Am. Ophthalmol. Soc.,* 50: 421–467.

55. *Retinoschisis*

Retinoschisis is detachment of the retina due to congenital degeneration. The affected males show cystic degeneration leading to split in the retina, detachment of the retina, and finally complete retinal atrophy with sclerosis of the choroid. Gieser and Falls observed a macular cyst in one eye of a possible female carrier in a kindred with nine affected males and suggested that it might represent an expression of the carrier state.

Hereditary forms of retinal detachment, with and without severe myopia as the underlying mechanism, have been described. One would presume that the disease with myopia is fundamentally distinct from that without myopia. In addition to the X–linked form, autosomal recessive and autosomal irregular dominant forms (the last being most frequent) are known.

Retinoschisis is, in the opinion of Gieser and Falls, the same condition as that described by Mann and MacRae as congenital vascular veil in the vitreous and also the same as the X–linked retinal detachment described by Sorsby and colleagues. Retinoschisis is probably distinct from pseudoglioma, although possibly even this cannot be considered settled. So-called congenital falciform fold of the retina (ablatio falciformis retinae congenita) is probably yet another expression of the same gene as that for retinoschisis. Weve (1938) observed falciform fold and pseudoglioma in the same family.

GIESNER, E. P., and H. FALLS. 1961. Hereditary retinoschisis. Am. J. Ophthalmol., 51: 1193–1200.
KLEINERT, W. 1953. Eine rezessiv-geschlechtsgebundene Form der idiopathischen Netzhautsplattung bei nichtmyopen Jugendlichen. Graefes Arch. Ophthamol., 154: 295–305.
MANN, I., and A. MACRAE. 1938. Congenital vascular veil in the vitreous. Brit. J. Ophthalmol., 22: 1–10.
SORSBY, A., M. KLEIN, J. H. GANN, and G. SIGGINS. 1951. Unusual retinal detachment, possibly sex linked. Brit. J. Ophthalmol., 35: 1–10.
WEVE, H. 1938. Ablatio falciformis congenita (retinal fold). Brit. J. Ophthalmol., 22: 456–470.

56. Pseudoglioma

Only an X–linked form is clearly established. The disorder is a not infrequent cause of congenital blindness. Affected males show detachment of the retina from birth. The picture may simulate glioma of the retina (hence the name), or retrolental fibroplasia. In the family reported by Forssman, pseudoglioma was combined with mental deficiency present from infancy and apparently of progressive nature.

FORSSMAN, H. 1960. Mental deficiency and pseudoglioma, a syndrome inherited as an X–linked recessive. Am. J. Mental Deficiency, 64: 984–987.
WILSON, W. M. C. 1949. Congenital blindness (pseudoglioma) occurring as a sex-linked developmental anomaly. Can. Med. Assoc. J., 60: 580–584.

57. Van den Bosch syndrome

The components of this syndrome transmitted as an X–linked recessive are 1) mental deficiency, 2) choroideremia, 3) acrokeratosis verruciformis, 4) anhidrosis, and 5) skeletal deformity. An interesting and possibly important point is that at least four of these five components have been described as isolated X–linked traits. The syndrome has been observed in a single kindred.

VAN DEN BOSCH, J. 1957. A new syndrome in 3 generations of a Dutch family. In: Genetica della tubercolosi e dei tumori. Atti del "Secundum Symposium Internationale Geneticae Medicae," Torino. Edited Ist. Gregorio Mendel. Pp. 143–144.

58. Menkes syndrome

In a family of English-Irish descent living in New York, Menkes and colleagues (1962) described an X–linked recessive disorder characterized by early retardation in growth, peculiar hair and focal cerebral and cerebellar degeneration. Four males were affected but the gene could by inference be identified in four generations. The failure to grow brought the affected infants to medical attention at the age of a few weeks and death occurred in the first or second year of life. The hair was stubby and white; microscopically it showed twisting, varying diameter along the length of the shaft and often fractures of the shaft at regular intervals. Rather extensive biochemical investigations showed elevated plasma glutamic acid as the only consistent abnormality. The anatomic change in the central nervous system was described on the basis of two autopsies.

MENKES, J. H., M. ALTER, G. K. STEIGLEDER, D. R. WEAKLEY, and J. H. SUNG. 1962. A sex-linked recessive disorder with retardation of growth, peculiar hair and focal cerebral and cerebellar degeneration. Pediatrics, 29: 764–779.

59. Albinism—deafness syndrome

Margolis (1962) has described a "new" X–linked syndrome—deaf-mutism and total albinism. Also from Israel, Ziprkowski and his colleagues (1962) described an X–linked syndrome consisting of deaf-mutism and partial albinism (without ocular albinism). The relationship, if any, between the syndromes remains to be established.

MARGOLIS, E. 1962. A new hereditary syndrome—sex-linked deaf-mutism associated with total albinism. *Acta Genet. Statist. Med.* 12: 12–19.

ZIPRKOWSKI, L., A. KRAKOWSKI, A. ADAM, H. COSTEFF, and J. SADE. 1962. Partial albinism and deaf-mutism due to a recessive sex-linked gene. *A.M.A. Arch. Dermat.,* 86: 530–539.

B. Conditions for which the evidence of X–linkage is considered inconclusive

1. *Inability to smell cyanide*

Initial studies (reviewed by Stern) showed male : female frequencies and family data consistent with X–linked recessive inheritance of inability to smell cyanide. Further studies seem to indicate that the situation is more complex (Kirk).

FUKUMOTO, Y., and COLLEAGUES. 1957. Small ability to smell solutions of potassium cyanide and its inheritance. (In Japanese) *Japan. J. Human Genet.* 2: 7–16.

KIRK, R. L. 1961. Personal communication, University of Western Australia.

——, and N. S. STENHOUSE. 1953. Ability to smell solutions of potassium cyanide. *Nature,* 171: 698–699.

STERN, C. 1960. *Principles of Human Genetics* (2nd edition). W. H. Freeman, San Francisco. P. 232, Table 35.

2. *Incontinentia pigmenti*

Incontinentia pigmenti is a disturbance of skin pigmentation inconstantly associated with a variety of malformations of the eye, teeth, skeleton, heart, etc. The pigmentary disturbance, an autochthonous tattooing, is evident at or soon after birth and may be preceded by a phase suggesting inflammation in the skin. In the fully developed disease, the skin shows swirling patterns of melanin pigmentation, especially on the trunk, suggesting the appearance of "marble cake." The pigmentation gradually fades and is often gone completely by age 20 years. Histologically, deposits of melanin pigment are seen in the corium; the designation was based on the idea that the basal layer of the epidermis is "incontinent" of melanin. Pedigree patterns suggest X–linked dominance with lethality in the male. The phenotype in the affected females might be consistent with random X chromosome inactivation as in the Lyon hypothesis (see text).

The cutaneous phenotype has other interesting features, namely, that in the first months of life it has some characteristics of an inflammatory process and that the pigmentary changes have usually disappeared completely by the age of 20 years. Caffey's disease (infantile hyperostosis), which is familial and possibly genetic, displays a similar behavior, with pronounced signs suggesting an inflammatory process in many bones with subsequent quiescence and in many cases disappearance of all evidence of previous disease.

Cytoplasmic (or other nonchromosomal) inheritance with lethality in the male could account for the pedigree pattern. Features of the histologic and clinical picture have suggested viral etiology to several workers (e.g., Haber). Cytoplasmic inclusions like those of molluscum contagiosum have been identified (Thomas W. Murrell, Jr., personal communication, Richmond, Va.).

As a third possibility, the pedigree pattern is probably consistent also with an autosome/X chromosome translocation. No chromosomal abnormality was found in two cases of incontinentia pigmenti studied by Benirschke (personal communication). In the family studied, the mother and two daughters were affected; there had been one male abortion.

HABER, H. 1952. The Bloch-Sulzberger syndrome (incontinentia pigmenti). *Brit. J. Dermatol.,* 64: 129–140.

LENZ, W. 1961. *Medizinische Genetik. Eine Einfuhrung in ihre Grundlagen und Probleme.* Georg Thieme Verlag, Stuttgart., p. 89.

PFEIFFER, R. A. 1960. Zur Frage der Vererbung der Incontinentia pigmenti Bloch-Siemens. *Z. Menschl. Vererb. Konstitutionslehre,* 35: 469–493.

3. *Wildervanck syndrome*

The Wildervanck syndrome consists of congenital perceptive deafness, Klippel-Feil anomaly (fused cervical vertebrae), and abducens palsy with retractio bulbi (Duane syndrome). The disorder is limited, or almost completely limited, to females, raising the question of sex-linked dominance with lethality in the hemizygous male or one of the other mechanisms discussed with incontinentia pigmenti (B2) and in the text (p. 10).

WILDERVANCK, L. S. 1960. Een cervico-oculo-acusticussyndroom. *Ned. Tijdschr. Geneesk.,* 104: 2600–2605.

——. 1961. A cervico – oculo – acusticous syndrome belonging to the status dysraphicus. *Proc. II Intern. Conf. Human Genet., Rome.*

4. *Male hypogonadism*

Variously termed in the literature are several conditions which affect only persons with the usual male karyotype and are familial with a pattern often suggesting X–linked inheritance. At least five distinct entities are probably involved: 1) male hypogonadism with or without gynecomastia, 2) male pseudohermaphroditism (B7), 3) the testicular feminization syndrome (B6), 4) gynecomastia (C2), and 5) the Kallmann syndrome (B8). As seen later, there may be at least two distinct forms of the testicular feminization syndrome. Male pseudohermaphroditism is also probably a heterogeneous category. The testicular feminization syndrome is indeed a variety of male pseudohermaphroditism. When hypospadias and gynecomastia are associated with hypogonadism, the designation of male pseudohermaphroditism is often attached. Gynecomastia may occur alone as a familial anomaly or be a feature of one of the other three classes. The necessity for studies, genetic and physiologic, to bring order out of this nosologic chaos is evident. Yet another form of male hypogonadism—that associated with ichthyosis (B5)—will be separately discussed.

Sohval and Soffer described mentally deficient brothers with small testes, aspermatogenesis, and gynecomastia. The seminiferous tubules showed no spermatogenic cells. Reifenstein (1947; also quoted by Sohval) found nine of 10 males in two generations of a Syrian family affected. Hypospadias was present in some and seven of the nine had gynecomastia. Peters and colleagues described gynecomastia, inguinal testes, and slight hypogonadal traits in two half-brothers (sons of the same mother) and in a cousin, the son of the mother's sister. One affected male had intercourse and ejaculation. The family of Gilbert–Dreyfus and colleagues is yet another example; maternal uncles were affected. The family pictured in Figure 53 is probably of the same type as that described by all the above mentioned authors. We have recently restudied this family reported by Young (1937). The anomaly is clearly identical to that in Reifenstein's family which we have also restudied recently (see Fig. 54). Since a separate, rather clear-cut entity seems to be represented in these cases, I propose to refer to it as *Reifenstein's syndrome*.

Volpé's cases had eunochoid skeletal features and low urinary gonadotropins, and in addition there was cerebellar ataxia.

There is likely to be heterogeneity left within the group of male hypogonadism even after the types discussed separately hereafter are removed. Some cases may be primary as indicated by high levels of urinary gonado-

tropins whereas others are cases of secondary hypogonadism with low gonadotropins. The cases of Sohval and Soffer and those of Reifenstein were of the primary type.

BIBEN, R. L., and G. S. GORDAN. 1955. Familial hypogonadotropic eunuchoidism. *J. Clin. Endocrinol. Metab.*, 15: 931–942.

BRIMBLECOMBE, S. L. 1946. Bilateral cryptorchidism in three brothers. *Brit. Med. J.*, 1: 526.

GILBERT-DREYFUS, SAVOIE, SEBAOUN, C. ALEXANDRE and J. BELAISCH. 1957. Etude d'un cas familial d'androgynoïdisme avec hypospadias grave, gynécomastie et hyperoestrogénie. *Ann. endocrinol. Paris*, 18: 93–101.

HURXTHAL, L. M. 1943. Sublingual use of testosterone in 7 cases of hypogonadism: report of 3 congenital eunuchs occurring in one family. *J. Clin. Endocrinol. Metab.*, 3: 551–556.

PETERS, J. H., W. K. SIEBER, and N. DAVID. 1955. Familial gynecomastia associated with genital abnormalities: report of a family. *J. Clin. Endocrinol. Metab.*, 15: 182.

REIFENSTEIN, E. C., JR. 1947. Hereditary familial hypogonadism. *Proc. Am. Federation Clin. Res.*, 3: 86; *Recent Progr. Hormone Res.*, 3: 224–225.

SIMPSON, S. L. 1946. Two brothers with infantilism or eunuchoidism. *Proc. Roy. Soc. Med.*, 39: 512–513.

SOHVAL, A. R. and L. J. SOFFER, 1953. Congenital familial testicular deficiency. *Am. J. Med.*, 14: 328–348.

VOLPÉ, R. M, W. S. METZLER, and MacA. W. JOHNSTON. 1963. Familial hypogonadotrophic eunochoidism with with cerebellar ataxia. *J. Clin. Endocrinol.*, 23: 107–115.

YOUNG, H. H. 1937. *Genital Abnormalities, Hermaphroditism and Related Adrenal Diseases*. Williams & Wilkins, Co., Baltimore. Pp. 405–409.

5. *Ichthyosis and male hypogonadism*

In the apparently unique family reported by Lynch and his colleagues five males in three generations showed both secondary hypogonadism (associated with low titers of pituitary gonadotrophic hormones) and congenital ichthyosis. This is classed as a definite X–linked recessive trait because if the syndrome were inherited as an autosomal dominant, the ichthyosis component would be expected to have been displayed by females. The authors suggested that close linkage (p. 33) may be responsible for the occurrence of hypogonadism with ichthyosis, a well-known X–linked trait (No. A24). However, ichthyosis and hypogonadism is listed as a separate mutation since linkage can only be postulated. If indeed the two traits are due to two linked genes one can say with 95 per cent confidence that the recombination value is not greater than 20 per cent. The disorder was transmitted by six females in whom there was opportunity for cross-over.

LYNCH, H. T., F. OZER, C. W. McNUTT, J. E.

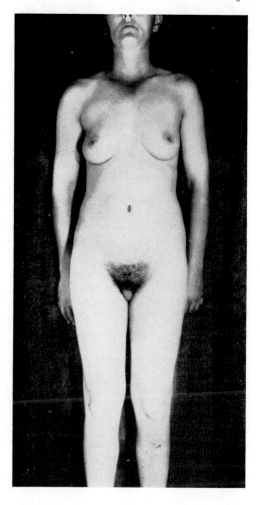

a

FIG. 53. HYPOGONADISM WITH GYNECOMASTIA AND HYPOSPADIAS (REIFENSTEIN'S SYNDROME)

The two brothers shown here were reported by Young in 1937. The older brother (a and b) was 35 years old and the younger (c and d) was 24 at the time of these photographs in 1935. They had identical conditions, as did also two maternal uncles. In addition to hypospadias with chordee, small right testis and undescended testis on the left, there was striking gynecomastia. The distribution of hair was feminine, and they shaved rarely. After correction of the hypospadias and chordee, intercourse was practiced with success and ejaculation occurred. The flattening of the breasts in the younger brother (c) was due to prolonged wearing of a tight binder. (e) Pedigree of the family originally reported by Young (1937).

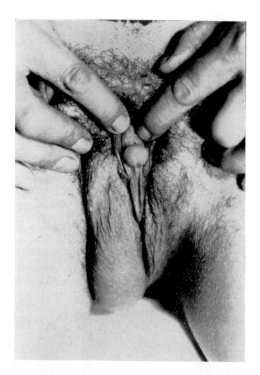

FIG. 53b.

JOHNSON, and N. A. JAMPOLSKY. 1960. Secondary male hypogonadism and congenital ichthyosis. Association of two rare genetic diseases. *Am. J. Human Genet.,* 12: 440–456.

6. *The syndrome of testicular feminization*

This variety of sex anomaly has been of relatively long interest to geneticists largely through the publications of Pettersson and Bonnier (1937). Both the nature of the basic defect and the mode of inheritance are in question. The affected males have female external genitalia, female breast development, blind vagina, absent uterus and female adnexa, abdominal or inguinal testes, and a normal male (2A + XY) karyotype. The patients often come to medical attention because of a presumed inguinal hernia. Many have absent pubic and axillary hair ("hairless pseudofemale"). The hair of the head is luxuriant, without temporal balding. The phenotype is often voluptuously feminine; Netter (1958) reported this disorder in a famous photographic model, Marshall and Harder (1958) reported affected monozygotic twins who worked as airline stewardesses, and Polaillon (1891) observed prostitution.

In one such patient studied by Wilkins (Fig. 55b) the hair follicles of the axillary and pubic areas, although anatomically normal, were unresponsive to local or parenteral exhibition of androgens and the beard, voice, and clitoris are similarly unresponsive. Female carriers, presumed heterozygotes, may show no, or almost no, secondary sex hair but have normal menstruation, conception and pregnancies. The basic defect in cases of the hairless pseudo-female type might be end-organ unresponsiveness to androgen, a situation comparable to nephrogenic diabetes insipidus (No. A16), and pseudohypoparathyroidism (inherited as an autosomal dominant). (These conditions are analogous to the situation in the Seabright bantam cock which has a female comb structure despite obvious demonstrations of viril-

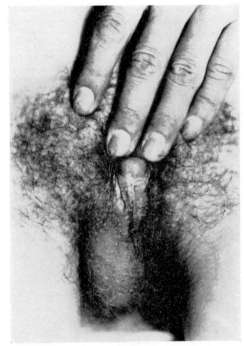

Fig. 53d.

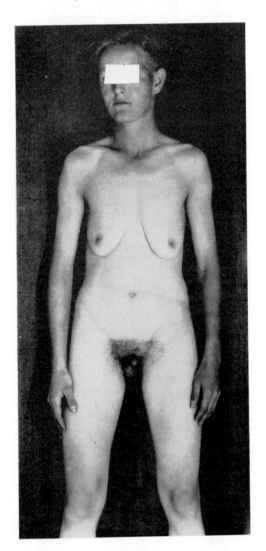

Fig. 53c.

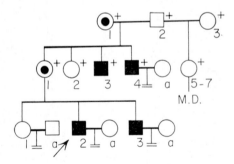

⊥ No issue   + Dead

M.D. Many Descendents

⊙ Presumed carrier

■ Reifenstein's
        syndrome

Fig. 53e.

ity.) An alternative view on the nature of the basic defect in other or all cases is that the testis produces a feminizing hormone (see Southren and Saito). Yet a third suggestion has been that the testis is damaged at an early stage in utero (Lubs, et al.). It is likely that more than one distinct entity is included in the testicular feminization syndrome. Wilkins states: "In about one-third of the cases of male pseudohermaphroditism 'of feminine

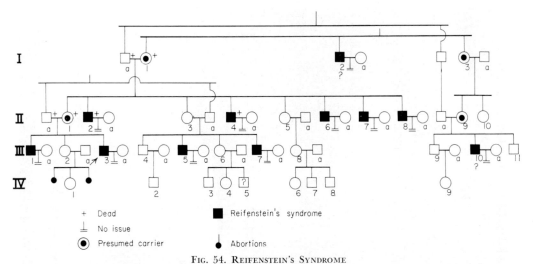

FIG. 54. REIFENSTEIN'S SYNDROME

The pedigree of the family first reported by Reifenstein (1947) and recently reinvestigated is shown here. [Note: II 3 should be indicated as a carrier.]

type' sexual hair has been entirely lacking." Miller considers "feminizing labial testes" of the type described by Lubs, Vilar and Bergenstal (1959) to be a separate form of male pseudohermaphroditism.

The histological changes in the testis in this syndrome tend to be characteristic and not the non-specific ones of cryptorchidism. Furthermore, the degree of feminization appears to be correlated with the degree of change in the testis.

Whether the trait is X–linked or autosomal is uncertain. The evidence from linkage studies is inconclusive (p. 33).

Mainly using data on the frequency of inguinal hernia in females, Jagiello and Atwell estimated the frequency of testicular feminization as being of the order of one in 65,000 males. This value implies a mutation rate of 0.5–0.4×10^{-5} genes per generation (depending on whether the disorder is autosomal dominant or X–linked recessive).

Professor J. McL. Morris, Yale University, called my attention to the following case of Gayral and colleagues (1960): a woman, who was sister, mother, and grandmother of affected males, showed asymmetry in the development of the breasts, body hair, and vulva. The right breast was smaller than the left and there was no pubic hair to the right of the mid-line. She had always had menstrual irregularity but had three children, an affected male, a carrier daughter, and a daughter who was the mother of three unaffected sons. The findings may be best explained by an X–linked recessive (or incompletely recessive) gene whose effects are to render tissues resistant to male hormone.

ALBRIGHT, F., C. H. BURNETT, P. H. SMITH, and W. PARSON. 1942. Pseudohypoparathyroidism, an example of "Seabright-bantam syndrome." Report of 3 cases. *Endocrinilogy*, 30: 922–932.

BURGERMEISTER, J. J. 1953. Contributions à l'étude d'un type familial d'intersexualité. *J. Génét. hum.*, 2: 51.

GAYRAL, L., M. BARRAND, J. CARRIE, and L. CANDEBAT. 1960. Pseudo-hermaphrodisme à type de "testicule féminisant": 11 cas. Etude hormonale et etude psychologique. *Toulouse méd.*, 61: 637–647.

GRUMBACH, M. M., and M. L. BARR. 1958. Cytologic tests of chromosomal sex in relation to sexual anomalies in man. *Recent Progr. Hormone Res.*, 14: 255–334.

HAUSER, G. A. 1961. Testikuläre Feminisierung. In: *Die Intersexualität*, Overzier, I., editor. Georg Thieme, Verlag, Stuttgart.

JAGIELLO, G., and J. D. ATWELL. 1962. Prevalence of testicular feminisation. *Lancet*, 1: 329.

LUBS, H. A., JR., O. VILAR, and D. M. BERGENSTAL. 1959. Familial male pseudohermaphroditism with labial testes and partial feminization: endocrine studies and genetic aspects. *J. Clin. Endocrinol. Metab.*, 19: 1110–1120.

MARSHALL, H. K., and H. I. HARDER. 1958. Testicular feminization syndrome in male pseudohermaphroditism; report of two cases in identical twins. *Obstet. Gynecol.*, 12: 284–293.

MILLER, O. J. 1961. Developmental sex abnormalities. In *Recent Advan. Human Genet.*, L. S. Penrose, editor, pp. 39–55. J. & A. Churchill, Ltd., London.

PETTERSSON, G., and G. BONNIER. 1937. Inherited sex-mosaic in man. *Hereditas*, 23: 49–69.

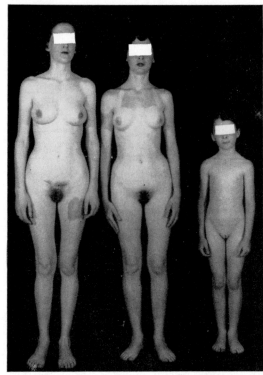 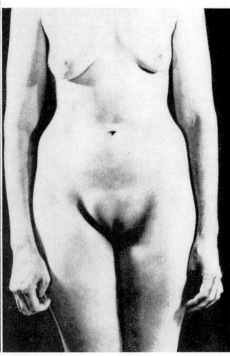

a   b

FIG. 55. TESTICULAR FEMINIZATION SYNDROME

a. Three sibs, ages 24, 19, and nine years. One brother and one sister are normal. Another sib, presumably normal female, died at nine months. The family was discovered when the oldest affected sib was admitted to the surgical clinic for presumed inguinal hernia. Skin graft from the left thigh was used in vaginal reconstruction. The affected persons are more feminine than their normal sister and the oldest of these three is happily married. Hair is rather ample. All three are chromatin-negative. The karyotype has been shown to be XY in one who was included in the report of Alexander and Ferguson-Smith (1961). Linkage studies are presented in Figure 21c, d (This family was described in detail by Jones and Scott (1958) and was restudied with the assistance of Dr. Howard W. Jones.) b. Testicular feminization syndrome, "hairless pseudofemale" type. At age 30 E. L. (423266) came to medical attention because of infertility. She had been happily married for eight years with normal libido and satisfactory intercourse. Testes were located in the inguinal canals. The vagina was blind. No uterus was present. Labial, pubic and axillary hair was totally absent, although the hair of the scalp was normal and a little fine down was located on the extremities. Biopsy of skin from the pubic area showed rudimentary hair follicles. Rubbing the pubis daily with testosterone ointment and methyl-testosterone given by mouth failed to stimulate growth of sexual hair, enlargement of the clitoris, change in the voice, or other clinical effects. Often quoted as evidence that the defect concerns end-organ response to endogenous androgen, this is apparently the only experiment of the type which has been performed in one of these cases. From Wilkins (1957). (Hauser and his colleagues (cited by Nowakowski and Lenz, 1961) were able to stimulate growth of pubic and axillary hair, but the subject was a somewhat atypical case.) Rudimentary Fallopian tubes and uterus were present in this patient and some of the other reported cases of testicular feminization syndrome.

On recent restudy at the age of 45 years, the findings were as described earlier, with total absence of axillary and pubic hair as the striking feature. Her only sib, a half sister by the same mother, had the same condition. The sister was killed in an automobile accident at age 25 years. The mother, who died at age 48 years of age, was born in Finland. The patient has no knowledge of her mother's sibs and other relatives.

PUCK, T. T., A. ROBINSON, and J. H. TJIO. 1960. Familial primary amenorrhea due to testicular feminization: a human gene affecting sex differentiation. Proc. Soc. Exp. Biol. Med., 103: 192–196.

SCHREINER, W. E. 1959. Über eine hereditäre Form von Pseudohermaphrodismus masculinus ("testiculare Feminisierung). Gynaecologia, 148: 355–357.

SOUTHREN, A. L., and A. SAITO. 1961. The syndrome of testicular feminization. A report of three cases with chromatographic analysis of the urinary neutral 17-ketosteroids. *Ann. Internal Med.,* 55: 925–931.

WILKINS, L. 1957. *The Diagnosis and Treatment of Endocrine Disorders in Childhood and Adolescence* (2nd edition). Charles C Thomas, Springfield, Ill.

7. *Male pseudohermaphroditism*

The testicular feminization syndrome is one type of male pseudohermaphroditism and in itself may comprise, as noted above, at least two distinct entities. In addition there is at least one other form in which the external genitalia are ambiguous and masculinization is striking. Testes are the only gonads present. Some cases (for example six of the nine cases in the series of Alexander and Ferguson-Smith) have a rudimentary uterus and Fallopian tubes. The sex chromosome constitution is XY (Alexander and Ferguson-Smith). It will be evident that it is often difficult to know whether cases belong in the general category discussed here or in that of hypogonadism (B4). Whereas the histologic findings in the testis of testicular feminization syndrome is characteristic, those in the form of male pseudohermaphroditism discussed here are only the non-specific ones found in any cryptorchid testis. The defect in male pseudohermaphroditism may involve the male morphogenetic hormone normally produced by the fetal testis.

Male pseudohermaphroditism is familial in many instances, although the now available information on this point is less extensive than for testicular feminization. Multiple affected sibs have been reported by several authors (e.g., Alexander and Ferguson-Smith, Evans and Riley, and Witschi and Mengert). Male-limited autosomal recessive inheritance is not excluded for at least some of the cases, and of course autosomal dominant inheritance is possible if maternal uncles are affected. Assembly of more pedigree data, information on the frequency of consanguinity, and linkage studies may be of value.

In two sibs (L. L. A. 921527 and M. A. 920004) with ambiguous genitalia, testes, and XY karyotype, recently studied in this hospital, we have found that one was Xg(a+) and the other Xg(a−), suggesting no close linkage. The finding may indicate autosomal inheritance.

ALEXANDER, D. S., and M. A. FERGUSON-SMITH. 1961. Chromosomal studies in some variants of male pseudohermaphroditism. *Pediatrics,* 28: 758–763.

BERGADA, C., W. W. CLEVELAND, H. W. JONES, JR., and L. WILKINS. 1962. Gonadal histology in patients with male pseudohermaphroditism and atypical gonadal dysgenesis. Relation to theories of sex differentiation. *Acta Endocrinol.,* 40: 493–520.

EVANS, T. N., and G. M. RILEY. 1953. Pseudohermaphroditism. A clinical problem. *Obstet. Gynecol.,* 2: 363–378.

WITSCHI, E. and W. F. MENGERT. 1942. Endocrine studies on human hermaphrodites and their bearing on the interpretation of homosexuality. *J. Clin. Endocrinol. Metab.,* 2: 279–286.

8. *Kallmann syndrome* (secondary [hypogonadotropic] hypogonadism with anosmia; dysplasia olfactogenitalis [de Morsier]).

Affected males show anosmia and hypogonadism secondary to low gonadotropin production. Transmitting females have partial or complete anosmia. Gonadotropins have to our knowledge not been studied in the carrier females. Affected males at times have children. Unilateral renal agenesis has occurred in some affected males. Anosmia is due to agenesis of the olfactory lobes. Whether a mutation resulting in anosmia is separate from that for the Kallmann syndrome is discussed later (No. B9). As indicated on p. 33, color blindness was also segregating in Kallmann's families. However, the information was too limited to give conclusive evidence on possible X–linkage of this syndrome.

KALLMANN, F. J., W. A. SCHOENFELD, and S. E. BARRERA. 1944. The genetical aspects of primary eunuchoidism. *Am. J. Mental. Deficiency.,* 48: 203–236.

NOWAKOWSKI, H., and W. LENZ. 1961. Genetic aspects in male hypogonadism. *Recent Progr. Hormone Res.,* 17: 53–95.

9. *Anosmia*

Anosmia may be an X–linked dominant trait; no male-to-male transmission has been observed, although only a few affected males have had children (Altricher; Glaser). The main reason for considering anosmia separately is that it is not clear whether it is always merely part of the Kallmann syndrome (No. B8: hypogonadism and anosmia) or may be a distinct mutation. Affected males in Glaser's family in which X–linked inheritance was suggested had "excessive sex interest." It was a Russian Jewish family like those of Kallmann and colleagues (B8). Mainland's family showed autosomal dominant inheritance.

The anatomic basis of anosmia is agenesis of the olfactory lobes. De Morsier collected 28 reported cases of agenesis of the olfactory

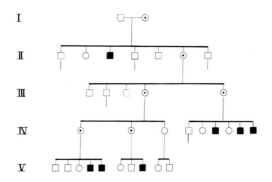

■ · Testicular feminization

FIG. 56. TESTICULAR FEMINIZATION SYNDROME
Full pedigree of the family of the patients pictured in Fig. 55a.

lobes in which complete autopsy was performed and found that abnormalities of the sexual organs, mainly cryptochidism and testicular atrophy, had been noted in 14. He suggested that the genital atrophy is secondary to involvement of the hypothalamus as well as the olfactory lobes.

> DE MORSIER, G. 1954. Études sur les dysraphies crânio-encephaliques; agénésie des lobes olfactifs (télencéphaloschizis lateral) et des commissures calleuse et anterieure (télencéphaloschisis médian); la dysplasie olfacto-génitale. *Schweiz. Arch. Neurol. Psychiat.*, 74: 309–361.
> GLASER, O. 1918. Hereditary deficiencies in the sense of smell. *Science*, 48: 647–648.

10. *Zonular cataract and nystagmus*

Falls reported a family in which this combination of traits appeared to be X–linked. He pointed out that the family was "incompletely studied."

> FALLS, H. F. 1952. The role of the sex chromosome in hereditary ocular pathology. *Trans. Am. Ophthalmol. Soc.*, 50: 421–467.

11. *Myoclonic nystagmus*

This condition may be an X–linked dominant and distinct from simple nystagmus (A46).

In the family described by van Bogaert and de Savitsch, ten sons of four affected men were all normal with the exception of one instance of an affected son of an affected man who was married to a relative; ten of the sons of 13 daughters of affected men were affected.

> VAN BOGAERT, L., and E. DE SAVITSCH. 1937. Sur une maladie congénitale et hérédo-

familiale comportant un tremblement rythmique de la tête, des globes oculaires et des membres supérieurs. (Ses rélations avec le nystagmus-myoclonie et le nystagmus congénital héréditaire.) *Encéphale*, 32: 113–139.

12. *Combined Charcot–Marie–Tooth peroneal muscular atrophy and Friedreich's ataxia*

In the families reported by van Bogaert and Moreau, Charcot–Marie–Tooth disease and Friedreich's ataxia occurred in the same individuals in a pattern of sex-linked recessive inheritance. Possibly this is a mutation distinct from that responsible for the two disorders separately. If the genes for peroneal muscular atrophy and Friedreich's ataxia are closely situated on the X chromosome, deletion is another possible explanation for the finding in this family. In Biemond's kindred some individuals had Charcot–Marie–Tooth disease (in a pedigree pattern consistent with X–linked inheritance), whereas two females of one sibship had Friedreich's ataxia. In addition many members of the kindred had deaf-mutism (in a pattern consistent with autosomal recessive inheritance). Thus, three seemingly independent hereditary traits were observed in the same family. van Bogaert's family is probably the only one in which the two neurologic diseases occurred always together in an X–linked pattern.

> BIEMOND, A. 1928. Neurotische Muskelatrophie und Friedreichsche Tabes in derselben Familie. *Deut. Z. Nervenheilk.*, 104: 113–145.
> VAN BOGAERT, L., and M. MOREAU. 1939–1941. Combinaison de l'amyotrophie de Charcot–Marie–Tooth et de la maladie de Friedreich, chez plusieurs membres d'une même famille. *Encéphale*, 34: 312–320.

13. *Choroidal sclerosis*

In his *Atlas of the Fundus Oculi* (1934), Wilmer showed (Plate 82) the fundus of a 35-year-old affected man whose maternal grandfather was also affected. Furthermore two brothers and the maternal grandfather of the proband's maternal grandfather were also affected, i.e., the proband had inherited the disorder from his great-great-grandfather through the intermediacy of a carrier mother and great-grandmother. Follow-up by letter in 1962 provided no further information.

Stankovic reported a similar family, which is of further interest because female carriers showed partial expression.

A difficulty in interpretation of these reports is the uncertainty that the disorder is distinct from retinitis pigmentosa (A53) and perhaps choroideremia (A52). In retinitis pigmentosa (see Jacobson and Stephens, A53) the fundi are sometimes reported as showing "severe choroidal sclerosis." Because of the uncertainty that choroidal sclerosis is a separate condition, it is listed in the uncertain group.

> STANKOVIC, I. 1958. L'angiosclérose choroidienne familiale liée au sexe. *Bull. Soc. Franc. Ophthalmol.*, 71: 411–417.

14. *White occipital lock of hair*

Only a single pedigree showing X–linked inheritance is known to us—that of Karl Pearson, who stated that the pedigree (redrawn in Fig. 41, retaining Pearson's numbers) was that "of a well-known family."

A case of some interest, the partial albinism, consisting of a white lock, appears to be inherited only through the female and to occur only in the males. II.3 (reported by IV.7), IV.7 and VI.1 had patches of white hair on the back of the head. The patch on VI.1 is about the size of a shilling, it is slightly to the right of the median plane and above the occiput; the skin from which it springs does not appear less pigmented or otherwise differentiated from the adjacent skin. Offspring of V.3 are known to exist and are said not to be affected, but details could not be ascertained. (K. Pearson, Sept., 1909).

> PEARSON, NETTLESHIP, USHER. 1911–1913. *A Monograph on Albinism.* Drapers Company Research Memoirs. Cambridge Press. Fig. 638, Plate LIII, p. 255 of part I.

15. *Diffuse cortico-meningeal angiomatosis of Divry and van Bogaert*

Features in addition to the cortico-meningeal angiomatosis were demyelination of the white substance of the centrum ovale with hemianopsia, and "marbled skin" resulting from a telangiectatic network. Three affected brothers were described.

> DIVRY, P., and L. VAN BOGAERT. 1946. Une maladie familiale charactérisée par une angiomatose diffuse corticomeningée non calcifiante et une démyélinisation progressive de la substance blanche. *J. Neurol., Neurosurg. Psychiat.*, 9: 41–54.

16. *Albright's hereditary osteodystrophy*

This condition comprises both pseudohypoparathyroidism and pseudo-pseudohypoparathyroidism, which are probably aspects of a single entity. The facts 1) that no indubitable

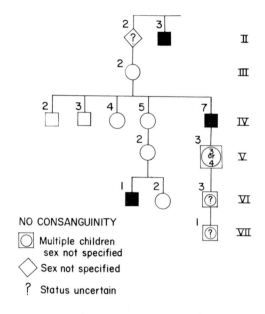

NO CONSANGUINITY

⬡ Multiple children sex not specified

◇ Sex not specified

? Status uncertain

FIG. 57. PEARSON'S PEDIGREE (1913)

instance of male-to-male transmission has been observed and 2) that females are affected twice as often as males support the view that the disorder is an X–linked dominant. On the other hand, hemizygous males are not more severely affected than are heterozygous females. In fact, the tabulation of reported pedigrees (Mann, et al.) shows that whereas only four of 36 female cases were of the incomplete form, six of 14 male cases failed to show full expression. This finding, contrary to that in other X–linked traits and contrary to present concepts on the X chromosome, makes it possible that this disorder is in fact a sex-influenced autosomal dominant.

> MANN, J. B., S. ALTERMAN, and A. G. HILL. 1962. Albright's hereditary osteodystrophy comprising pseudohypoparathyroidism and pseudo-pseudohypoparathyroidism: with a report of two cases representing the complete syndrome occurring in successive generations. *Ann. Internal Med.*, 56: 315–342.

17. *Aptitude for spatial visualization*

Stafford, using the Identical Blocks Test as a measure of spatial visualization, studied 104 fathers and mothers and their 58 teen-age sons and 70 daughters. Males showed higher average scores than females in both the paternal and offspring group. No correlation of scores existed between fathers and mothers and none between fathers and sons. The correlations between fathers and daughters, between mothers and sons and between mothers and daughters was what would be expected on the assumption that the aptitude for visualizing space is an X–linked recessive trait.

> STAFFORD, R. E. 1961. Sex differences in spatial visualization as evidence of sex-linked inheritance. *Perceptual Motor Skills*, 13: 428.

18. *Paine's syndrome* (microcephaly with spastic diplegia)

In the French Canadian family described by Paine (1960) the pattern of inheritance was quite consistent with X–linkage. Myoclonic fits were one feature and another was elevated level of amino acids in the spinal fluid with inversion of the usual ratio of plasma level to spinal fluid level. Autopsy in one case showed an apparent developmental malformation (hypoplasia of the cerebellum, inferior olives and pons), supporting the view that this entity is distinct from the two forms of diffuse sclerosis (Nos. A38 and A39) and from No. A40 which is sometimes accompanied by spastic paraplegia and microcephaly after arrest of the hydrocephalus.

Dr. John H. Menkes has recently shown us a 15-month-old-male patient who presented features suggesting this disorder. A family tree with at least four known affected males in four sibships in two generations is strongly suggestive of X–linked inheritance. Myoclonic fits and elevated spinal fluid amino acids are also present. Autopsy in this case and in other affected members of the family reveals agenesis of the corpus callosum and pronounced hypogyria (J. H. Menkes, personal communication, November, 1962.) This is, then, a condition distinct from Paine's syndrome. Since the pattern of inheritance is quite clearly X–linked, it is likely that this and Paine's syndrome are conditions to be added to the first list.

> PAINE, R. S., Personal communication, Boston.
> PAINE, R. S. 1960. Evaluation of familial biochemically determined mental retardation in children, with special reference to aminoaciduria. *New Engl. J. Med.*, 262: 658–665.

19. *Familial obstructive jaundice of infancy*

McElfresh described a form of neo-natal hyperbilirubinemia in six males of two generations in a pattern consistent with X–linked recessive inheritance. One affected member of the earlier generation was jaundiced with light stools for the first five months of life. He was 31 and well, with two normal children, at the time of report

> McELFRESH, A. E. 1962. Familial obstructive jaundice during infancy. (Abstract) *A.M.A.J. Diseases Children*, 104: 531–532.

20. *Paget's disease of bone*

Montagu reviewed the reported families with multiple instances of Paget's disease of bone and concluded that "when inherited, [it] is transmitted as an incompletely dominant gene carried on an X-chromosome." McKusick reviewed 35 pedigrees reported to 1956 and added two others. In only one family, that of van Bogaert, was there male-to-male transmission. All the persons affected by the bone disease and some members of the family not so affected also had retinitis pigmentosa, which may have been an independent, i.e., coincidental, genetic disorder.

> McKUSICK, V. A. 1956. *Heritable Disorders of Connective Tissue* (1st edition). C. V. Mosby Co., St. Louis.
> MONTAGU, M. F. A. 1949. Paget's disease (osteitis deformans) and heredity. *Am. J. Human Genet.*, 1: 94–95.
> VAN BOGAERT, L. 1933. Ueber eine hereditäre und familiäre Form der Pagetschen Ostitis deformans mit Chorioretinitis pigmentosa. *Z. Ges. Neurol.*, 147: 327–345.

21. *Phosphorylase-deficient glycogen storage disease of liver.*

Williams and Field (1961) found low leukocyte phosphorylase activity in two affected brothers and normal in an unaffected brother and in the father. An intermediately low level in the mother, together with affected males, suggested X–linked inheritance. The finding of affected females by Hers (1959) is against the X–linked hypothesis which deserves further study.

> HERS, H. G. 1959. Études enzymatiques sur fragments hépatiques; application à la classification des glycogénoses. *Rev. Intern. Hepatol.*, 9: 35.
> WILLIAMS, N. E., and J. B. FIELD. 1961. Low leukocyte phosphorylase in hepatic phosphorylase deficient glycogen storage disease. *J. Clin. Invest.*, 40: 1841–1845.

C. Conditions probably not X–linked although this genetic mechanism has been suggested.

1. *Leber's optic atrophy*

Part of the difficulty in studying the genetics of this disorder arises from diagnostic confusion in a disease category which is almost certainly heterogeneous. There are many peculiarities to the familial distribution of Leber's optic atrophy. In Europeans 84.8 per cent of cases are male but in Japanese only 59.1 per cent. In Europeans the peak age of onset seems to be about age 20 years. The disorder is usually transmitted through the mother. Ninety-five per cent of affected males apparently get their disease from the mother, some of whom (about a seventh) are affected whereas the remainder have affected relatives. Eighty-four per cent of affected females get their disease from the mother and about half of their mothers are affected. (See Table below.)

Source of Disease in Hereditary Optic Atrophy (from Bell)

| Source | Affected Offspring | | | |
| | Male | | Female | |
	No.	Per cent	No.	Per cent
Transmission through mother	545	95.1	74	84.1
Mother affected	85	14.8	38	43.2
Relatives of mother affected	460	80.3	36	40.9
Transmission through father	28	4.9	14	15.9
Father affected	23	4.0	12	13.6
Relatives of father affected	5	0.9	2	2.3

Recent studies raise doubts about whether males ever transmit the condition. Furthermore, the interrelationship of a genetic factor with an environmental factor (perhaps tobacco) has been raised (Wilson). The genetic component may well prove to be autosomal. Imai and Moriwaki suggest cytoplasmic inheritance.

BELL, J. 1933. Hereditary optic atrophy (Leber's disease). *Treasury of Human Inheritance* (Part IV), 2: 325.

IMAI, Y., and D. MORIWAKI. 1936. A probable case of cytoplasmic inheritance in man: a critique of Leber's disease. *J. Genet.*, 33: 163–167.

WAARDENBURG, P. J. 1924. Beitrag zur Vererbung der familiären Sehnervenatrophia (Leberschen Krankheit). *Klin. Monatsbl. Augenh.*, 73: 619–652.

WILSON, J. 1963. Leber's hereditary optic atrophy—some clinical and aetiological considerations. *Brain*, 86: 347–362.

2. Gynecomastia

This is, of course, only a manifestation and has many causes. It is a feature of many of the cases of male hypogonadism referred to in B4.

Bonhoff observed gynecomastia with delayed puberty and sparse beard and axillary pubic hair in two cousins whose mothers were sisters. In Ljungberg's family hypogonadism was not a striking feature and male-to-male

transmission of gynecomastia excluded X–linkage. Gynecomastia was reported in identical twins by Eisenstodt and we have observed a pair of identical Negro twins with gynecomastia without hypogonadism or chromosomal aberration.

BONHOFF, F. 1926. Über Ursache und familiäres Auftreten von Gynäkomastie. *Z. Konstitutionslehre*, 12: 528.

EISENSTODT, L. W. 1952. Mastectomy by mammaplasty for gynaecomastia (gynaecomastia in identical twins). *J. Intern. Coll. Surgeons*, 18: 1–14.

LJUNGBERG, T. 1960. Hereditary gynaecomastia. *Acta Med. Scand.*, 168: 371–380.

3. Acrokeratosis verruciformis

Van den Bosch reanalyzed Niedelman's pedigree and concluded that the probability of X–linked dominant inheritance is many times that of autosomal dominant inheritance, even allowing for an *a priori* probability of one in 17 of X–linkage. However, we have recently restudied this kindred and found an affected son of an affected male and three unaffected daughters of affected males (Fig. 58).

NIEDELMAN, M. L. 1947. Acrokeratosis verruciformis (Hopf); report of 14 cases in one family of four generations with review of literature. *Arch. Dermatol. Syph.*, 56: 48–63.

NIEDELMAN, M. L. and V. A. McKUSICK. 1962. Acrokeratosis verruciformis (Hopf). A follow-up study. *A.M.A. Arch. Dermatol.*, 86: 779–782.

VAN DEN BOSCH, J. 1961. New loci on the human X-chromosome. *Proc. II Intern. Conf. Human Genet.*, Rome.

4. The OFD (orofaciodigital) syndrome

Gorlin and colleagues first reported this condition in the English literature. Clefts of the jaw and tongue in the area of the lateral incisors and canines, other malformations of the face and skull, malformation of the hands, specifically syndactyly, familial trembling, and mental retardation are features. All cases are female. Ruess and colleagues state that the sex ratio in affected sibships differs significantly from 1:1 in the direction of 2:1 (F:M). Furthermore, an excessive number of abortions in affected sibships is reported. X–linked dominant inheritance is suggested, with the trait lethal in the hemizygous male. However, Patau and colleagues interpret this syndrome as a partial autosomal trisomy which is lethal in the male. The existence of an autosomal aberration has been claimed in several of the cases studied by this group. The possibility that

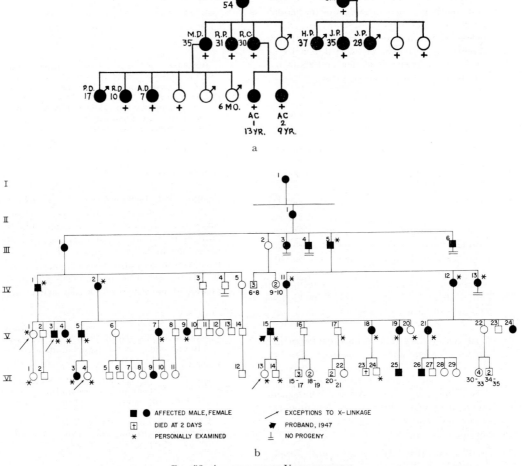

FIG. 58. ACROKERATOSIS VERRUCIFORMIS

a. The pedigree as reported by Niedelman (1947) is consistent with X–linked dominant inheritance. b. Brought up to date (1962) the pedigree does not support X–linked dominant inheritance since male-to-male transmission occurred in one instance and in three instances daughters of affected males were unaffected (see arrows). The spouse of IV 1 is an unaffected and unrelated person of different ethnic origin. The three unaffected daughters of affected males have passed the age when the disease is always manifest. The severity of involvement is of the same degree in affected males and females.

the chromosomal segment inserted into a large autosome was derived from an X chromosome and that the phenotypic changes were the result of position effects were considered unlikely by Patau (personal communication).

GORLIN, R. J., V. E. ANDERSON, and C. R. SCOTT. 1961. Hypertrophied frenuli, oligophrenia, familial trembling, and anomalies of the hand. Report of four cases in one family and a forme fruste in another. New Engl. J. Med., 264: 486–489. See also, Proc. Second. Intern. Conf. Human Genet., Rome, Sept., 1961.

PATAU, K., E. THERMAN, S. L. INHORN, D. W. SMITH, and A. L. RUESS. 1961. Partial trisomy syndromes. II. An insertion as cause of the OFD syndrome in mother and daughter. Chromosoma, 12: 573–584.

5. Plain radial loop on right index finger

Walker suggested that this pattern is sex linked.

WALKER, J. F. 1941. Sex linked recessive fingerprint pattern. J. Heredity, 32: 379–380.

S. B. Holt (personal communication, Galton Laboratory, London) cannot confirm the suggestion of X–linkage.

Csik, L., and J. Mather. 1937. The sex incidence of certain hereditary traits in man. *Ann. Eugenics*, 8: 126–145.

Cunier, F. 1838. Observations curieuse d'une achromatopsie hereditaire depuis 5 generations. *Ann. Oculist.*, 1: 488–489.

Czörsz, B. 1929. *Monatsschr. Ungar. Mediz.*, 2: 180. Cited by E. A. Cockayne. 1933. *Inherited Abnormalities of the Skin and its Appendages*, Oxford University Press, London. P. 213.

Dalton, J. 1798. Extraordinary facts relating to the vision of colours, with observations. *Mem. Lit. Phil. Soc. Manchester*, 5: 28–45.

Darlington, C. D. 1953. Polyploidy in animals. *Nature*, 171: 191–194.

Davenport, C. B. 1906. *Inheritance in Poultry*. Carnegie Institute of Washington, Washington.

———. 1909. *Inheritance of Characteristic in Domestic Fowl*. Carnegie Institute of Washington, Washington.

———. 1911. *Heredity in Relation to Eugenics*. Henry Holt and Company, New York.

Davidson, R. G., H. M. Nitowsky, and B. Childs. 1963a. Glucose–6–phosphate dehydrogenase deficiency studies in human cell cultures. *Pediatrics*, 63: 719.

———, ———, and ———. 1963b. Demonstration of two populations of cells in the human female heterozygous for glucose–6–phosphate dehydrogenase variants. *Proc. Natl. Acad. Sci. U.S.*, 50: 481–485.

Davidson, W. M., and D. R. Smith. 1954. A morphological sex difference in polymorphonuclear neutrophil leucocytes. *Brit. Med. J.*, 2: 6–7.

———. 1960. Sex determination: diagnostic methods. *Brit. Med. J.*, 2: 1901–1906.

———, and P. T. Flute. 1962. Sex dimorphism in polymorphonuclear neutrophil leucocytes. *Acta cytol.*, 6: 13–21.

Davies, S. H., et al. 1963. The linkage relations of hemophilia A and hemophilia B to the Xg blood group system. *Am. J. Human Genet.*, in press.

Day, R. W., S. W. Wright, W. Larson, and J. D. Mann. 1963. Abnormal sex-chromosome complements and the Xg blood-groups. (Letter) *Lancet*, 1: 665.

de Assis, L. M., D. Epps, C. Bottura, and I. Ferrari. 1960. Chromosomal constitution and nuclear sex of a true hermaphrodite. *Lancet*, 2: 129–130.

De Carli, L., F. Nuzzo, B. Chiarelli, and E. Poli. 1960. Trisomic condition of a large chromosome. *Lancet*, 2: 130–131.

De Castro, N. 1963. Frequency variations of "drumsticks" of peripheral blood neutrophiles in the rabbit in different alimentary conditions. *Acta Anat.*, 52: 341.

de Grouchy, J., M. Lamy, H. Yaneva, et al. 1961. Further observations of the X chromosome in primary amenorrhoea or in severe oligomenorrhoea. *Lancet*, 2: 777–778.

de la Chapelle, A., E. Ikkala, and H. R. Nevanlinna. 1961. Hæmophilia A in a girl. *Lancet*, 3: 578–581.

———. 1962a. Chromosomal mosaicism, X chromosome anomaly and sex chromosome discrepancy in case of gonadal dysgenesis. *Acta Endocrinol.*, 39: 175–182.

———. 1962b. Cytogenetical and clinical observations in female gonadal dysgenesis. *Acta Endocrinol. Suppl.* 65, 40: 1–122.

Delhanty, J., J. R. Ellis, and P. T. Rowley. 1961. Triploid cells in a human embryo. *Lancet*, 1: 1287.

DeMars, R. 1962. Sex chromatin mass in living, cultivated human cells. *Science*, 138: 980–981.

Demerec, M., and P. E. Hartman. 1959. Complex loci in microorganisms. *Ann. Rev. Microbiol.*, 13: 377–406.

———. 1961. The nature of the gene. *Am. J. Human Genet.*, 13: 122–127.

Dent, C. E., and H. Harris. 1956. Hereditary forms of rickets and osteomalacia. *J. Bone Joint Surg.*, 38B: 204–226.

Deraemaeker, R. 1958. Sex-linked congenital deafness. *Acta Genet. Statist. Med.*, 8: 228–231.

Derrick, E. H. 1953. The epidemiology of "Q" fever, a review. *Med. J. Australia*, 1: 245–253.

Didisheim, P., and R. L. E. Vandervoort. 1962. Detection of carriers for factor IX (PTC) deficiency. *Blood*, 20: 150–155.

Digby, Sir Kenelm. 1645. *The Immortality of Reasonable Souls*. John Williams, London.

Dock, W. Predilection of atherosclerosis for coronary arteries. *J. Am. Med. Assoc.*, 131: 875–878.

Doncaster, L., and G. H. Raynor. 1906. On breeding experiments with *Lepidoptera*. *Proc. Zool. Soc. London*, 125–133.

———. 1911. Note on the inheritance of characters in which dominance appears to be influenced by sex. *J. Genet.*, 1: 377–379.

———. 1912. Sex-limited inheritance in cats. *Science*, 36: 144.

Dorn, H. 1956. Dominant-geschlechts-chromosomen-gebundener Erbgang bei Trichoclasis: Trichoptilosis in Kombination mit Trichorrhexis nodosa. *Z. Haut- Geschlechtskrankh.*, 20: 129–133.

Doxiadis, S. A., P. Fessas, and T. Vales. 1960. Erythrocyte enzyme deficiency in unexplained kernicterus. *Lancet*, 2: 44–45.

Dronamraju, K. R. 1961. Hypertrichosis of the pinna of the human ear: Y-linked pedigrees. *J. Genet.*, 57: 230–243.

———, and J. B. S. Haldane. 1962. Inheritance of hairy pinnae. (Letter) *Am. J. Human Genet.*, 14: 102–103.

Dubowitz, V. 1963. Myopathic changes in muscular dystrophy carriers. *Proc. Roy. Soc. Med.*, 56: 810–812.

Dunn, L. C., and E. Caspari. 1942. Close linkage between mutations with similar effects. *Proc. Natl. Acad. Sci. U. S.*, 28: 205–210.

Edwards, A. W. F. 1963. Human sex ratio and maternal immunity to male antigen. *Nature*, 198: 1106–1107.

Eichwald, E. J., and E. C. Lustgraff. 1961. Histology of sex-specific graft rejection. *J. Natl. Cancer Inst.*, 26: 1395–1403.

——, C. R. Silsmen, and H. Wheeler. 1957. The genetics of skin grafting. *Ann. N. Y. Acad. Sci.*, 64: 737–766.

Eldridge, F. E., and F. W. Atkeson. 1953. Streaked hairlessness in Holstein-Friesian cattle. A sex-linked, lethal character. *J. Hered.*, 44: 265–271.

Ellis, J. R., O. J. Miller, L. S. Penrose, and G. E. B. Scott. 1961. A male with XXYY chromosomes. *Ann. Human Genet.*, 25: 145–151.

Elves, M. W., and M. C. G. Israëls. 1962. An abnormal large chromosome in a haemophiliac with congenital abnormalities. *Lancet*, 2: 909–911.

Emery, A. E. H. 1963. Clinical manifestations in two carriers of Duchenne muscular distrophy. *Lancet*, 1: 1126–1128.

Eng. L.-I. L. 1962. Glucose-6-phosphate dehydrogenase activity in the red blood cells of monkeys. *Nature*, 195: 1110.

Engel, E., and A. P. Forbes. 1961. An abnormal medium-sized metacentric chromosome in a woman with primary gonadal failure. *Lancet*, 2: 1004–1005.

——, ——, L. C. Mantooth, and E. L. Socolow. 1963. Chromosomal abnormalities associated with diabetes mellitus and Hashimoto's thyroiditis in Turner's syndrome. Paper read at meeting of *Am. Soc. Human Genet.*, New York.

Falconer, D. S. 1953. Total sex-linkage in the house mouse. *Z. Induktive Abstammungs-Vererbungslehre*, 85: 210–219.

——. 1960. *Introduction to Quantitative Genetics*. The Ronald Press Company, New York. p. 21, figs. 1, 3.

——, and J. H. Isaacson. 1962. The genetics of sex-linked anaemia in the mouse. *Genet. Res.*, 3: 248.

Falls, H. F., and C. W. Cotterman. 1948. Choroidoretinal degeneration. A sex-linked form in which heterozygous women exhibit a tapetal-like retinal reflex. *Arch. Ophthalmol.*, 40: 685–703.

Ferguson-Smith, M. A., A. W. Johnston, and S. D. Handmaker. 1960. Primary amentia and micro-orchidism associated with an XXXY sex chromosome constitution. *Lancet*, 2: 184–187.

——, ——, and W. Weinberg. 1960. A chromo-some complement in true hermaphroditism. *Lancet*, 2: 126–128.

——. 1961a. Trisomy of a large chromosome. (Letter). *J. Am. Med. Assoc.*, 175: 414–415.

——. 1961b. Chromosomes and human disease. In *Progress in Medical Genetics*. A. G. Steinberg, editor. Grune and Stratton, New York. Vol. 1.

——, and S. D. Handmaker. 1961. Observations on the satellited human chromosomes. *Lancet*, 1: 638–640.

——. 1962. Chromosome abnormalities as a cause of human infertility. *Fertility Sterility*, 13: 34–46.

Finney, D. J. 1939. Tests for sex-linkage in a quantitative character. *Ann. Eugenics*, 9: 203–207.

——. 1940. The detection of linkage. *Ann. Eugenics*, 10: 171–214.

Fisher, R. A. 1921. On the mathematical foundations of theoretical statistics. *Phil. Trans. Royal Soc.*, London, Ser. A 222: 309–368.

——. 1931. The evolution of dominance. *Biol. Rev. Cambridge Phil. Soc.*, 6: 345–368.

——. 1935. The detection of linkage with "dominant" abnormalities. *Ann. Eugenics*, 6: 187–201.

Forbes, A. P., and E. Engl. 1963. The high incidence of diabetes mellitus in 41 patients with gonadal dysgenesis, and their close relatives. *Metabolism*, 12: 428–439.

Ford, C. E., and J. L. Hamerton. 1956. The chromosomes of man. *Nature*, 178, 1020–1023.

——, K. W. Jones, O. J. Miller, et al. 1959. The chromosomes in a patient showing both Mongolism and the Klinefelter syndrome. *Lancet*, 1: 709–710.

——, ——, P. E. Polani, et al. 1959. A sex-chromosome anomaly in a case of gonadal dysgenesis (Turner's syndrome). *Lancet*, 1: 711–713.

——, P. E. Polani, J. H. Briggs, and P. M. F. Bishop. 1959. A presumptive human XXY/XX mosaic. *Nature*, 183: 1030–1032.

Fraccaro, M., K. Kaijser, and J. Lindsten. 1960a. A child with 49 chromosomes. *Lancet*, 2: 899–902.

——, ——, and ——. 1960b. Letter. *Lancet*, 2: 1303.

——, D. Ikkos, J. Lindsten, and K. Kaijser. 1960b. A new type of chromosomal abnormality in gonadal dysgenesis. (Letter) *Lancet*, 2: 1144–1145.

Fraccaro, M., A. I. Taylor, M. Bodian and G. H. Newns. 1962. A human intersex ("true hermaphrodite") with XX/XXY/XXYYY sex chromosomes. *Cytogenetics*, 1: 104–112.

François, J. 1961. *Heredity in Ophthalmology*. C. V. Mosby Company, St. Louis.

——, F. Gosset, and L. Haustrate. 1956. In *XC delle Leggi Mendeliani.* L. Gedda, editor. Instituto Gregorio Mendel, Rome.

——, and Verriest, G. 1957. État actuel de nos connaissances sur la vision colorée dans le règne animal. *Ann. d'occul.,* 190: 633–683.

Fraser, F. C. 1963. Taking the family history. *Am. J. Med.,* 34: 585–593.

Fraser, G. R. 1963. Parental origin of the sex chromosomes in the XO and XXY karyotypes in man. *Ann. Human Genet.,* 26: 297–304.

Fraser, J. H., E. Boyd, B. Lennox, and W. M. Dennison. 1961. A case of XXXXY Klinefelter's syndrome. *Lancet,* 2: 1064–1067.

Freire-Maia, N. 1957. Inbreeding levels in different countries. *Eugenics Quart.,* 4: 127–138.

Frey, H. G. 1961. Chromosomale Anomalien und die Verebung angeborener Farbensinnstörungen. *Graefes Arch. Ophthal.,* 163: 117.

Frézal, J., J. de Grouchy, M. Lamy, and C. Pignan. 1957. Myopathie et daltonisme. Analyse d'un pedigree. *Ann. Human Genet.,* 21: 237–243.

Frota-Pessoa, O. 1961a. On the number of gene loci and the total mutation rate in man. *Am. Naturalist* 95: 217–222.

——. 1961b. The evaluation of mutation rates of sex-linked genes in man when a carrier test is available. *Proc. II Intern. Conf. Human Genet.,* Rome.

——, and P. H. Saldanha. 1960. The rate of spontaneous sex-linked mutations and the doubling dose in man. *Ann. Human Genet.,* 24: 367–373.

Futterweit, W., M. L. Chapman, J. P. Salvaneschi, and R. E. Moloshok. 1961. Multiple congenital defects in a twelve-year-old boy with cryptorchidism—"male Turner's syndrome." *Metab. Clin. Exptl.,* 10: 1074–1084.

Gartler, S. M., C. Vuzzo, and S. Gandini. 1962. Glucose–6–phosphate dehydrogenase deficiency in an XO individual. *Cytogenetics,* 1: 1–4.

——, S. H. Waxman, and E. Giblett. 1962. An XX/XY human hermaphrodite resulting from double fertilization. *Proc. Natl. Acad. Sci. U. S.,* 48: 332–335.

——, and R. S. Sparkes. 1963. The Lyon-Beutler hypothesis and isochromosome X patients with the Turner syndrome. (Letter) *Lancet,* 2: 411.

Gee, S. 1877. A contribution to the history of polydipsia. *St. Bart's. Hosp. Rep.,* 13: 71–77.

Geitler, L. 1937. Die analyse des kernbaus und der kernteilung der wasserläufer gerris lateralis und gerris lacustris (Hemiptera Heteroptera) und die soma-differenzierung. *Z. Zellforsch. mikroskop. Anat. Abt. Histochem.,* 26: 641–672.

German, J. L., III. 1962a. Synthesis of deoxyribonucleic acid during interphase. *Lancet,* 1: 744.

——. 1962b. DNA synthesis in human chromosomes. *Trans. N. Y. Acad. Sci.,* 24: 395–407.

——, A. G. Bearn, and J. H. McGovern. 1962. Chromosomal studies of three hermaphrodites. *Am. J. Med.,* 33: 83–87.

Giannelli, F. 1963. The pattern of X-chromosome deoxyribonucleic acid synthesis in two women with abnormal sex-chromosome complements. *Lancet,* 1: 863–865.

Giblett, E. R., S. M. Gartler, and S. H. Waxman. 1963. Blood group studies on the family of an XX/XY hermaphrodite with generalized tissue mosaicism. *Am. J. Human Genet.,* 15: 62–68.

Gilbert, C. W., S. Muldal, L. G. Lajtha, and J. Rowley. 1962. Time-sequence of human chromosome duplication. *Nature,* 195: 869.

Gilchrist, L. 1961. A female case of hæmophilia. *Proc. Roy. Soc. Med.,* 54: 813–814.

Githens, J. H., and P. J. Wilcox. 1962. The carrier state in hemophilia. *Pediatrics,* 60: 77–83.

Glass, B. 1954. Genetic changes in human populations, especially those due to gene flow and genetic drift. *Advan. Genet.,* 6: 95–139.

——, and R. K. Ritterhof. 1956. Spontaneous mutation rate at specific loci in *Drosophila* males and females. *Science,* 124: 314–315.

Goldschmidt, R. B. 1955. *Theoretical genetics.* University of California Press, Berkeley. pp. 1–107.

Gorman, J. G., J. Di Re, A. M. Treacy, and A. Cahan. 1963. The application of Xg^a antiserum to the question of red cell mosaicism in female heterozygotes. *J. Lab. Clin. Med.,* 61: 642–649.

Gough, J. H. 1961. Coarctation of the aorta in father and son. *Brit. J. Radiol.,* 34: 670–672.

Gowen, J. W. 1933. Anomalous human sex-linked inheritance of color blindness in relation to attached sex chromosomes. *Human Biol.,* 5: 130–134.

Gowers, W. 1879. Cited by J. Bell. 1943. On pseudohypertrophic and allied types of progressive muscular dystrophy. In *Treasury of Human Inheritance.* Cambridge University Press, New York and London. Vol. IV, Pt. IV, pp. 283–341.

Graham, J. B. 1959a. The inheritance of vascular hemophilia: a new and interesting problem in human genetics. *J. Med. Educ.,* 34: 385–396.

——. 1959b; 1960. Hereditary chronic kidney disease. *Am. J. Human Genet.,* 11: 333–338; 12: 382–384.

——, and C. E. Badgley. 1955. Split-hand with unusual complications. *Am. J. Human Genet.,* 7: 44–50.

——, H. L. Tarleton, R. R. Race, and R. Sanger. 1962. A human double cross over. *Nature,* 195: 834.

GREEN, M. C., and M. M. DICKIE. 1959. Linkage map of the mouse. *J. Heredity*, 50: 3–5.

GRETHER, W. F. 1939. Color vision and color blindness in monkeys. *Comp. Psych. Mono.*, 15: 1–38.

GRÖNHOLM, V. 1921. Ueber die Vererbung der Megalocornea nebst einem Beitrag zur Frage des genetischen Zusammenhanges zwischen Megalocornea und Hydrophthalmus. *Klin. Monatsbl. Augenh.*, 67: 1–15.

GROSS, J. B., E. E. WOLLAEGER, W. G. SAUER, ET AL. 1959. Whipple's disease; report of four cases, including two in brothers, with observations on pathologic physiology, diagnosis, and treatment. *Gastroenterology*, 36: 65–93.

GROSS, R. T., R. E. HURWITZ, and P. A. MARKS. 1958. An hereditary enzyme defect in erythrocyte metabolism: glucose–6–phosphate dehydrogenase deficiency. *J. Clin. Invest.*, 37: 1176–1184.

GRUMBACH, M. M., P. A. MARKS, and A. MORISHIMA. 1962. Erythrocyte glucose-6-phosphate dehydrogenase activity and X-chromosome polysomy. *Lancet*, 1330–1332.

——, and A. MORISHIMA. 1962. Sex chromatin and the sex chromosomes: on the origin of sex chromatin from a single X-chromosome. *Acta Cytol.*, 6: 46–60.

——, ——, and E. H. Y. CHU. 1960. On the sex chromatin and the sex chromosomes in sexual anomalies in man; relation to origin of the sex chromatin. (Abstract) *Acta Endocrinol. Suppl.*, 51: 633.

——, ——, and J. H. TAYLOR. 1963. Human sex chromosome abnormalities in relation to DNA replication and heterochromatization. *Proc. Natl. Acad. Sci. U.S.*, 49: 581–589.

HALDANE, J. B. S. 1930. A note on Fisher's theory of the origin of dominance and on a correlation between dominance and linkage. *Am. Naturalist*, 64: 87–90.

——. 1932. Genetical evidence for a cytological abnormality in man. *J. Genet.*, 26: 341–344.

——. 1935. The rate of spontaneous mutation of a human gene. *J. Genet.*, 31: 317–326.

——. 1936. A search for incomplete sex-linkage in man. *Ann. Eugenics*, 7: 28–57.

——. 1939a. The spread of harmful autosomal recessive genes in human populations. *Ann. Eugenics*, 9: 232–237.

——. 1939b. The theory of the evolution of dominance. *J. Genet.*, 37: 365–374.

——. 1941. The partial sex-linkage of recessive spastic paraplegia. *J. Genet.*, 41: 141–147.

——. 1947. The mutation rate of the gene for hæmophilia and its segregation ratios in males and females. *Ann. Eugenics*, 13: 262–271.

——. 1956. Mutation in the sex-linked recessive type of muscular dystrophy. A possible sex difference. *Ann. Human Genet.*, 20: 344–347.

——, and C. A. B. SMITH. 1947. A new estimate of the linkage between the genes for colour-blindness and hæmophilia in man. *Ann. Eugenics*, 14: 10–31.

HAMERTON, J. L. 1961. Sex chromatin and human chromosomes. *Intern. Rev. Cytol.*, 12: 1–68.

——, V. A. COWIE, F. GIANELLI, ET AL. 1961. Differential transmission of Down's syndrome (mongolism) through male and female translocation carriers. *Lancet*, 2: 956–958.

——, M. FRACCARO, L. DECARLI, et al. 1961. Somatic chromosomes of the gorilla. *Nature*, 192: 225–228.

——, G. M. JAGIELLO, and B. H. KIRMAN. 1962. Sex-chromosome abnormalities in a population of mentally defective children. *Brit. Med. J.*, 1: 220–223.

HANDLEY, R. S., and A. N. NUSSBRECHER. 1935. Hereditary pseudo-hæmophilia. *Quart. J. Med.*, 4: 165–190.

HANSEN-MELANDER, E., and Y. MELANDER. 1963. Sex chromosome dimorphism in germline and soma. *Hereditas*, 49: 48.

HARDISTY, R. N. 1957. Christmas disease in a woman. *Brit. Med. J.*, 1: 1039–1040.

HARNDEN, D. C. 1961a. The chromosomes. In *Recent Advan. Human Genet.*, L. S. Penrose, editor. Little, Brown and Company, Boston. pp. 19–38.

——. 1961b. Nuclear sex in triploid XXY human cells. (Letter). *Lancet*, 2: 488.

——, and C. N. ARMSTRONG, 1959. The chromosomes of a true hermaphrodite. *Brit. Med. J.*, 2: 1287–1288.

——, and P. A. JACOBS. 1961. Cytogenetics of abnormal sexual development in man. *Brit. Med. Bull.*, 17: 206–212.

——, O. J. MILLER, and L. S. PENROSE. 1960. The Klinefelter-mongolism type of double aneuploidy. *Ann. Human Genet.*, 24: 165–167.

HARRIS, H. 1948. On sex limitation in human genetics. *Eugenics Rev.*, 40: 70–76.

——, D. A. HOPKINSON, N. SPENCER, W. M. COURT BROWN, and D. MANTLE. 1963. Red cell glucose-6-phosphate dehydrogenase activity in individuals with abnormal numbers of X chromosomes. *Ann. Human Genet.*, 27: 59–66.

HARRIS, R., and H. M. GILES. 1961. Glucose–6–phosphate dehydrogenase deficiency in the peoples of the Niger delta. *Ann. Human Genet.*, 25: 199–206.

HARVEY, W. 1657. Letter quoted by Sir Archibald Garrod (1928). The lessons of rare maladies. *Lancet*, 1: 1055–1059.

HAUSCHKA, T. S. 1955. Probable Y-linkage of a

histocompatibility gene. Discussion of Eichwald and Silmser's data. *Transplant. Bull.*, 2: 154–155.

——, J. E. HASSON, M. N. GOLDSTEIN, ET AL. 1962. An XYY man with progeny indicating familial tendency to non-disjunction. *Am. J. Human Genet.*, 14: 22–30.

HAY, J. 1813. Account of a remarkable hæmorrhagic disposition, existing in many individuals of the same family. *New Engl. J. Med. Surg.*, 2: 221–225.

HELLER, C. G., and Y. CLERMONT. 1963. Spermatogenesis in man: an estimate of its duration. *Science*, 140: 184–185.

HERRINGHAM, W. P. 1889. Muscular dystrophy of the peroneal type affecting many members of a family. *Brain*, 11: 230–236.

HERS, H. G. 1959. Etudes enzymatiques sur fragments hépatiques; application à la classification des glycogénoses. *Rev. Intern. Hépatol.*, 9: 35.

HERSKOWITZ, I. H. 1950. An estimate of the number of loci in the X-chromosome of *Drosophila melanogaster*. *Am. Naturalist*, 84: 255–260.

HIRSCHHORN, K., W. H. DECKER, and H. L. COOPER. 1960. Human intersex with chromosome mosaicism of type XY/XO. *New Engl. J. Med.*, 263: 1044–1048.

HOGBEN, L. 1932. Filial and fraternal correlations in sex-linked inheritance. *Proc. Roy. Soc. Edinburgh*, 52: 331–336.

HORNER, J. F. 1876. Die Erblichkeit des Daltonismus. Ein Beitrag zum Vererbungsgesetz. *Amtlicher Bericht über die Verwaltung des Medizinalwesens des Kantons Zürich*; Vom Jahr 1876, pp. 208–211.

HSIA, D.-Y., and F. A. WALKER. 1961. Variability in the clinical manifestation of galactosemia. *J. Pediat.*, 59: 872–883.

HUNGERFORD, D. A., A. J. DONNELLY, P. C. NOWELL, ET AL. 1959. The constitution of a human phenotypic intersex. *Am. J. Human Genet.*, 11: 215–236.

HUTT, F. B. 1953. Homologous sex-linked mutations in man and other mammals. *Am. Naturalist*, 87: 160–162.

——, C. G. RICKARD, and R. A. FIELD. 1948. Sex-linked hemophilia in dogs. *J. Heredity*, 39: 3–10.

IKKALA, E. 1960. Hæmophilia. A study of its laboratory, clinical, genetic, and social aspects based on known hæmophiliacs in Finland. *Scand. J. Clin. Lab. Invest.* 12: (Suppl. 46).

INGRAM, V. M., and A. O. W. STETTEN. 1961. Human haemoglobin A₂: chemistry, genetics, and evolution. *Nature*, 190: 1079–1084.

ISRAËLS, M. C. G., H. LEMPERT, and E. GILBERTSON. 1951. Hæmophilia in the female. *Lancet*, 1: 1375–1380.

JACKSON, C. E., W. E. SYMON, and J. D. MANN. 1962. Colour-blindness and blood-group Xgᵃ. (Letter) *Lancet* 2.

JACOB, F., and J. MONOD. 1961. Genetic regulatory mechanisms in the synthesis of proteins. *J. Molecular Biol.*, 3: 318–356.

JACOBS, P. A., A. G. BAIKIE, W. M. C. BROWN, ET AL. 1959a. Chromosomal sex in the syndrome of testicular feminization. *Lancet*, 2: 591–592.

——, ——, W. M. C. BROWN, ET AL. 1959b. Evidence for the existence of a human "super female." *Lancet*, 2: 423–428.

——, M. BRUNTON, W. M. C. BROWN, R. DOLL, and H. GOLDSTEIN. 1963. Change of human chromosome count distribution with age: evidence for a sex difference. *Nature*, 197: 1080–1081.

——, D. G. HARNDEN, W. M. COURT BROWN, and A. G. BAIKIE. 1960a. Comment: trisomic condition of a large chromosome. *Lancet*, 2: 368.

——, ——, ——, ET AL. 1960b. Abnormalities involving the X chromosome in women. *Lancet*, 1: 1213–1216.

——, ——, F. BUCKTON, ET AL. 1961. Cytogenetic studies in primary amenorrhea. *Lancet*, 1: 1183–1188.

——, and J. A. STRONG. 1959. A case of human intersexuality having a possible XXY sex-determining mechanism. *Nature*, 183: 302.

JAEGER, W. 1952. Beitrag zur Frage der Genlokalisation der Farbensinnstörungen. *Graefes Arch. Ophthalmol.*, 152: 385–388.

JAMES, T. N. 1960. The arteries of the free ventricular walls in man. *Anat. Record*, 136: 371–376.

JANSSENS, F. A. 1909. La théorie de la chiasmatypie. *Cellule*, 25: 389–412.

JENNINGS, H. S. 1917. The numerical results of diverse systems of breeding, with respect to two pairs of characters, linked or independent, with special relation to the effect of linkage. *Genetics* 2: 97–154.

JOHNSTON, A. W., M. A. FERGUSON-SMITH, S. D. HANDMAKER, ET AL. 1961. The triple-X syndrome. *Brit. Med. J.*, 2: 1046–1052.

JOHNSTON, A. W., and J. K. PETROKIS. 1963. Mongolism and Turner syndrome in the same sibship. *Ann. Human Genet.*, 26: 407–413.

——, and V. A. McKUSICK. 1962. Sex-linked recessive inheritance of spastic paraplegia. *Am. J. Human Genet.*, 14: 83–94.

JONES, H. W., and W. W. SCOTT. 1958. *Hermaphroditism, Genital Anomalies and Related Endocrine Disorder*. Williams and Wilkins Co., Baltimore. Pp. 172–177.

JOST, A. 1947. Sur les effects de castration precoce de l'embryon male du lapin. *Compt. Rend. Soc. Biol.*, 141: 126–129.

KALLMAN, F. J., W. A. SCHOENFELD, and S. E. BAR-

RERA. 1944. The genetic aspects of primary eunuchoidism. *Am. J. Mental Deficiency*, 48: 203–236.

KALMUS, H. 1955–1956. The familial distribution of congenital tritanopia, with some remarks on some similar conditions. *Ann. Human Genet.*, 20: 39–56.

——, and C. A. B. SMITH. 1960. Evolutionary origin of sexual-differentiation and the sex-ratio. *Nature*, 186: 1004–1006.

——. 1962. Distance and sequence of the loci for protan and deutan defects and for glucose–6–phosphate dehydrogenase deficiency. *Nature*, 194: 215.

KEY, J. A. 1927. Hypermobility of joints as a sex-linked hereditary character. *J. Am. Med Assoc.*, 88: 1710–1712.

KIDSON, C., and J. G. GORMAN. 1962. A challenge to the concept of selection by malaria in glucose–6–phosphate dehydrogenase deficiency. *Nature*, 196: 49–51.

KIRKMAN, H. N. and E. BYNUM. 1959. Enzymic evidence of a galactosemic trait in parents of galactosemic children. *Ann. Human Genet.*, 23: 117–126.

KLINE, A. H., J. B. SIDBURY, JR., and C. P. RICHTER. 1959. The occurrence of ectodermal dysplasmia and corneal dysplasmia in one family. An inquiry into the mode of inheritance. *J. Pediat.*, 55: 355–366.

KLINGER, H. P., and H. G. SCHWARZACHER. 1963. XY/XXY and sex chromatin-positive cell distribution in a 60 mm. human fetus. *Cytogenetics*, 1: 266–290.

KODANI, M. 1957. Three diploid chromosome numbers of man. *Proc. Natl. Acad. Sci. U. S.*, 43: 285–292.

KOLLER, P. C. 1937. The genetical and mechanical properties of sex chromosomes. III. Man. *Proc. Roy. Soc. Edinburgh*, 55: 197–216.

——, and C. D. DARLINGTON. 1934. The genetical and mechanical properties of the sex chromosomes. I. *Rattus norvegicus. J. Genet.*, 29: 159–173.

KOSIN, I. L., and H. ISHIZAKI. 1959. Incidence of sex chromatin in *Gallus domesticus. Science*, 130: 43–44.

KOSOWER, N., R. CHRISTIANSEN, and N. E. MORTON. 1962. Sporadic cases of hæmophilia and the question of a possible sex difference in mutation rates. *Am. J. Human Genet.*, 14: 159–169.

LANMAN, J. T., B. S. SKLARIN, H. L. COOPER, and K. HIRSCHHORN. 1960. Klinefelter's syndrome in a ten month old Mongolian idiot: report of a case with chromosome analysis. *New Engl. J. Med.*, 263: 887–890.

LEE, C. S. N., and P. BOWEN. 1963. Unpublished observations.

LEHMANN, O., and J. FORSSMAN. 1960. Klinefelter's syndrome and mongolism in the same person. *Acta Paediat.*, 49: 536–539.

LEJEUNE, J. 1962. Macy Conference on Genetics, Oct., 1962. To be published.

——, M. GAUTIER, and R. TURPIN. 1959. Les chromosomes humains en culture de tissus. *Compt. Rend.*, 248: 602–603.

——, and R. TURPIN. 1961. Détection chromosomique d'une mosaique artificielle humaine. *Compt. Rend.*, 252: 3148–3150.

LENNOX, B. 1961. Indirect assessment of number of X chromosomes in man, using nuclear sexing and colour vision. *Brit. Med. Bull.*, 17: 196–199.

LENZ, W. 1957. Rotgrün-blindheit bei einem heterogametischen Schein-Mädchen zugleich ein Beitrag zur Genetik der heterogametischen Pseudofemininität. *Acta Genet. Med. Gemell.*, 6: 231–246.

——. 1959. Der Einfluss des Alters der Eltern und der Geburtennummer auf angeborene pathologische Zustände beim Kind. *Acta Genet. Statis. Med.*, 9: 249–283.

——. 1961. *Medizinische Genetik. Eine Einführung in ihre Grundlagen und Probleme.* Georg Thieme Verlag, Stuttgart. P. 89.

LEVAN, A., and T. C. HSU. 1959. The human idiogram. *Hereditas*, 45: 665–672.

LEVIJ, I. S., and P. N. MEULENDIJK. 1962. The localization of sex chromatin. *Lab. Invest.*, 11: 192–194.

LEVIT, S. G. 1936. The problem of dominance in man. *J. Genet.*, 33: 411–434.

LEWIS, E. B. 1950. The phenomenon of position effect. *Advan. Genet.*, 3: 73–115.

LEWIS, J. H., P. DIDISHEIM, J. H. FERGUSON, and C. C. LI. 1963. Genetic considerations in familial hemorrhagic disease. I. The sex-linked recessive disorders, hemophilia and PTC deficiency. *Am. J. Human Genet.*, 15: 53–61.

LEWIS, T. 1933. Material relating to coarctation of the aorta of the adult type. *Heart*, 16: 205–261.

LI, C. C. 1955. *Population Genetics.* Chicago: University of Chicago Press. Pp. 91–93.

LIMA-DE-FARIA, A. 1959. Incorporation of tritiated thymidine into meiotic chromosomes. *Science*, 130: 503–504.

——, J. REITALU, and S. BERGMAN. 1961. The pattern of DNA synthesis in the chromosome of man. *Hereditas*, 47: 695–704.

——. 1963. *The nature and origin of X chromosome aberrations in Turner's syndrome. A cytogenetical and clinical study of 57 patients.* Almqvist and Wilssell, Stockholm.

LINDSTEN, J. 1961. New type of chromosomal mosaicism in ovarian dysgenesis. (Letter) *Lancet*, 1: 1228–1229.

——, and K. G. TILLINGER. 1962. Self-perpetuating ring chromosome in patient with gonadal dysgenesis. *Lancet*, 1: 593–594.

——, P. Bowen, C. S. N. Lee, V. A. McKusick, et al. 1963. Source of the X in XO females: the evidence of Xg (letter). *Lancet*, 1: 558–559.

——, M. Fraccaro, P. E. Polani, et al. 1963. Evidence that Xg blood group genes are on the short arm of the X chromosome. *Nature*, 197: 648–649.

——, ——, D. Ikkos, K. Kaijser, H. P. Klinger, and R. Luft. 1963. Presumptive iso-chromosomes for the long arm of X in man. Analysis of five families. *Ann. Human Genet.*, 26: 383–405.

Little, C. C. 1912. Preliminary note on the occurrence of a sex-linked character in cats. *Science*, 35: 784–785.

——, and M. Gibbons. 1921. Evidence for sex-linked lethal factors in man. *Proc. Soc. Exptl. Biol. Med.*, 18: 111–115.

Lynch, H. T., F. Ozer, C. W. McNutt, et al. 1960. Secondary male hypogonadism and congenital ichthyosis: association of two rare genetic diseases. *Am. J. Human Genet.*, 12: 440–456.

Lyon, M. F. 1961a. Gene action in the X-chromosomes of the mouse (*Mus musculus L.*). *Nature*, 190: 372–373.

——. 1961b. Gene action in the X-chromosomes of mammals including man. *Proc. II Intern. Conf. Human Genet.*, Rome.

——. 1961c. Genetic factors on the X chromosome. (Letter) *Lancet*, 2: 434.

——. 1962a. Attempts to test the inactive-X theory of dosage compensation in mammals. (Abstract) *Ann. Human Genet.*, 25: 423.

——. 1962b. Sex chromatin and gene action in the mammalian X-chromosome. *Am. J. Human Genet.*, 14: 135–148.

Maclean, N., G. Harnden, and W. M. C. Brown. 1961. Abnormalities of sex chromosome constitution in newborn babies. *Lancet*, 2: 406–408.

——. 1962. The drumstick of polymorphonuclear leucocytes in sex-chromosome abnormalities. *Lancet*, 1: 1154–1158.

——, et al. 1962. A survey of sex-chromosome abnormalities among 4514 mental defects. *Lancet*, 1: 293–299.

Macklin, M. T. 1952. Sex ratios in partial sex-linkage. I. Excess of affected females from consanguineous matings. *Am. J. Human Genet.*, 4: 14–30.

Mackson, L. M., R. B. A. Carnaghan, and G. B. Young. 1959. Familial cerebellar degeneration and atrophy—a sex linked disease affecting light Sussex pullets. *J. Comp. Path. Therap.*, 69: 223–230.

Madlener, M. 1928. Eine Bluterfamilie. *Arch. Rassenk Ges. Biol.*, 20: 390–394.

Mann, J. D., A. Cahan, A. G. Gelb, et al. 1962. A sex-linked blood group. *Lancet*, 1: 8–10.

Markert, C. L. 1961. Nucleocytoplasmic interactions during development. In *First International Conference on congenital malformations* M. Fishbein, editor, J. B. Lippincott Company, Philadelphia. pp. 158–165.

Martensson, L. 1963. On "a key point of modern biochemical genetics." (Letter) *Lancet*, 1: 946–947.

Masouredis, S. P. 1960. Rh_0 (D) genotype and red cell Rh_0 (D) antigen content. *Science*, 131: 1442.

Matthey, R. 1951. The chromosomes of the vertebrates. *Advan. Genet.*, 4: 159–180.

——. 1957. Les bases cytologique de l'hérédité "relativement" liée au sexe chez les mammifères. *Experientia*, 13: 341–346.

McClung, C. E. 1902. The accessory-chromosome —sex determinant? *Biol. Bull.*, 3: 43–84.

McGovern, J. J., and A. G. Steinberg. 1958. Anti-hemophilic factor deficiency in the female. *J. Lab. Clin. Med.*, 51: 386–397.

McIlraith, C. H. 1892. Notes on some cases of diabetes insipidus with marked family and hereditary tendencies. *Lancet*, 2: 767–768.

McKusick, V. A. 1960a. *Heritable Disorders of Connective Tissue*. Second Edition. C. V. Mosby Company, St. Louis.

——. 1960b. Walter S. Sutton and the chromosomal basis of Mendelism. *Bull. Hist. Med.*, 34: 487–497.

——. 1962a. The earliest record of hemophilia in America? *Blood*, 19: 243–244.

——. 1962b. Hemophilia in early New England. A follow-up of four kindreds in which hemophilia occurred in the pre-Revolutionary period. *J. Hist. Med.*, 17: 342–365.

——, and S. I. Rapaport. 1962. History of classical hemophilia in a New England family. *A.M.A. Arch. Internal Med.*, 110: 144–149.

Mellman, W. J., I. J. Wolman, H. A. Wurzel, et al. 1961. A chromosomal female with hemophilia A. *Blood*, 17: 719–727.

Merskey, C. 1951. The occurrence of hæmophilia in the female. *Quart. J. Med.*, 20: 299–312.

Milch, R. A. 1960. Studies of alcaptonuria: inheritance of 47 cases in eight highly inter-related Dominican kindreds. *Am. J. Human Genet.*, 12: 76–85.

Miller, O. J., W. R. Breg, R. D. Schmickel, et al. 1961. A family with an XXXXY male, a leukemic male and two 21-trisomic mongoloid females. *Lancet*, 2: 78–79.

——, B. B. Mukherjee, W. R. Breg, and A. Van N. Gamble. 1963. Non-random distribution of chromosomes in metaphase figures from cultured human leucocytes. I. The peripheral location of the Y chromosome. *Cytogenetics*, 2: 1–14.

MILLER, R. W. 1963. Down's syndrome (mongolism), other congenital malformations and cancers among the sibs of leukemic children. *New Engl. J. Med.*, 268: 393–401.

MITCHELL, F. N. and J. E. MITCHELL. 1957. Vitamin–D–resistant rickets. *A.M.A. J. Diseases Children*, 93: 385–390.

MITTWOCH, U. 1961. Properties of X chromosomes. (Letter) *Lancet*, 2: 880–000.

——. 1963. Barr bodies and nuclear size in cultured human fibroblasts. *Nature*, 198: 975–977.

——, and J. D. A. DELHANTY. 1961. Nuclear sex in triploid XXY human cells. (Letter) *Lancet*, 2: 552.

MONEY, J. 1963. Cytogenetic and psychosexual incongruities with a note on space-form blindness. *Am. J. Psychiat.*, 119: 820–827.

MONTAGU, M. F. A. 1963. *The Natural Superiority of Women*. The Macmillan Company, New York.

MORGAN, L. V. 1922. Non criss-cross inheritance in *Drosophilia melanogaster*. *Biol. Bull.*, 42: 267–274.

MORGAN, T. H. 1910a. The method of inheritance of two sex-limited characters in the same animal. *Proc. Soc. Exptl. Biol. Med.*, 8: 17–19.

——. 1910b. Sex-limited inheritance in *Drosophilia*. *Science*, 32: 120–122.

——. 1911a. The application of the conception of pure lines to the sex-limited inheritance and to the sexual dimorphism. *Am. Naturalist*, 45: 65–89.

——. 1911b. An attempt to analyse the constitution of the chromosomes on the basis of sex-limited inheritance in *Drosophilia*. *J. Exptl. Zool.*, 11: 365–413.

——. 1913. *Heredity and Sex*. Columbia University Press, New York.

MORISHIMA, A. and M. M. GRUMBACH. 1961. Karotypic analysis in a case of Turner's syndrome in a phenotypic male. (Abstract) *A.M.A. J. Diseases Children*, 102: 585–586.

——, ——, and J. H. TAYLOR. 1962. Asynchronous duplication of human chromosomes and the origin of sex chromatin. *Proc. Natl. Acad. Sci. U. S.*, 48: 756–763.

MORTON, N. E. 1955. Non-randomness in consanguinous marriage. *Ann. Human Genet.*, 20: 116–134.

——. 1957. Further scoring types in sequential linkage tests with a critical review of autosomal and partial sex linkage in man. *Am. J. Human Genet.*, 9: 55–75.

——. 1961. Morbidity of children from consanguineous marriage. In *Progress in Medical Genetics* (Vol. 1), A. G. Steinberg, editor. Grune and Stratton, New York, pp. 261–291.

——. 1962. Segregation and linkage. In *Methodology in Human Genetics*, Walker J. Burdette, editor, Holden-Day, Inc., San Francisco, California.

——, J. F. CROW, and H. J. MULLER. 1956. An estimate of the mutational damage in man from data on consanguineous marriage. *Proc. Natl. Acad. Sci. U. S.*, 42: 855–863.

——, and C. S. CHUNG. 1959. Formal genetics of muscular dystrophy. *Am. J. Human Genet.*, 11: 360.

MOTULSKY, A. G. 1960. Metabolic polymorphisms and the role of infectious diseases in human evolution. *Human Biol.*, 32: 28–162.

——. 1961. Glucose–6–phosphate dehydrogenase deficiency, hemolytic disease of the newborn and malaria. (Letter) *Lancet*, 1: 1168–1169.

MULDAL, S., and G. H. OCKEY. 1960. The "double male": a new chromosome constitution in Klinefelter's syndrom. *Lancet*, 2: 492–493.

——, and ——. 1961. The Denver classification and group III. *Lancet*, 2: 462–463.

MULDAL, S., C. W. GILBERT, L. G. LAJTHA, J. LINDSTEN, J. ROWLEY, and M. FRACCARO. 1963. Tritiated thymidine incorporation in an isochromosome for the long arm of the X chromosome in man. *Lancet*, 1: 861–863.

MULLER, H. J. 1947–1948. Evidence of the precision of genetic adaptation. *Harvey Lectures Ser. 43*, 165–229.

MURAKAMI, V., K. OKABA, and K. TAKIKAWA. 1951. A pedigree with both hæmophilia and color blindness. Crossing over between these genes. *Nagoya J. Med. Sci.*, 14: 58–61.

MURPHY, E. A., R. W. SHERWIN, and M. F. GLYNN. A note on the rate of equilibrium for two X-linked loci. To be published.

MUSTARD, J. F., H. C. ROWSELL, G. A. ROBINSON, ET AL. 1960. Canine hæmophilia B (Christmas disease). *Brit. J. Haematol.*, 6: 259–266.

NASSE, C. F. 1820. Von einer erblichen Neigung zu tödlichen Blutungen. *Arch. Med. Erfahrung Geb. Praktischen Med. Staatsarzneikunde*, May–June, p. 385.

NEEL, J. V. 1961a. A geneticist looks at modern medicine. *Harvey Lectures, Ser. 56*, 127–150.

——. 1961b. The hemoglobin genes: A remarkable example of the clustering of related genetic functions on a single mammalian chromosome. *Blood*, 18: 769–777.

——, and R. H. POST. 1963. Transitory "positive" selection for color blindness. *Eugenics Quart.*, 10: 33–35.

——, and W. J. SCHULL. 1954. *Human Heredity*. University of Chicago Press, Chicago. pp. 58.

NILÉHN, J.-E. and I. M. NILSSON. 1962. Hæmophilia B in a girl. *Thromb. Diath. Hæmorrhag.*, 7: 552–558.

NILSSON, I. M., S. BERGMAN, J. REITALU, and J. WALDENSTRÖM. 1959. Hæmophilia A in a "girl" with male sex-chromatin pattern. *Lancet*, 2: 264–266.

——, M. BLOMBÄCK, O. RAMGREN, and I. V. FRANCKEN. 1962. Hæmophilia in Sweden. II. Carriers of hæmophilia A and B. *Acta Med. Scand.*, 171: 223–235.

NISHIMURA, E. T., H. B. HAMILTON, T. Y. KOBARA, ET AL. 1959. Carrier state in human actalasemia. *Science*, 130: 333–334.

NORTON, H. W. 1949. Estimation of linkage in Rucker's pedigree of nystagmus and color blindness. *Am. J. Human Genet.*, 1: 55–65.

NOSSEL, H. L., R. K. ARCHER, and R. G. MACFARLANE. 1962. Equine hæmophilia: report of a case and its response to multiple infusions of heterospecific AHG. *Brit. J. Hæmat.*, 8: 335–342.

NOWAKOWSKI, H. and W. LENZ. 1961. Genetic aspects in male hypogonadism. *Recent Progr. Hormone Res.*, 17: 53–95.

——, ——, and J. PARADA. 1959. Discrepanz zwischen Chromatin-Befund und genetischem Geschlecht beim Klinefelter Syndrom. *Acta Endocrinol.*, 30: 296–320.

O'BRIEN, J. R., J. B. HARRIS, R. R. RACE, R. SANGER and OTHERS. 1962. Hæmophilia (VIII) and the Xg blood-groups. *Lancet*, 1: 1026.

OHNO, S. 1962. More about the mammalian X chromosome. (Letter) *Lancet*, 2: 152–153.

——. 1961a. Properties of X Chromosomes. (Letter) *Lancet*, 2: 723–724.

——. 1961b. Sex chromosomes and microchromosomes of *Gallus domesticus*. *Chromosoma*, 11: 484–498.

——. 1963a. Dynamics of the condensed female X-chromosome. *Lancet*, 1: 273–274.

——. 1963b. Dynamics of the condensed female C chromosome. (Letter) *Lancet*, 1: 273.

——, and B. M. CATTANACH. 1963. Cytological study of an X-autosome translocation in *mus musculus*. *Cytogenetics*, 1: 129–140.

——, and T. S. HAUSCHKA. 1960. Allocycly of the X-chromosome in tumors and normal tissues. *Cancer Res.*, 20: 541–545.

——, W. D. KAPLAN, and R. KINOSITA. 1956. Concentration of RNA on the heteropycnotic XY bivalent of the rat. *Exptl. Cell Res.*, 11: 520–526.

——, ——, and ——. 1957a. Conjugation of the heteropycnotic X and Y chromosomes of the rat spermatocyte. *Exptl. Cell Res.*, 12: 395–397.

——, ——, and ——. 1957b. Heterochromatic regions and nucleolus organizers in chromosomes of the mouse, *Mus musculus*. *Exptl. Cell Res.*, 13: 358–364.

——, ——, and ——. 1959a. Formation of the sex chromatin by a single X-chromosome in liver cells of *Rattus norvegius*. *Exptl. Cell Res.*, 18: 415–418.

——, ——, and ——. 1959b. On the end-to-end association of the X and Y chromosomes of *Mus musculus*. *Exptl. Cell Res.*, 18: 282–290.

——, ——, and ——. 1959c. Do XY and O sperm occur in *Mus musculus*? *Exptl. Cell Res.*, 18: 382–384.

——, ——, and ——. 1959d. On the sex chromatin of *Gallus domesticus*. *Exptl. Cell Res.*, 19: 180–183.

——, ——, and ——. 1960. On the isopycnotic behavior of the XX-bivalent in cocytes of *Rattus norvegicus*. *Exptl. Cell Res.*, 19: 637–639.

——, ——, and ——. 1961. Female germ cells of man. *Exptl. Cell Res.*, 24: 106–110.

——, H. P. KLINGER and N. B. ATKIN. 1962. Human oögenesis. *Cytogenetics*, 1: 42–51.

——, J. M. TRUJILLO, C. STENIUS, L. C. CHRISTIAN, and R. L. TEPLITZ. 1962. Possible germ cell chimeras among newborn dizygotic twin calves (*Bos taurus*). *Cytogenetics*, 1: 258–265.

——, and S. MAKINO. 1961. The single-X nature of sex chromatin in man. *Lancet*, 1: 78–79.

——, and C. WEILER. 1961. Sex chromosome behavior pattern in germ and somatic cells of *Mesocricetus auratus*. *Chromosoma*, 12: 362–373.

——, ——, and C. STENIUS. 1961. Nucleolus-organizer in guinea pig. *Exptl. Cell Res.*, 25: 498–503.

OREL, H. 1929. Die Vererbung von Ichthyosis congentia und der Ichthyosis vulgaris. *Z. Kinderheilk.*, 47: 312–340.

OSLER, W. 1885. *A System of Practical Medicine*, Vol. 3, W. Pepper, editor. Lea Brothers, Philadelphia. pp. 882–973.

OSWALD, A. 1911. Hereditary tendency to defective sight in males only of a family. *Brit. Med. J.*, 1: 18.

OTTO, J. C. 1803. An account of an hæmorrhagic disposition existing in certain families. *Med. Repository*, 6: 1.

OWEN, D. C. L. 1882. An illustration of hereditary nystagmus. *Ophthalmol. Rev.*, 1: 239–242.

PAGENSTECHER, H. A., 1878. Erblichkeit der Hemeralopie. *Beilage Zentralb. praktische Augenheilk.*, 2: 40–00.

PAIGEN, K. and W. K. NOELL. 1961. Two linked genes showing a similar timing in mice. *Nature*, 190: 148–150.

PAINTER, T. 1924. The sex chromosomes of man. *Am. Naturalist*, 58: 506–524

PARK, W. W. 1957. The occurrence of sex chromatin in early human and macaque embryos, *J. Anat.*, 91: 369–373.

PARKES, A. S. 1956. *Marshall's Physiology of Reproduction.* Vol. 1. Longmans, New York. Pp. 425–427.

PATAU, K. 1960. The identification of individual chromosomes, especially in man. *Am. J. Human Genet.,* 12: 250–276.

——, E. THERMAN, S. L. INHORN, ET AL. 1961. Partial-trisomy syndromes. II. An insertion as cause of a OFD syndrome in mother and daughter. *Chromosoma,* 12: 573–584.

PEARL, R. and F. M. SUFFACE. 1910. Further data regarding the sex-limited inheritance of the barred color patterns in poultry. *Science,* 32: 870–874.

PEARSON, C. M., W. M. FOWLER, and S. W. WRIGHT. 1963. X-chromosome mosaicism in females with muscular dystrophy. *Proc. Natl. Acad. Sci. U.S.,* 50: 24–31.

PENROSE, L. S. 1955. Parental age and mutation. *Lancet,* 2, 312–313.

——. 1961. Mutation. *Recent Advan. Human Genet.* L. S. Penrose, editor. Little, Brown and Company, Boston. pp. 1–18.

——. 1963. Finger-prints, palms and chromosomes. *Nature,* 197: 933–938.

——, and J. DELHANTY. 1961. Triploid cell cultures from a macerated foetus. *Lancet,* 1: 1261–1262.

——, and C. STERN. 1958. Reconsideration of the Lambert pedigree (icthyosis hystrix gravior). *Ann. Human Genet.,* 22: 258–283.

PERKOFF, G. T., C. A. NUGENT, JR., D. A. DOLOWITZ, ET AL. 1958. A follow-up study of hereditary chronic hereditary chronic nephritis. *A.M.A. Arch. Internal Med.,* 102: 733–746. Also *Am. J. Human Genet.,* 12: 381–382. (1960)

PETERS, J. A. 1959. editor. *Classic Papers in Genetics.* Prentice-Hall, Englewood Cliffs, N. J.

PHILIP, U. 1955. On the inheritance of muscular dystrophy. A note on colour vision and linkage studies. *Ann. Human Genet.,* 20: 16–17.

——, and J. N. Walton. 1956. Colour blindness and the Duchenne-type of muscular dystrophy. *Ann. Human Genet.,* 21: 155–158.

PINKERTON, J. H. M., D. G. McKAY, E. C. ADAMS, and A. T. HERTIG. 1961. Development of the human ovary—a study using histochemical technics. *Obstet. Gynec.,* 18: 152–181.

PLATT, SIR R. 1961. Concepts of medicine. In *Collection of Essays on Aspects of Medicine.* B. Lush, editor. Pergamon Press, New York.

POLA, V. and J. SVOJITKA. 1957. Klassische Hämophilie bei Frauen. *Folia Hæmatol.,* 75: 43–51.

POLANI, P. E. 1960. In *Molecular Genetics and Human Disease.* L. T. Gardner, editor. Charles C Thomas, Springfield, Ill. Pp. 153–178.

——. 1961. Turner's syndrome and allied conditions: Clinical features and chromosome abnormalities. *Brit. Med. Bull.,* 17: 200–205.

——. 1962. In *Chromosomes in Medicine.* Ed. J. L. Hamerton. Wm. Heinemann, Ltd., London.

——. 1963. Chromosome aberrations and birth defects. In *Birth Defects,* M. Fishbein, editor, Chapter 14, J. B. Lippincott Co., Philadelphia, Pennsylvania.

——, P. M. F. BISHOP, B. LENNOX, ET AL. 1958. Colour vision studies and the X-chromosome of patients with Klinefelter syndrome. *Nature,* 182: 1092–1093.

——, and J. L. HAMERTON 1961. Genetic factors on the X chromosome. (Letter) *Lancet,* 2: 262–263.

——, M. H. LESSOF, and P. M. F. BISHOP. 1956. Colour-blindness in "ovarian agenesis" (gonadal dysplasia). *Lancet,* 2: 118–120.

POPIVANOV, R., and V. H. VULCHANOV. 1962. Segregation of man's AB-group spermatozoa in A- and B- spermatozoa through agglutination with immune anti-A rabbit serum. *Z. Immunitaetsforsch.,* 124: 206–210.

PORTER, I. H., J. SCHULZE, and V. A. McKUSICK. 1962. Linkage of glucose–6–phosphate dehydrogenase and colour-blindness. *Nature,* 193: 506.

PORTER, I. H., J. SCHULZE, and V. A. McKUSICK. 1962. Genetic linkage between the loci for glucose–6–phosphate dehydrogenase deficiency and colour-blindness in American Negroes. *Ann. Human Genet.,* 20: 107–122.

POST, R. H. 1962. Population differences in red and green color vision deficiency: a review, and a query on selection relaxation. *Eugenics. Quart.,* 9: 131–146.

PRIESTLEY, J. 1777. An account of persons who could not distinguish colours. (Letter from J. Huddart). *Phil. Trans. Roy. Soc. London,* 67: 260–265.

PUITE, R. H., and H. TESLUK. 1953. Whipple's disease. *Am. J. Med.,* 19: 383–400.

PUNNETT, R. C. 1950. Early days of genetics. *Heredity,* 4: 1–10.

QUICK, A. J. 1960. Sporadic hemophilia. *Arch. Internal Med.,* 106: 335–340.

RABOCH, J., and I. SIPOVA. 1961. The mental level in 47 cases of "true Klinefelter's syndrome." *Acta Endocrinol.,* 36: 404–408.

RACCUGLIA, G., and J. V. NEEL. 1960. Congenital vascular defect associated with platelet abnormality and antihemophilic factor deficiency. *Blood,* 15: 807–829.

RAPAPORT, S. I., M. J. PATCH, and F. J. MOORE. 1960. Antihemophilic globulin levels in carriers of hemophilia A. *J. Clin. Invest.,* 39: 1619–1625.

——, R. R. PROCTOR, M. J. PATCH, and M. YETTRA. 1961. The mode of inheritance of PTA deficiency: evidence for the existence of major PTA deficiency and minor PTA deficiency. *Blood.* 18: 149–165.

RATH, B. V. 1938. Rotgrünblindheit in der Calmbacker Blutersippe. *Arch. Rass.- Ges. Biol.*, 32: 397–406.

RAYLEIGH, LORD. 1881. Experiments on colour. *Nature*, 25: 64–66.

REED, T. E., N. E. SIMPSON, and B. CHOWN. 1963. The Lyon hypothesis. (Letter) *Lancet*, 2: 467–468.

RENKONEN, K. O. 1963. Human sex ratio and maternal immunity to male antigen. *Nature*, 198: 1107–1108.

——, O. MÄKELÄ, and R. LEHTOVAARA. 1962. Factors affecting the human sex ratio. *Nature*, 194: 308–309.

RENPENNING, H., J. W. GERRARD, W. A. ZALESKI, and T. TABATA. 1962. Familial sex-linked mental retardation. *Canad. Med. Assoc. J.*, 87: 954–956. (See also, DUNN, L. C., H. RENPENNING, et al., *Am. J. Mental Def.*, 67: 827, 1963.)

RENWICK, J. H., and J. SCHULZE. 1961. A computer programme for the processing of linkage data from large pedigrees. *Proc. II Intern. Conf. Human Genet.*, Rome.

RHOADES, M. M. 1961. Meiosis. In *The Cell*, J. Brachet and A. E. Mirsky, editors. Academic Press, New York and London. pp. 1–75.

RICHTERICH, R., S. ROSIN, V. AEBI, and E. ROSSI. 1963. Progressive muscular dystrophy. V. The identification of the carrier state in the Duchenne type by serum creatine kinase determination. *Am. J. Human Genet.*, 15: 133–154.

RIDDEL, W. J. B. 1938. A hæmophilia and colourblind pedigrees. *J. Genet.*, 36: 45–51.

RIDLER, M. A. C., A. SCHAPIRO, and W. R. McKIBBEN. 1963. Sex chromatin abnormalities in female subnormal patients. *Brit. J. Psychiat.*, 109: 390–394.

ROBBINS, R. B. 1918. Some applications of mathematics to breeding problems III. *Genetics* 3: 375–389.

ROBERTS, E. 1929. The inheritance of anhidrosis associated with anadontia. *J. Am. Med. Assoc.*, 93: 277–279.

ROBINSON, A., ED. 1960. Proposed standard system of nomenclature of human mitotic chromosomes. *New Engl. J. Med.*, 262: 1245–1246: *Eugenics Quart.*, 7: 96–100; *J. Am. Med. Assoc.*, 174: 159–162.

ROOSEN-RUNGE, E. C. 1962. The process of spermatogenesis in mammals. *Biol. Rev.*, 37: 343–377.

ROSENBERG, H. S., G. W. CLAYTON, and T. C. HSU. 1963. Familial true hermaphroditism. *J. clin. Endocrinol. Metab.*, 23: 203–206.

ROSENFELD, L. 1959. Renal agenesis. (Questions and answers) *J. Am. Med. Assoc.*, 170: 1247.

ROSIN, S., J. K. MOOR-JANKOWSKI, and M. SCHNEEBERGER. 1958. Die Fertilität im Bluterstamm von Tenna (Hämophilie B). *Acta Genet. Statist. Med.*, 8: 186–208.

ROSTAND, J. 1961. *Human Heredity.* Philosophical Library, New York.

ROTHSCHILD, RT. HON. LORD. 1960. X and Y spermatozoa. *Nature*, 187: 253–254.

ROWLEY, J., S. MULDAL, C. W. GILBERT, et al. 1963. Synthesis of deoxyribonucleic acid on X–chromosomes of an XXXXY male. *Nature*, 197: 251–252.

RUCKER, C. W. 1949. Sex-linked nystagmus associated with red-green color-blindness. *Am. J. Human Genet.*, 1: 52–54.

RUSSELL, L. B. 1961. Genetics of mammalian sex chromosomes. *Science*, 133: 1795–1803.

——. 1962. Chromosome aberrations in experimental mammals. In *Progress in Medical Genetics*, A. G. Steinberg, editor, Vol. II, pp. 230–294, Grune and Stratton, New York, New York.

——. 1963. Mammalian X chromosome action: inactivation limited in spread and in region of origin. *Science*, 140: 976–978.

——, and J. W. BANGHAM. 1961. Variegated-type position effects in the mouse. *Genetics*, 46: 509–525.

——, and E. H. CHU. 1961. An XXY male in the mouse. *Proc. Natl. Acad. Sci. U.S.*, 47: 571–575.

——, and C. L. SAYLORS. 1960. Factors causing a high frequency of mice having the XO chromosome constitution. (Abstract) *Science*, 131: 1321–1322.

——, and ——. 1962. Induction of paternal sex chromosome losses by irradiation of mouse spermatozoa. *Genetics*, 47: 7–10.

RUSSELL, W. L., L. B. RUSSELL, and J. S. GOWER. 1959. Exceptional inheritance of a sex-linked gene in the mouse explained on the basis that X/O sex chromosome constitution is female. *Proc. Natl. Acad. Sci. U.S.*, 45: 554–560.

SACHS, L. 1954. Sex-linkage and the sex chromosomes in man. *Ann. Eugenics*, 18: 255–261.

SAKSELA, E., and P. S. MOORHEAD. 1962. Enhancement of secondary constrictions and the heterochromatic X in human cells. *Cytogenetics*, 1: 225–244.

SANDBERG, A. A., L. N. CROSSWHITE, and E. GORDY. 1960. Trisomy of a large chromosome. *J. Am. Med. Assoc.*, 174: 221–225.

——, G. F. KROEPF, L. H. CROSSWHITE, and T. S. HAUSCHKA. 1960. The chromosome constitution of human marrow in various developmental blood disorders. *Am. J. Human Genet.*, 12: 231–249.

SANGER, R., and R. R. RACE. 1962. Personal communication, cited by Gorman, et al. (1963).

——, and ——. 1963. The Xg blood groups and familial hypogammaglobulinemia. *Lancet*, 1: 859–860.

SANGHVI, L. D., D. S. VARDE, and H. R. MASTER.

1956. Frequency of consanguineous marriage in twelve endogamous groups in Bombay. *Acta Genet. Statist. Med.*, 6: 41–49.

SARKER, S. S., A. R. BANERJEE, P. BHATTACHARJEE, and C. STERN. 1961. A contribution to the genetics of hypertrichosis of the ear rims. *Am. J. Human Genet.*, 13: 214–223.

SASAKI, M., and S. MAKINO. 1960. The chromosomal constitution of a human hermaphrodite. *Texas Rept. Biol. Med.*, 18: 493–500.

SCHAEFER, L. E., D. ADLERSBERG, and A. G. STEINBERG. 1958a. Heredity, environment and serum cholesterol; a study of 201 health families. *Circulation*, 17: 537–542.

——, ——, and ——. 1958b. Serum phospholipids; genetic and environmental influences. *Circulation*, 18: 341–346.

SCHLESSINGER, M. J. 1940. Relation of anatomic pattern to pathologic conditions of the coronary arteries. *Arch. Pathol.*, 30: 403–415.

SCHREINER, W. E. 1959. Über eine hereditäre Form von Pseudohermaphrodismus masculinus ("testiculäre Feminisierung"). *Geburtsch. Frauenheilk.*, 19: 1110–1118.

SCHULL, W. J., and J. V. NEEL. 1958. Radiation and the sex ratio in man. *Science*, 128: 343–348.

SCHULL, W. J., and J. V. NEEL. 1963. Sex linkage, inbreeding, and growth in childhood. *Am. J. Human Genet.*, 15: 106–114.

SCHULTZ, J. 1936. Variegation in *Drosophila* and the inert chromosome regions. *Proc. Natl. Acad. Sci. U. S.*, 22: 27–33.

SCHULZE, J. 1962. Discussion of the digital computer in the analysis of genetic linkage. In *Methodology in Human Genetics*. W. J. Burdette, editor. Holden-Day, San Francisco. Pp. 125–126.

SCHUSTER, J., and A. G. MOTULSKY. 1962. Exceptional sex-chromatin pattern in male pseudohermaphroditism with XX/XY/XO mosaicism. (Letter). *Lancet*, 1: 1074–1075.

SCHWARZ, G., and K. WALTER. 1962. Chromosomal analysis in gonadal dysgenesis with pseudo-pseudohypoparathyroidism. (Letter). *Lancet*, 1: 1075.

SCOTT, E. M. 1960. The relation of diaphorase of human erythrocytes to inheritance of methemoglobinemia. *J. Clin. Invest.*, 39: 1176–1179.

SCOTT, P. W., and R. T. HOSIE. 1957. Whipple's disease. *A.M.A. Arch. Internal Med.*, 100: 280–282.

SEARLE, A. G. 1962. Is sex-linked *Tabby* really recessive in the mouse? (Abstract). *Ann. Human Genet.*, 25: 423.

SEDGWICK, W. 1861. On sexual limitation in hereditary disease. *Brit. Foreign Medico-Chirurg. Rev.*, 27: 477–489; 28: 198–214.

——. 1863. On the influence of sex in hereditary disease. *Brit. Foreign Medico-Chirurg. Rev.*, 31: 445; 32: 159.

SHAW, R. F., and R. A. GLOVER. 1961. Abnormal segregation in hereditary renal disease with deafness. *Am. J. Human Genet.*, 13: 89–97.

SHETTLES, L. B. 1958. Biological sex differences with special reference to disease, resistance, and longevity. *J. Obstet. Gynaecol. Brit. Empire*, 65: 288–295.

——. 1960a. Nuclear morphology of human spermatozoa. *Nature*, 186: 648–649.

——. 1960b. Nuclear morphology of human spermatozoa. *Nature*, 188: 918–919.

——. 1960c. Nuclear morphology of human spermatozoa. *Obstet. Gynaecol.*, 16: 10–14.

——. 1961. Sperm morphology and sex ratios. *J. Urol.*, 86: 450–455.

SHIWAGO, P. I., and A. H. ANDRES. 1932. Die Geschlechtschromosomen in der Spermatogenese des Menschen. *Z. Zellforsch. Mikroskop. Anat. Abt. Histochem.*, 16: 413–431.

SIMPSON, N. E., and R. BIGGS. 1962. The inheritance of Christmas factor. *Brit. J. Hæmatol.*, 8: 191–202.

SINISCALCO, M., L. BERNINI, B. LATTIE, and A. G. MOTULSKY. 1960. Indagini genetici sulla predisposizione al favismo. II. Dati familiari. Associazione genica con il daltonismo. *Rend. Accad. Nazl. Lincei*, 28: 903.

——, ——, ——, and ——. 1961. Favism and thalassaemia in Sardinia and their relationship to malaria. *Nature*, 190: 1179–1180.

SJØLIN, K.-E. 1961. *A Classification of the Clotting Defects in 78 Hæmophilia Families*. Oxford University Press, New York and London.

SLATIS, H. M., and A. APELBAUM. 1963. Hairy pinna of the ear in Israeli populations. *Am. J. Human Genet.*, 15: 74–85.

SLIZYNSKI, B. M. 1955. Chiasmata in the male mouse. *J. Genet.*, 53: 597–605.

——. 1961. The pachytene state in mammalian oocytes. *Nature*, 189: 683–684.

SMITH, A. 1962. Large chromosome in hæmophiliac. (Letter) *Lancet*, 2: 1059.

SMITH, C. A. B. 1953. The detection of linkage in human genetics. *J. Roy. Statist. Soc. Ser. B* 150: 153.

——, and S. J. KILPATRICK. 1958. Estimates of the sex ratio of mutation rates in sex-linked conditions by the method of maximum likelihood. *Ann. Human Genet.*, 22: 244–249.

SMITH, S. G. 1945. Heteropycnosis as a means of diagnosing sex. *J. Heredity*, 36: 195–196.

SOUTHREN, A. L., and A. SAITO. 1961. The syndrome of testicular feminization. A report of three cases with chromatographic analysis of the urinary neutral 17-ketosteroids. *Ann. Internal Med.*, 55: 925–931.

SPARKES, R. S., and A. G. MOTULSKY. 1963. Hashimoto's disease in Turner's syndrome with isochrome X. (Letter) *Lancet*, 1: 947.

SPUHLER, J. N. 1948. On the number of genes in man. *Science*, 108: 279–280.

SRIVASTAVA, R. P. 1961. Ability to smell solutions of sodium cyanide. *East. Anthrop.*, 14: 189–191.

STEIKER, D. D., W. J. MELLMAN, A. M. BONGIOVANNI, ET AL. 1961. Turner's syndrome in the male. *J. Pediat.*, 58: 321–329.

STEINBERG, A. G. 1962. Progress in the study of genetically determined human gamma globulin types (the Gm and Inv groups). In *Progress in Medical Genetics*, A. G. Steinberg and A. G. Bearn, editors, 2: 1–33.

STEFFENSEN, D. M. 1959. A comparative view of the chromosome. In *Structure and Function of Genetic Elements. (Brookhaven Symposium)*. Brookhaven National Laboratory, Upton, N. Y. P. 103–124.

——. 1961. Chromosome structure with special reference to the role of metal ions. *Intern. Rev. Cytol.*, 12: 163–197.

STEPHENS, F. E., and F. H. TYLER. 1951. The inheritance of childhood progressive muscular dystrophy in 33 kindreds. *Am. J. Human Genet.*, 3: 111–125.

STERN, C. 1931. Zytologisch-genetische Untersuchungen als Beweise für die Morgansche Theorie des Faktorenaustausches. *Biol. Zentralblatt.*, 51: 547–585.

——. 1936. Somatic crossing over and segregation in *Drosophilia melanogaster*. *Genetics*, 21: 625–730.

——. 1957. The problems of complete Y linkage in man. *Am. J. Human Genet.*, 9: 147–166.

——. 1958. La Daltonisme lié au chromosome X à-t-il une localisation unique ou double? *J. Génét. Hum.*, 7: 302–307.

——. 1959a. The chromosomes of man. *Am. J. Human Genet.*, 11: 301–314.

——. 1959b. Colour-blindness in Klinefelter's syndrome. *Nature*, 183: 1452–1453.

——. 1960a. Dosage compensation. Development of a concept and new facts. *Can. J. Genet. Cytol.*, 2: 105–118.

——. 1960b. *Principles of Human Genetics*, second edition. W. H. Freeman, San Francisco.

——, and G. L. WALLS. 1957. The Cunier pedigree of color blindness. *Am. J. Human Genet.*, 9: 249–273.

STEVENS, N. M. 1905. *Studies in spermatogenesis with especial reference to the "accessory chromosome."* Carnegie Institution of Washington, Washington, D. C.

——. 1908. A study of the germ-cells of certain diptera. *J. Exptl. Zool.*, 5: 359–374.

STEVENSON, A. C. 1958. Muscular dystrophy in Northern Ireland. IV. Some additional data. *Ann. Human Genet.*, 22: 231–234.

——, M. Y. DUDGEON, and H. O. McCLURE. 1959. Observations on the results of pregnancies in women resident in Belfast. II. Abortions, hydatidiform moles and ectopic pregnancies. *Ann. Human Genet.*, 23: 395–415.

——, and E. A. CHEESEMAN. 1956. Hereditary deaf mutism, with particular reference to Northern Ireland. *Ann. Human Genet.*, 20: 177–231.

STEWART, J. S. S. 1959. Testicular feminization and colour-blindness. *Lancet*, 2: 592–594.

——. 1960. Genetic mechanisms in human intersexes. *Lancet*, 1: 825–826.

——. 1961. Genetic factors on the X-chromosome. (Letters) *Lancet*, 2: 104–105; 317.

——. 1962. Mechanisms of non-disjunction in man. *Nature*, 194: 258–260.

——, and A. R. SANDERSON. 1961. Sex-chromatin body in normal human testis. *Lancet*, 1: 79–80.

STURDEVANT, A. H. 1913. The linear arrangement of six sex-linked factors in *Drosophila*, as shown by their mode of association. *J. Exptl. Zool.*, 14: 43–59.

SWANSON, C. P. 1957. *Cytology and Cytogenetics*. Prentice-Hall, Englewood Cliffs, N. J.

SYMPOSIUM. 1962. (18 papers, with comments, on sex chromatin). *Acta cytol.*, 6: 1–142.

SZILARD, L. 1960. Dependence of the sex ratio at birth on the age of the father. *Nature*, 186: 649–650.

SZONTAGH, F. E., A. JAKOBOVITS, and C. MÉHES. 1961. Primary embryonal sex ratio in normal pregnancies determined by the nuclear chromatin. *Nature*, 192: 476.

TANAKA, K. and K. OHKURA. 1958. Evidence for genetic effects of radiation in offspring of radiological technicians. *Japan J. Human Genet.*, 3: 135.

TANAKA, K. R., W. N. VALENTINE and S. MIWA. 1962. Pyruvate kinase (PK) deficiency hereditary nonspherocytic hemolytic anemia. *Blood*, 19: 267–268.

TANNER, J. M., A. PRADER, H. HABICH and M. A. FERGUSON-SMITH. 1959. Genes on the Y chromosome influencing rate of maturation in man. Skeletal age studies in children with Klinefelter's (XXY) and Turner's (XO) syndromes. *Lancet*, 2: 141–144.

TAYLOR, A. 1963. Sex chromatin in the newborn. *Lancet*, 1: 912–914.

TAYLOR, J. H. 1960. Asynchronous duplication of chromosomes in cultured cells of Chinese hamster. *J. Biophys. Biochem. Cytol.*, 7: 455–464.

——, and R. BIGGS. 1961. Female with mild hæmophilia. (Letter) *Brit. Med. J.*, 2: 960.

THERKELSEN, A. J. and G. B. PETERSON. 1962. Frequency of sex-chromatin-positive cells in the logarithmic and postlogarithmic growth phases of human cells in tissue culture. *Exp. Cell Res.*, 28: 588–590.

THERMEN, E., K. PATAU, D. W. SMITH and R. I. DEMARS. 1961. The D trisomy syndrome and XO gonadal dysgenesis in two sisters. *Am. J. Human Genet.*, 13: 193–204.

THULINE, H. C. and D. E. NORBY. 1961. Spontaneous occurrence of chromosome abnormality in cats. *Science*, 134: 554–555.

TILLER, W. M., J. W. ROSEVEAR, and E. C. BURKE. 1961. Identification of heterozygous carriers of gargoylism. *Proc. Soc. Exptl. Biol. Med.*, 108: 193–204.

TOBLER, R., A. PRADER, and W. TAILLARD. 1956. Die familiäre primäre vitamin–D–resistente Rachitis (Phosphatdiabetes). *Helv. Paediat. Acta*, 11: 209–255.

TREVES, F. 1886. A case of hæmophilia; pedigree through five generations. *Lancet*, 2: 533–534.

TRUJILLO, J., V. FAIRBANKS, S. OHNO, and E. BEUTLER. 1961. Chromosomal constitution in glucose–6–phosphate dehydrogenase deficiency. (Letter) *Lancet*, 2: 1454–1455.

TURPIN, R., J. LEJEUNE, J. LAFOURCADE, ET AL. 1961. Présomption de monozygotisme en dépit d'un dimorphisme sexuel: sujet masculin XY et sujet neutre haplo X. *Compt. Rend.*, 252: 2945–2946.

——, ——, and M. O. RETHORE. 1956. Etude de la descendance de sujets traités par radiothérapie pelvienne. *Acta Genet. Statist. Med.*, 6: 204–216.

TWIESSELMANN, F., E. DEFRISE-GUSSENHOVEN, and A. LEGUEBE. 1962. Incidence on genetics of mechanism of segregation and disjunction at meiosis in man. *Nature*, 196: 1232–1233.

UCHIDA, I. A., and J. M. BOWMAN. 1961. XXX 18-trisomy. (Letter) *Lancet*, 2: 1094.

——, A. J. LEWIS, J. M. BOWMAN, and H. C. WANG. 1962. A case of double trisomy: trisomy No. 18 and triplo-X. *J. Pediat.*, 60: 498–502.

VALENTINE, W. N., K. R. TANAKA, and S. MIWA. 1961. A specific erythrocyte glycolytic enzyme defect (pyruvate kinase) in three subjects with congenital hemolytic anemia. *Trans. Assoc. Am. Physicians*, 74: 100–109.

VAN DE KERCKHOVE, D. 1959. Content of deoxyribonucleic acid of the germinal vesicle of the primary oocyte in the rabbit. *Nature*, 183: 329.

VANDENBERG, S. G., V. A. McKUSICK, and A. B. McKUSICK. 1962. Twin data in support of the Lyon hypothesis. *Nature*, 194: 505–506.

VANDERDONCK, R., and G. VERRIEST. 1960. Femme protanomale et hétérozygote mixte (gènes de la protanomalie et de la deutéranopie en position de repulsion) ayant deux fils deutérranopes, un fils protanomal et deux fils normaux. *Biotypologie*, 21: 110–120.

VANDUIJN, C., JR. 1960. Nuclear structure of human spermatozoa. *Nature*, 188: 916–918.

VENDRELY, R. 1955. In *The Nucleic Acids*, editors E. Chargoff and J. N. Davidson. Vol. II. p. 155. Academic Press, New York.

VERSCHUER, O. v. 1959. *Genetik des Menschen. Lehrbuch der Humanangenetik*. Urban and Schwarzenberg, Berlin. Pp. 1–759.

VOGEL, F. 1955. Vergleichende Betrachtungen über die Mutationsrate der geschlechtgebundenen-rezessiven Hemophilieformen in der Schweiz und in Dänmark. *Blut*, 1: 91–109.

——. 1958. Verzogerte Mutation beim Menchen? Einige kritische Bernerkungen zu Ch. Auerbachs Arbeit (1956). *Ann. Human Genet.*, 22: 132–137.

WAARDENBURG, P. J., A. FRANCESCHETTI, and D. KLEIN. 1961. *Genetics and Ophthalmology.* Vol. 1. Charles C Thomas, Springfield, Ill.

——, and J. VAN DEN BOSCH. 1956. X-chromosomal ocular albinism in a Dutch family. *Ann. Human Genet.*, 21: 101–122.

WALLS, G. L. 1959. Peculiar color-blindness in peculiar people. *A.M.A. Arch. Ophthalmol.*, 62: 13–62.

WALTON, J. N. 1956. The inheritance of muscular dystrophy; further observations. *Ann. Human Genet.*, 21: 40–57.

——. 1957. The inheritance of muscular dystrophy. *Acta Genet. Statist. Med.*, 7: 318–325.

WAXMAN, S. H., S. M. GARTLER, and V. C. KELLEY. 1962. Apparent masculinization of the female fetus diagnosed as true hermaphrodism by chromosome studies. *J. Pediat.*, 60: 540–544.

WEATHERALL, D. J. 1960. Enzyme deficiency in hemolytic disease of the newborn. *Lancet*, 2: 835–837.

WEBB, J. B., and A. ST. J. DIXON. 1960. Hemophilia and hemophilic arthropathy. An historical review and a clinical study of 42 cases. *Ann. Rheumatic Diseases*, 19: 143–157.

WELSHONS, W. J., and L. B. RUSSELL. 1959. The Y chromosome as the bearer of male determining factors in the mouse. *Proc. Natl. Acad. Sci. U.S.*, 45: 560–566.

WESTERGAARD, M. 1948. The relation between chromosomal contitution and sex in the offspring of triploid melandrium. *Hereditas*, 34: 257–279.

WHALEN, R. E., S. HUANG, E. PESCHEL, and H. D. McINTOSH. 1961. Hereditary nephropathy, deafness, and renal foam cells. *Am. J. Med.*, 31: 171–186.

WHITE, M. J. D. 1960. Are there no mammalian species with XO males—and if not, why not? *Am. Naturalist*, 94: 301–312.

WHITE, T. 1940. Linkage and crossing-over in the human chromosomes. *J. Genet.*, 40: 403–437.

WHITTAKER, D. L., D. L. COPELAND, and J. B. GRAHAM. 1962. Linkage of color blindness to hemophilias A and B. *Am. J. Human Genet.*, 14: 149–158.

WILKINS, L. 1957. *The Diagnosis and Treatment of Endocrine Disorders in Childhood and Adolescence.* 2nd ed. Charles C Thomas, Springfield, Ill.

WILKINSON, J. F., F. NOUR-ELDIN, M. C. G. ISRAELS, and K. E. BARRETT. 1961. Hæmophilia syndrome. A survey of 267 families. *Lancet*, 2: 947–950.

WILLIAMS, N. E., and J. B. FIELD. 1961. Low leukocyte phosphorylase in hepatic phosphorylase deficient glycogen storage disease. *J. Clin. Invest.*, 40: 1841–1845.

WILLIAMS, T. F., R. W. WINTERS, and C. H. BURNETT. 1960. Familial hypophosphatemia and vitamin-D-resistant rickets. In *The Metabolic Basis of Inherited Disease.* J. B. Stanbury, J. B. Wyngaarden and D. S. Fredrickson, editors. McGraw-Hill, New York. Pp. 1177–1221.

WILSON, E. B. 1905. The behavior of the idiochromosomes in Hemiptera. *J. Exptl. Zool.*, 2: 377–405.

——. 1911. The sex chromosomes. *Arch. Mikrobiol. Anat.* 77: 249–271.

——. 1925. *The Cell in Development and Heredity*, 3rd ed. Macmillan, New York.

WINGE, O. 1921. On a partial sex-linked inheritance of eye-colour in man. *Compt. Rend. Lab. Carlsberg, Copenhagen*, 14: 1–4.

WINIWARTER, H. VON. 1912. Etudes sur la spermatogenèse humaine. I. Cellule de Sertoli. II. Hétérochromosome et mitoses de l' épithelium séminal. *Arch. Biol.*, 27: 91–189.

WINTERS, R. A., J. B. GRAHAM, T. F. WILLIAMS, ET AL. 1957. A genetic study of familial hypophosphatemia and vitamin D resistant rickets. *Trans. Assoc. Am. Physicians*, 70: 234–242.

WRIGHT, S. 1951. The genetical structure of populations. *Ann. Eugenics*, 15: 323–354.

YARDLEY, J. H., and T. R. HENDRIX. 1961. Combined electron and light microscopy in Whipple's disease. Demonstration of "bacillary bodies" in the intestine. *Bull. Johns Hopkins Hosp.*, 109: 80–98.

YERGANIAN, G. 1957. Cytologic maps of some isolated human pachytene chromosomes. *Am. J. Human Genet.*, 9: 42–54.

——. 1960. "Brittle-bristle", genetic evidence for the triheterosomic scheme of sex determination. (Abstract) *Genetics*, 45: 1018.

——, R. KATO, M. J. LEONARD, ET AL. 1960. Sex chromosomes in malignancy, transplantibility of growths, and aberrant sex determination. In *Cell Physiology of Neoplasia.* University of Texas Press, Austin. Pp. 49–73.

ZIRKLE, C. 1946. The discovery of sex-influenced, sex-limited and sex-linked heredity. In *Studies and Essays in the History of Science and Learning in Honor of George Sarton.* M. F. A. Montagu, editor. Schuman, New York.

INDEX